UNVEILING THE UNIVERSE

UNVEILING THE UNIVERSE

The Aims and Achievements of Astronomy

HARLEY WOOD

Government Astronomer for New South Wales
Sydney Observatory

AMERICAN ELSEVIER PUBLISHING COMPANY, INC.

NEW YORK 1968

Library of Congress Catalog Card Number: 67-31258

Copyright (1967, H. Wood), *in Australia*

American Edition Published in 1968 by

AMERICAN ELSEVIER PUBLISHING COMPANY, INC.

52 Vanderbilt Avenue
New York, New York 10017

PRINTED IN AUSTRALIA

ACKNOWLEDGMENTS

THE whole manuscript has been read by Mrs. Kathleen O'Neil, Mr. James O'Neil, Mr. W. H. Robertson and my wife Una, and significant parts by Professor B. J. Bok, Dr. Priscilla F. Bok, Dr. R. G. Giovanelli, Professor W. M. O'Neil and my daughter Rosamond. The criticism they have given me has been invaluable. Besides being especially indebted to the astronomers and institutions who have provided the illustrations I naturally owe much to astronomical colleagues for their published work in periodicals and books. One constantly used reference work was C. W. Allen's *Astrophysical Quantities* (University of London Press).

CONTENTS

ILLUSTRATIONS

22. The Crab Nebula photographed in colour with the 200-inch telescope (Mount Wilson and Palomar Observatories, copyright California Institute of Technology). Spectra of an incandescent lamp (continuous spectrum), a cadmium arc (line spectrum) and the Sun (Dr S. C. Baker, University of Newcastle).

23. Portion of the Bahama Islands from Gemini 4 in June 1965 (National Aeronautics and Space Administration).

24. The Great Nebula in Orion photographed in colour with the 200-inch telescope (Mount Wilson and Palomar Observatories, copyright California Institute of Technology).

25. The Great Galaxy in Andromeda photographed in colour with the 48-inch Schmidt camera (Mount Wilson and Palomar Observatories, copyright California Institute of Technology).

26. Sunspot in white light (R. J. Bray and R. E. Loughhead, Division of Physics, Commonwealth Scientific and Industrial Research Organization).

27. A large active solar prominence photographed in calcium light (Mount Wilson and Palomar Observatories).

28. The solar corona of 15 February 1961 (Dr. M. Waldmeier).

29. The globular cluster 47 Toucanae (Sydney Observatory).

30. The Sun photographed in Hα light (Division of Physics, Commonwealth Scientific and Industrial Research Organization).

31. Classes of stellar spectra (Observatory of the University of Michigan).

32. The open cluster Δ 289 (Sydney Observatory).

33. The spiral galaxy M101 (Mount Wilson and Palomar Observatories).

34. Star clouds in Sagittarius (Mount Wilson and Palomar Observatories).

35. The nebula around Eta Carinae (The Uppsala-Schmidt camera at Mount Stromlo Observatory).

36. The Horsehead Nebula in Orion (Mount Wilson and Palomar Observatories).

37. A field of clusters in the Large Magellanic Cloud (Mount Stromlo Observatory).

38. The 30 Doradus Nebula in the Large Magellanic Cloud (Mount Stromlo Observatory).

39. Types of galaxies (Mount Wilson and Palomar Observatories).

40. The edge-on spiral galaxy NGC 891 (Mount Wilson and Palomar Observatories).

41. The spiral galaxy M51 photographed with the 200-inch telescope (Mount Wilson and Palomar Observatories).

42. The barred spiral galaxy NGC 1300 (Mount Wilson and Palomar Observatories).

43. The galaxy NGC 5128 (Mount Stromlo Observatory).

44. Portion of cluster of galaxies in Coma Berenices (Mount Wilson and Palomar Observatories).

45. The relation between red-shift and distance for galaxies (Mount Wilson and Palomar Observatories).

INTRODUCTION

ASTRONOMERS are stimulated to write popular books, not only by their own enthusiasm, but also by the evident interest of others in their subject. A chance acquaintance who unmasks an astronomer soon finds questions he must ask and topics he must discuss, just as he feels the urgent need of talking anatomy and aches and pains to a medical man. Do you think life is possible on other worlds? Why does an artificial satellite not fall immediately? What keeps the Sun shining? How large, and how old, is the universe? Is it expanding? To these questions we are not always able to give the confident, satisfying answers we would wish, but we must be prepared to discuss whatever evidence science has yielded and to disclose, without too much reserve or reluctance, the places where our knowledge is incomplete.

Astronomy is a vital part of present-day science and a key to the understanding of its history. The knowledge gained during patient centuries has not decreased for us the wonder with which our ancestors looked at the heavens, but it has taught us to appreciate the place of our Earth in the family of planets that journey through space with the Sun, and the insignificance of even the Sun itself in the known universe. In the study of astronomy we may make a nearer acquaintance with the great forces of nature which nowhere else display their universality in so majestic a form, and gain understanding of the new ways of science which, in a few score years, have so enormously expanded our known environment and made such great changes in our ordinary lives. In astronomy, too, we find explanation of many common-place things which influence daily affairs—the seasons, the calendar and time-keeping, the phases of the Moon, tides, eclipses and the basis of navigation.

Fifteen hundred years or so ago, when the Roman Empire collapsed, most of the ancient scientific learning disappeared leaving Ptolemaic astronomy as the only branch of ancient science which survived almost intact. In this way, through its continuity, astronomy is a link between the ancient and the modern as well as a clue to the thought of our scientific ancestors. In the sixteenth and seventeenth centuries the revolution which occurred not only in knowledge of the universe, but also in the whole way of looking at its problems, was inspired by astronomy through the work of Copernicus, Tycho Brahe, Kepler, Galileo and Newton. Today it remains in the forefront of scientific endeavour, providing a host of problems which call for solution and serving as an inspiration and a testing ground for physical theory, since, in the stars and in space, matter is found in extreme conditions, hotter, denser or less dense than can be produced in our Earth-bound laboratories.

The Aim of the Book

My aim has been to provide a minimum serious account of astronomy in a book which strikes a balance between the brief account, whose danger lies in giving inadequate information, and the full statement, more formidable to read and to buy, of which there are several good examples. While an effort has been made to avoid over-confidence when knowledge is incomplete or not firmly founded, subjects have not been omitted only because they are difficult.

Two considerations have been kept in mind. The first is that it is just as interesting to understand the basic principles, the observational evidence and reasoning, which lead to complex pieces of knowledge as it is to know the spectacular result itself. Yet most of us would find it hard to explain without warning how we know that the Earth revolves about the Sun or what is meant by the direction north, or even harder to give evidence that we see objects in space from which the light set forth on its journey to us millions of years ago. While it may not have been possible to build up in full detail the arguments which justify every statement in the pages which follow, an attempt has been made to give, with enough emphasis on basic explanation, a credible and consistent picture of the knowledge we have. The intention is to provide particularly for the reader who, for any result, is likely to ask, if the foundation is not given, "How do you know this?"

The second consideration is to cater for the person who, when a class of objects in the sky is mentioned, will say, "Now where can I see one?". As many interesting things can be seen by the naked eye or with small optical aid such as binoculars or small telescopes, Chapter 12 contains information for finding the more interesting and spectacular of these and gives positions of the objects which are mentioned in the text and which can be seen with ordinary telescopes. This chapter, while rather disconnected, is an essential part of the book for those who have telescopes and wish to see things for themselves or who wish to compile programmes for demonstrations at the telescope.

The Plan of the Book

The book is designed, except for Chapter 12, to be read straight through. Those to whom the ideas of Chapter 1 are new may find it hard reading but, even so, it is probably better to keep to the plan, passing temporarily over the points where an obstacle occurs. The ideas will be found useful, and clearer, if later reference is made to them as they are used to assist in observation of the sky. Chapter 3 can be skimmed by anyone who has read some physics.

It is not easy to decide how much mathematics should be allowed to enter into an account of this kind. It seems that to exclude it completely, as some people do, is to handicap both the writer and the reader by not recognising that astronomy is a branch of quantitative physical science. However, all the mathematics that I have required is the realization that an equation between physical quantities is a useful way of displaying their relations and that if all of the quantities except one entering into an equation can be measured, then that one may usually be found from the equation. Although rigorous derivations of equations, which would interrupt the argument and make it unpalatable to some, are not included I have tried to make the few equations used appear reasonable.

1

THE CELESTIAL SPHERE

IF we look at the sky on a clear night, we can distinguish nothing about the distances of the stars. We perceive only their directions and can easily imagine that the stars are set inside a huge sphere canopied above us. In ancient times people thought of the universe in just this manner. The idea still provides us with a way of describing what we see when we begin observing the sky and, in fact, even with a way of calculating in connection with quite refined measurement. Long ago men watching the skies noticed that, except for a few planets, or wanderers, the stars keep the same relative positions over long periods. The patterns they form in the sky look much the same to us as they did to our ancestors. This led to the tradition of calling them the fixed stars and adds point to the device of imagining them to be attached to a huge sphere which by convention is called the *celestial sphere*. (Italics are used in this book to indicate words which are expected to become part of the reader's language.)

THE APPARENT DAILY MOTION OF THE STARS

A watch on the celestial sphere for only an hour or two shows that it is in motion, relative to the horizon. Stars are rising over the eastern part of the horizon and setting towards the west. This apparent motion is easily explained if the celestial sphere is considered to be fixed while the Earth rotates within it giving us, and our horizon, a motion which continuously displays different parts of the heavens to us. For the moment let us accept this rotation as known, leaving further description of it until Chapter 4.

Figure 1 is drawn to assist in describing the features of this motion. The Earth is represented at the centre of the celestial sphere which, however, must be imagined as far larger relative to the Earth than can be shown on any diagram. The point P' represents the South Pole of the Earth and P the North Pole. The Earth is rotating towards the east, in the direction shown by the arrow, about a line joining these two points. Now suppose we are situated at a point O on the Earth and consider how the sky will appear to move. The point straight above our heads, the *zenith*, is marked Z on the diagram and, as we cannot see through the Earth, only that part of the sky above our horizon, labelled on the diagram, is visible to us. In other words, we see the part of the sky within 90° of our zenith. As we, standing on the Earth, are not directly conscious of the Earth's motion, it is easier to describe what we see by supposing the celestial sphere to rotate towards the west about the points U and L, the upper *celestial pole* and the lower

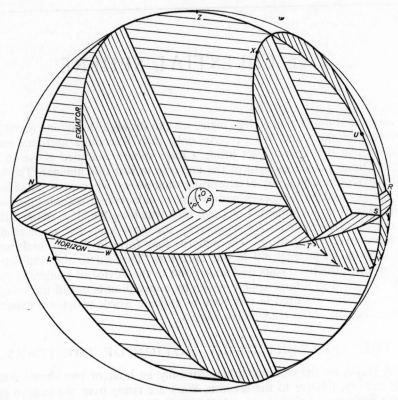

Figure 1.

celestial pole, where the axis of the Earth cuts the celestial sphere. This is how it seems to our senses. A star represented at X has a path which is shown by a full line above the horizon and a broken line below it. It rises at the point of the horizon marked R and sets, say 16 hours later, at the point marked T.

If we are in the Southern Hemisphere, and therefore, as in the Figure, nearer the South Pole than the North Pole, the South Celestial Pole will be above the horizon. Then a star whose distance from U is less than the distance from U to S will not set but just appear to move around the pole.

If there were a star at the celestial pole, it would appear not to move at all. Plate 1 is an exposure of four hours duration on the South Pole. The stars have traced their apparent motion around the pole during that period. The horizontal trace was made by the satellite Echo I which crossed the field during the exposure.

Similarly, for observers in the Northern Hemisphere, there will be stars close to the North Celestial Pole which do not set. Points on the Earth which are equidistant from its two poles are on the Earth's Equator which is drawn, and points on the celestial sphere equidistant from the celestial poles are on the *Celestial Equator* which is named on the Figure.

DIRECTIONS AND POSITIONS ON THE EARTH AND IN THE SKY

In Figure 2 is drawn a section of the Earth through its poles and the place *O*. The lettering on this Figure corresponds to that of Figure 1. The directions from *O* of the Celestial Equator and the upper celestial pole are shown, and since the celestial sphere is taken to be extremely large, the directions are parallel to those from the centre of the Earth. Several terms,

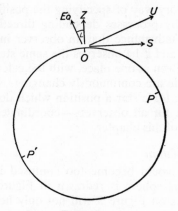

Figure 2.

some of which are used in everyday speech, may now be defined. The definitions call for careful reading, but they are necessary to give precision to the meaning of the terms.

The *meridian* of a place is the plane through the directions of the pole and the zenith of the place represented by *U* and *Z* in Figures 1 and 2.

The *latitude* of a place is the angle, marked *L* on Figure 2, between the directions of the zenith and the point of the Celestial Equator on the meridian cuts the horizon (*N* and *S* on the Figures).
south, negative. The latitude is 90° at the Earth's poles.

The *north* and *south* points of the horizon are the points where the meridian cuts the horizon (*N* and *S* on the Figures).

The *altitude* of any object is the angle at the observer between the horizon and the direction of the object.

The plane perpendicular to the horizon through the observer's zenith and an object cuts the horizon at one point on the same side of the zenith as the object. The angle at the observer between the south point of the horizon and this point is called the *azimuth* of the object. It is measured towards the west up to 360°. Thus west has azimuth 90° and east 270°.

Practical definitions should correspond to operations that can be carried out to observe the quantities defined. In this case it is chiefly the directions of the zenith and the pole that must be determined. The zenith may be found because it is the direction opposite to that in which a plumb line hangs or the direction perpendicular to a free liquid surface. The upper pole may be determined as the centre of the circle followed by a *circumpolar* star, that is, one above the horizon for all of its daily path. The direction of the pole, required to measure azimuth, may be found by pointing on a star when it is furthest east of the pole and again when it is furthest west. A point half way between these two pointings is the direction of the pole, which is also the direction of north or south depending on which pole was observed.

Notice that if the azimuth and altitude of a body—a star or an artificial satellite or an aeroplane—can be nominated, its direction is completely known. It is a satisfactory way of specifying the position because the quantities used are found by processes depending directly on their definition. However, it has the disadvantage that an observer in a different place will have a different zenith and if he observes the same star its azimuth and altitude will be different. Even at one place, with the celestial sphere in motion, the azimuth and altitude are continuously changing. Naturally there is need for a way of specifying for a star a position which does not change rapidly and which is the same for all observers—coordinates of this kind will be defined before the end of this chapter.

Hour Angle and Declination

Because Figure 1 would become too confused if we put many more lines on it, the celestial sphere is redrawn in Figure 3 as though viewed from outside. The lines on Figure 3 will not only help in some of the description but give the picture an appearance of perspective to emphasize that it really is a sphere that is being considered. The observer is supposed to be at the centre of the sphere, N is the North Celestial Pole, X the position of a star. The position of the Celestial Equator is marked. The point on the celestial sphere which at the moment is at the zenith of the observer is marked Z. The position of Z on the celestial sphere is continuously changing as the celestial sphere rotates, but everything else may be regarded as fixed on it. The lines radiating from N pass on through the South Celestial Pole. They are called hour circles. The one through Z is the meridian of the observer and the one through the star at X is called the *hour circle* of X because it is the same time since all objects on that circle were on the meridian.

The angle ZNX at the pole between the meridian and the hour circle

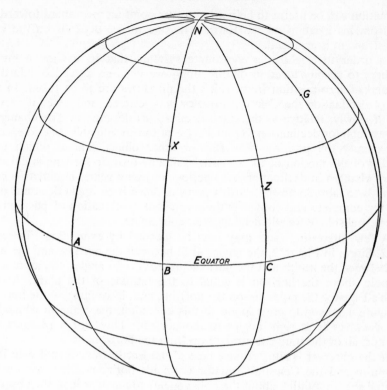

Figure 3.

of the star is called the *hour angle* of the star. It is so-called because it is convenient to evaluate it by taking the time since the star was on the meridian, and normally hour angle is quoted directly in hours, minutes and seconds without converting it to degrees as is more usual in other contexts. The hour angle of a star, or any other body, varies from 0 hours when it is on the meridian through all hours to 24 when it is on the meridian again to start the cycle. It is important to keep in mind that all distances on the celestial sphere are angles as seen at the eye of the observer.

The angular distance of a star from the Celestial Equator, *BX* on Figure 3, is called the *declination* of the star. The star and the equator may be regarded as fixed on the celestial sphere and so, in giving the position of a star, the declination is one measure which does not change quickly. It is called positive, or north, for objects north of the equator and negative, or south, for those south of it.

Hour angle and declination also specify direction in the sky just as altitude and azimuth do. Hour angle varies quickly because the meridian relative to which it is measured is carried right around the celestial sphere by each daily rotation of the Earth. Altitude and azimuth or hour angle and declination can be useful to help an observer point an instrument towards a star from his location on the Earth. The one to use depends on the way his instrument is arranged.

In order to establish a coordinate system—that is, a way of giving numbers to specify location or direction—we need an agreed standard of rest and of zero position from which the measures are to be taken. In the case of declination the Celestial Equator was selected, and, since it moves, even if slowly, relative to the stars, declinations do change. The change is slow enough for declination to remain one of the coordinates used to specify permanently the position of a star or other object. Tables which take account of the motion of the Celestial Equator provide for simple calculation of changes in declination over periods of many years. Declination corresponds to latitude on the Earth's surface. Since hour angle does not provide for complete and conveniently permanent specification of position on the celestial sphere we still need another coordinate.

A few interesting facts may now be gleaned by examining Figures 1 and 2. Since, in Figure 2, the angles at O between the equator and the pole and between the zenith and the horizon are both right angles, the altitude of the pole above the horizon is equal to the latitude of the place. At the Earth's Equator the poles are on the horizon, and, if we imagine the horizon of Figure 1 moved to correspond to this condition, the plane in which the star X moves is at right angles to the horizon. Thus, for a place at the Equator, all of the stars rise straight up from the horizon.

If the observer is situated at a pole of the Earth, the celestial pole is at his zenith and the Celestial Equator is on his horizon. Each star on the celestial sphere rotating about the pole appears to move around the observer at a constant altitude above the horizon.

Every point on the equator is 90° away from the pole. When an object on the Celestial Equator is rising or setting—W in Figure 1—it is also 90° from the zenith and so 90° away from every point on the meridian. The directions are thus 90° from south, for rising due east and for setting due west. Objects south of the equator with southerly declination rise and set south of east and west respectively and those north of the equator rise and set north of east and west. If the object is on the same side of the equator as the observer, as X is in Figure 1, more than half of the path is above the horizon, and, if it is on the opposite side of the equator, it is below the horizon most of the time.

THE MOTION OF THE SUN

In order to fix the standard of non-rotation which is required to complete the specification of coordinates on the celestial sphere some features of the motion of the Sun must be considered. The Sun, the Moon and the planets share in the apparent motion of the celestial sphere and show the phenomena, such as rising and setting, associated with this. In astronomical terms they are comparatively close to us, and so such individual motion as they have is soon revealed by their movement relative to the stars on the celestial sphere. The main features of the apparent motion of the Sun are due to the movement of the Earth about the Sun in a period of one year.

Imagine a line drawn from the Earth, and the observer, towards the Sun. As the observer on the Earth moves around the Sun, this line will change direction and the Sun will appear to move among the vastly distant stars on the celestial sphere. When the Earth returns to the same place at the end of a year, the Sun will occupy the same position on the celestial sphere. As the Earth's movement about the Sun is in a plane, the apparent movement of the Sun is also a plane. This plane or the path of the Sun is called the *ecliptic*. It is marked on the star maps in Chapter 2.

This movement is a very evident phenomenon associated with the seasons. The Sun is furthest south of the Equator, that is, has its greatest southerly declination, about December 22. It crosses the Equator going from south to north about March 22, and the point which it occupies at this time is called the vernal equinox or the first point of Aries because it was formerly at the beginning of that constellation. This is an important point of the sky. In fact, the necessity for introducing this point for the definitions is the reason why it was necessary to talk about the motion of the Sun here rather than leave it to a place where it might appear to fit in more naturally. The vernal equinox, often just called the *equinox*, is a fixed point on the celestial sphere, not affected by its apparent daily rotation. From March 22 the Sun is north of the Equator until about September 23 when it crosses again to southerly declination.

The way is now prepared to complete the definitions for specifying the position of a star but first it may be as well to finish consideration of the Sun's motion with a glance at some features which affect our everyday affairs. As the Sun's declination follows its yearly variation the period of each day when it is above the horizon changes as mentioned in discussion of Figure 1 and the times of sunrise and sunset vary. Figure 4 shows the character of this variation. Read the date along the bottom of the Figure and go straight up from this until you reach the line for the latitude in which you are interested. Then the time of sunrise or sunset may be read at this height from the left hand scale. See how much greater the variation is for high latitudes. This would be expected from Figure 1. (In the sunset diagram the hours of the day are numbered onward after 12 noon as though the clock had a 24 hour dial. This is a better way of avoiding confusion than using the letters a.m. or p.m.)

The direction in which the Sun rises or sets may be traced in the same way in Figure 5, which gives the azimuth of sunrise and sunset for latitudes 0°, 30° and 60°, either north or south. The graduations on the left give the direction of sunrise and those on the right of sunset. From the time of the equinox in March to that in September the Sun rises north of east and sets north of west and then from September to March rises and sets south of east and west respectively. As an example, if the direction of sunrise and sunset is wanted for latitude south 30° in the middle of February, the date may be read along the bottom of the Figure, then from the point of the 30° line above this the left hand scale of the Figure indicates that the Sun sets

SUNRISE

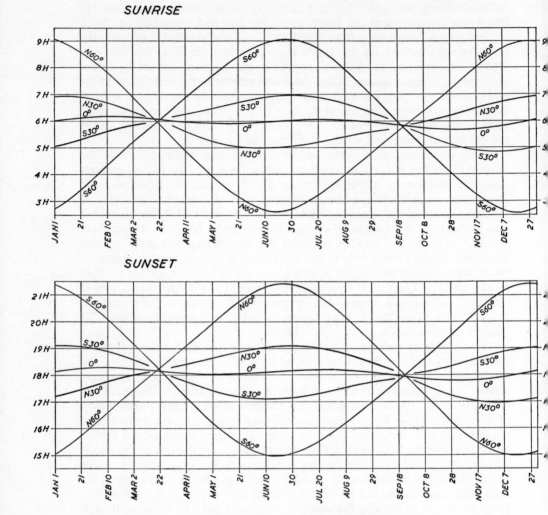

Figure 4.—Times of sunrise and sunset.

in azimuth 73°—that is 17° south of west—and on the same date rises 17° south of east.

After the Sun sets and before it becomes dark there is an interval called *twilight*. Civil twilight, the time during which ordinary outdoor occupations remain possible without artificial light, is taken to end when the Sun reaches 6° below the horizon. Some activities could be carried on longer, others not so long. If the Sun is imagined to be following the diurnal path of the star shown on Figure 1 and if the observer at O in Figure 1 were to move to the equator, his horizon would pass through the celestial poles. The Sun's path would then be perpendicular to it and the Sun would require a shorter path, and less time, to reach a distance of 6° below the horizon. This explains the well known short duration of twilight in the tropics.

As the observer moved away from the Equator, the apparent path of the Sun would tend to lie down more towards the horizon and the Sun would require a longer arc of movement to reach the standard 6°. If he were to go sufficiently far, the Sun, in summer, would not reach this distance below the horizon and his twilight would last all night. If he went inside the Arctic Circle the Sun would not set at all for a period the length of which would be longer the further he went.

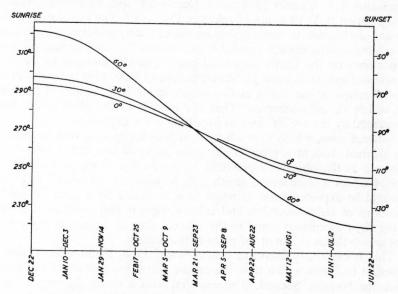

Figure 5.—Azimuth of sunrise and sunset.

RIGHT ASCENSION AND SIDEREAL TIME

The problem of finding a permanent way of specifying the position of a star can now be further considered. The poles, the Celestial Equator, the vernal equinox (marked A on Figure 3), and the stars, may be looked on as fixed on the celestial sphere. Already defined is one coordinate which does not change quickly, the declination marked XB on the figure. *Right ascension*, the other coordinate needed, is the angle, measured towards the east, made at the pole between the hour circle which passes through the vernal equinox and the hour circle of the star. On Figure 3 it is the angle ANX or equivalently the arc AB of the equator. If we regard the vernal equinox and the Celestial Equator as fixed, any point on the celestial sphere may be identified by naming its right ascension and declination. This way of specifying the position of any body is by far the most common and the most useful. Actually both the equator and, much more slowly, the ecliptic move relative to the stars, and so the equinox changes position and the right ascension of a star varies. However, as with declination, the changes are slow, and easy to evaluate. They are usually negligible for those who look at the sky with the naked eye.

The maps in Chapter 2 have lines to correspond to the right ascensions and declinations of the stars. The right ascension lines are numbered in hours around the polar maps and at the top and bottom of the remaining ones. The declination lines are numbered in degrees along a central line of the polar maps and at the sides of the others, the north and south being marked. For example, on the South Polar map, the bright star Canopus is in the position R.A. 6 hours 23 minutes, Dec. —53° and, on map V, Altair is in the position R.A. 19 hours 48 minutes, Dec. +9°. The use of right ascension and declination to name points on the celestial sphere may seem more natural and convincing if a parallel is drawn with the method used for naming positions on the Earth. Suppose Figure 3 for the moment to represent the celestial sphere at some particular instant of time. G is the point of the celestial sphere at the zenith at Greenwich and Z is the zenith of the place with which we are concerned. Then the latitude of the place is the angle represented by the arc ZC and its longitude is the angle GNZ.

Sidereal time, which is much used in astronomy, can now be defined. The sidereal time at a place is the hour angle of the vernal equinox as measured at the observer's position. In Figure 3 it is represented by the angle ANZ for a place whose zenith is Z. As with any other hour angle, and as would be expected from its name, it is measured by a clock. From the definitions of right ascension and sidereal time it may be seen that stars having right ascensions equal to the sidereal time of a place at a given instant are on the meridian of the place at that instant.

This is extremely useful in several ways. First, if the sidereal time is known, it indicates which stars are on the meridian, and which are visible above the horizon. Second, it means that with a clock showing accurate sidereal time, the positions of stars can be measured by setting up an instrument to measure the time when they cross the meridian—that is, the right ascension—and the distance from the Celestial Equator at which they do so, the declination. And third, if the right ascension of a star is known, the timing of its passage across the meridian with the same instrument gives the sidereal time. From Figure 3 it is clear that the hour angle of a star is equal to the sidereal time minus the right ascension of the star. The intimate association of hour angle and right ascension with sidereal time and clocks is the reason why they are expressed in time units.

The term right ascension is one that sounds strange to us, and, as it has a long history, a few words of explanation may be worthwhile. Ancient astronomers, such as those of Babylon, had not developed instruments for measuring angles in all directions, and for them the horizon was the best available reference device. It is still used in making astronomical observations for navigation. The phenomena near the horizon, such as rising and setting, were specially important. These astronomers divided the ecliptic, the path of the Sun around the celestial sphere, into twelve equal "signs", and these had special interest. The ascension of a sign was the arc of the

Celestial Equator that rose during the same time and came to apply to the whole arc from the equinox to the sign. The ascensions when the equator is perpendicular to the horizon—that is, when the observer is on the equator, and all objects rise straight up from the horizon—were called right ascensions and this is the term that has survived.

MEAN TIME AND STANDARD TIME

The most natural measure of time for ordinary use, the day, is provided by the movement of the Sun. Each day the Sun rises, reaches its highest point in the sky when it is on the meridian, and sets. Most of our everyday activities keep time with the cycle of light and heat which is thus provided for us. However, the motion of the Sun in the sky is such that intervals of time between succeeding passages across the meridian are not equal. This arises firstly because the Sun is at different distances from the Earth at different times of the year and therefore does not move uniformly on the celestial sphere. Secondly, because its oblique movement takes it back and forth across the Equator and so its hour angle, and the time when it crosses the meridian, usually differs from what it would be if the motion were along the Equator. Consequently, as accurate clocks were developed, it was not at all convenient to keep a time which would be exactly 12 o'clock each time the Sun was on the meridian. A new time was invented by imagining a body, called the mean Sun, whose motion is uniform along the Equator and as close as possible to the average motion of the Sun. It is defined by giving a formula for its right ascension which increases uniformly with time. The period between successive passages of this imagined body across the meridian is the mean day. It is divided into 24 hours which are broken into minutes and seconds, and this time is called mean solar time or mean time. Mean time at a place is the hour angle of the mean sun $+12$ hours, where the 12 hours is added because we like to start a new day at midnight.

Relation to Sidereal Time

The apparent westward rotation of the celestial sphere, due to the Earth's rotation towards the east, brings each point on it to the meridian once each day, but, as the Sun is moving towards the east in the sky, it takes longer to return to the meridian than does a fixed point on the celestial sphere, such as a star or the vernal equinox. While the Sun makes a complete circuit of the celestial sphere in a year, the stars, and the vernal equinox with them, will appear to have made one extra passage of the meridian in a year. The Sun crosses the meridian an average of $365\frac{1}{4}$ times a year and the stars $366\frac{1}{4}$ times—a sidereal clock, therefore, gains a day in the year or nearly four minutes each day.

Standard Time

Since the celestial sphere moves from east to west carrying all objects on it, including the vernal equinox and the mean Sun which was invented for defining time, it is obvious that they will cross the meridian earlier for an observer who is further east. If the mean time were used just as defined, each clock would have a different time according to the longitude of the place in which the observer happened to be. Clocks in Sydney would be 25 minutes ahead of those of Melbourne and those of Paris 9 minutes ahead of London. With the development of rapid means of communication and travel it was obviously an advantage to adopt exactly the same time for fairly wide areas. For the purpose of specifying position on the Earth's surface the longitude of Greenwich, already much used in navigation, was accepted in 1884 as the zero for measurement of longitude. Gradually the practice has been adopted of making the time of zones of the world differ by fixed amounts from the mean time at Greenwich. The amounts are usually in whole hours, and so the minutes and seconds of time are the same as at Greenwich. France made her time coincide with Greenwich Mean Time from 1911.

The eastern states of Australia keep a time exactly ten hours ahead of Greenwich, New York and Massachusetts are five hours behind, and other states of the United States various amounts, up to eight hours, behind Greenwich. When it is 22h in Sydney—that is, 10 p.m.—it is 12 noon at Greenwich, 7 hours in New York and 4 hours in California. Some countries, such as Britain, put clocks on an hour in the summer in order to have more daylight in the period after work or to conserve power. This is not usually satisfactory in countries which have a wide extent in longitude or for which the standard time meridian is already in the eastern part of the standard time zone.

A traveller going eastward, in a ship or plane, must at intervals put his watch on to conform to the longitude in which he finds himself. This process cannot be continued indefinitely, or he could arrive back at his point of departure, after a circuit of the globe, with his date one day ahead of those who had remained at home—in effect, having had one extra day. So it is agreed that at one point in his journey there will be a discontinuity in his time-keeping. This is on the 180th meridian, and, when he crosses it, he will set his date back by one day. If he were to cross from east to west, he would add one day to his date. This line is called the International Date Line. The date just west of it is one day ahead of the date just east of it. The 180th meridian does not pass through large land masses, but, where the arrangement might cause inconvenience, the line is deviated for some distance so that an agreed area will be on the one side of it.

Time Keeping

For astronomical determination of time the first step is to observe time shown by a sidereal clock when known stars cross the meridian of the observatory. This is done by using an instrument specially set up for the purpose, and, since the sidereal time when the star is on the meridian equals the right ascension of the star, every observation gives a correction to the sidereal clock. Stars are used for this purpose because there are many of them with accurately known positions, permitting the observation to be often repeated, and because their apparent smallness makes it easier to observe the precise instant when they cross the meridian than is the case with the Sun or a planet. The next step is to convert the sidereal time thus found to standard time. As the right ascension of the mean sun is given by a formula, it can be calculated for any sidereal time. Hence the interval since it would have been on the meridian is known and the calculation of this plus twelve hours gives the mean time. The passage to standard time is then simply done by adding a constant to allow for the difference of longitude of the observatory from the meridian agreed upon as the basis for standard time.

Astronomical time, the determination of which has been outlined, depends on the rate of rotation of the Earth which brings the observed stars to the meridian. In recent years time-keeping has been revolutionised by the development of man-made clocks which are more constant in their performance than the rotation of the Earth. The best of these depend on oscillations which are related to changes in atoms. The period of the oscillations used is so accurately fixed that the time which depends on them is now being made the basis for time-keeping. Time is kept by specialist observatories and physical laboratories from which it is distributed by signals on a wire or by radio. Atomic clocks are now used for maintaining the time. However, in order to keep the signals suitable for purposes—such as navigation—for which astronomical time is needed, the emissions are changed, at intervals, when the difference has become appreciable, by $\frac{1}{10}$ or $\frac{1}{20}$ of a second, so as to conform to astronomical time. Such changes have been made on several occasions since atomic time was introduced.

NAVIGATION

One important practical application of astronomy is to navigation. For navigation the observation consists of measuring the altitude of a body whose position is known—a star, a planet, or the Sun or Moon—and noting the Greenwich Mean Time at which the measurement is made.

Let us see what information is yielded. From the particular Greenwich Mean Time it is possible to derive the sidereal time at Greenwich and hence to know the orientation of the celestial sphere relative to the Earth. In terms of Figure 3 it is seen that the point on the Earth at which the observed star was directly overhead may be identified. The latitude of this place equals the declination of the star and its longitude is the hour angle of the star at Greenwich. This is the information derived from the time of the observation.

To see what is given by the altitude Figure 6 shows a section of the Earth through the position of the observer O, and S the point where the star is overhead. The direction of the star from each place and the direction of the observer's zenith is shown. The observed altitude of the star subtracted from 90° gives the angle z in the diagram. This proves to be equal to d, the angle which represents the distance of the observer from S. If this angle is expressed in minutes, it is the distance between the two places in *nautical miles*. Thus the observation of altitude tells how far the observer is from the place where the star is overhead; that is, he must be somewhere

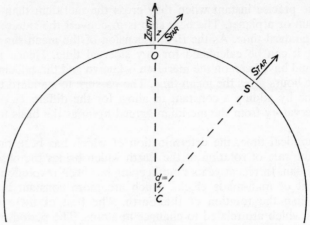

Figure 6.

on a circle with centre at S and radius d. Almost always he will have an approximate knowledge of his position and will need to draw only a small portion of the circle, his *position line*.

This information is represented in Figure 7. A star has been observed by a navigator. From the time of his observation he knows that it was overhead at the point marked S. Suppose he found the altitude of the star was 30°, he will know that he must be on a circle of radius 60° centred at S. A large part of this circle is shown, but he also knows that he is off the north coast of Africa, and so he need consider only the portion of the circle drawn as a full line. Usually the portion of the circle that needs to be drawn on his chart is so small that a straight ruled line on a chart of an area much

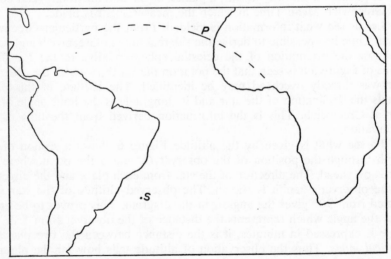

Figure 7.

smaller than in the figure is satisfactory for the purpose. To find his position completely all the navigator needs is to observe another body in a different direction and draw the corresponding position line to intersect the first one, perhaps after allowing for his motion between the two observations. His position must be at the intersection of the two lines.

These operations are of such importance that much ingenuity has been applied to devising instruments for measuring the altitude and to reducing the necessary calculations to a fairly simple routine. Keeping the Greenwich time for the observations—which in the beginning was the great difficulty—is now an easy part of the problem, since frequent time signals are available by radio, and the timepiece used by the navigator can continually be checked.

2

THE STAR MAPS

THE star maps of this chapter are designed to provide a way of recognising the more important stars and of identifying an object whose right ascension and declination are known.

There are six charts, which cover the whole sky. The first and last of these show circular sections around the North Pole and the South Pole respectively, and the remainder of the celestial sphere along the centre of which the Celestial Equator runs is divided into four sections. Each star is plotted on the map in the place corresponding to its right ascension and declination, and the size of the spot by which it is represented indicates its brightness. Three stars which vary in brightness are represented by open circles. In one place—the Pleiades cluster of stars on Map III—the stars are so close together in the sky that it was thought better to put only the brightest one, Alcyone, on the chart and to place at the foot of the page a diagram of the cluster on an eight times greater scale.

In ancient times the stars were divided into six classes of brightness. The few brightest stars in the sky were allotted to the first magnitude and the second, third, fourth and fifth magnitudes determined classes of decreasing brightness until those just visible to the naked eye were called sixth magnitude. The idea of stellar magnitude, which is of great importance, will be taken up in Chapter 8. The star maps here include all of the stars down to magnitude $4\frac{1}{2}$—that is, stars which are comfortably visible to the naked eye even in towns. The first purpose of the maps is to help the naked-eye observer to acquire some familiarity with the sky.

THE CONSTELLATIONS AND ANCIENT MYTHS

The sky is divided into areas, called constellations, which, in the northern sky, usually have names occurring in ancient myths although the divisions seem in some cases to predate the myths. In the southern part, which could not be seen by the ancient peoples of the northern hemisphere, the sky has been divided by astronomers and given names chosen by them.

The system of ancient constellations had its origin before 2000 B.C., possibly among the Sumerian and Babylonian peoples of Mesopotamia. Eudoxus, the great Greek scientist, wrote an account of the constellations as accepted in his time, and his description was incorporated, about 270 B.C., by Aratus in a poem which remains the source of our knowledge of the ancient constellation figures which represent characters in myths.

Sometimes there are several constellations associated with a particular myth or character. This is so in the story of Orion, the mighty hunter who was beloved by the goddess Diana. Her brother Apollo disapproved of the union and when he saw Orion in the sea, he challenged Diana to hit the distant object with an arrow. She accepted the challenge and her shot killed Orion, whose figure was then placed among the stars. Another story has it that Orion boasted that he would kill all animals and clear the Earth of wild beasts, but the Earth sent the scorpion whose sting was responsible for his death. This is supposed to be the reason why the constellations Orion and Scorpius are far apart in the sky. According to Aratus,

> "When the Scorpion comes
> Orion flies to the utmost end of Earth."

The hunter Orion is usually pictured with a sword at his belt, the skin of a lion flung over his left arm and a club brandished in his right hand. He is accompanied in the sky by the figures of the two dogs, Canis Major and Canis Minor and by the hare, Lepus. In Figure 8 is shown the form of Orion as depicted on maps by Flamsteed, the first Astronomer Royal of England.

Another group of constellations is associated with the legend of Perseus. Cassiopeia, the wife of Cepheus, King of Ethiopia, boasted of beauty surpassing that of the sea nymphs, who were so angered that they persuaded their father, the god Neptune, to send a monster to ravage the coast of the kingdom. The oracle said that the kingdom could be relieved from this scourge only if Cepheus chained his daughter Andromeda to a rock as a sacrifice to the monster, Cetus. They did this, but Perseus arrived, killed the monster, rescued the maiden and, very appropriately, married her. The constellations Perseus, Andromeda, Cepheus, Cassiopeia and Cetus are connected with this myth.

The ancient constellations left unnamed parts of the sky to which astronomers of a few hundred years ago did not hesitate to give names. Names that have survived were added mainly by Bayer, Hevelius and Lacaille. The constellations added by Lacaille are southern ones which he named when he visited the Cape in the middle of the eighteenth century. He used names like Telescopium and Microscopium associated with scientific apparatus. Astronomers have given up the habit of forming new constellations, and in 1930 the International Astronomical Union agreed on boundaries for the constellations. These boundaries are marked on the maps.

Figure 8.—The figure of Orion as in the atlas of Flamsteed, the first Astronomer Royal.

THE NAMES OF THE STARS

The names of some of the more conspicuous stars have been derived from the positions of the stars in the constellation figure or from some characteristic of the star. For example, in the constellation Orion, the name of the star Betelgeuse which is at the shoulder is a corruption of Arabic words meaning "the armpit of the central one", and the name Rigel comes from an Arabic word for the foot or leg. The name of Sirius, the brightest star in the sky, comes from the Greek word meaning sparkling or scorching. Many names of stars have gone out of use. The ones remaining most in use are marked on the charts.

Independently of any proper name they may have, most of the naked-eye stars are named by a Greek letter and the constellation in which they are situated. Sirius, for example, is Alpha Canis Majoris, that is, Alpha of the constellation Canis Major. The constellation names and the changes to indicate inclusion are Latin in form. This system was begun by Bayer in 1603. Usually the Greek letters are allotted in the order of brightness of the stars in the constellation, and Alpha will be brighter than Beta and so on. Bayer did not aim at following this rule exactly, and, although some later astronomers tried to do so, they did not always succeed very well. A list of the Greek letters is given below so that they may be recognised on the maps and used for naming the stars.

α Alpha	η Eta	ν Nu	τ Tau
β Beta	θ Theta	ξ Xi	υ Upsilon
γ Gamma	ι Iota	o Omicron	ϕ Phi
δ Delta	κ Kappa	π Pi	χ Chi
ϵ Epsilon	λ Lambda	ρ Rho	Ψ Psi
ζ Zeta	μ Mu	σ Sigma	ω Omega

CONSTELLATIONS AND STAR NAMES AND HOW TO SAY THEM

A list of the constellations now adopted is given. The first column gives the name of the constellation and, in brackets, the inflection required to indicate inclusion or possession. The second column gives a guide to pronunciation and, in brackets, the change for the possessive, and the final column contains the meaning and period from which the constellation dates —whether ancient, A, or modern, M. A list of the most used star names and their pronunciation is also given. The pronunciation is not always easy to decide with confidence as there are differences in different English-speaking countries, and I fully realize that in some cases there may be objections from other astronomers. Moreover, Latin scholars have more than once changed their way of pronunciation, and astronomers have not always followed the changes. However, it seemed better to give some guidance rather than to leave it to chance and, if you use the indicated pronunciation, you can be confident of being in accordance with some usage and understood by all.

NOTE: The main accent is indicated by the mark ′ at the end of the stressed syllable. The consonants used are: b, d, f, g (go), h, j (jest), k, l, m, n, n̄g (ring), p, r, s, t, v, w, y (yes), z, and the vowels: a, e, i, o, u (hat, get, it, hot, tub), ā, ē, ī, ō, ū, oo (fate, be, child, bone, tube, moon), ah, aw, ār, ēr (path, haul, care, her), and ĕ for the indeterminate vowel as in "sofa" or "circus".

The following cases exemplify the information on the maps and lists. The variable star Mira, right ascension 2 hours 20 minutes and declination —3° on Map II, is also o Ceti. Incidentally, its name means "the wonderful" as it was the first star recognised, in 1596, as variable. Arcturus, right ascension 14h 12m and declination +19° on Map IV is α Boötis. It is of first magnitude while η Boötis nearby is a third magnitude star.

THE CONSTELLATIONS

Constellation	Pronunciation	Meaning
Andromeda (ae)	androm′edĕ (−ē)	Andromeda, A.
Antlia (−ae)	ant′liĕ (−iē)	The Pump, M.
Apus (Apodis)	a′pus (ap′ĕdis)	The Bird of Paradise, M.
Aquarius (−ii)	ĕkwār′ius (−ī)	The Water Carrier, A.
Aquila (−ae)	ak′wilĕ(−ē)	The Eagle, A.
Ara (−ae)	ār′rĕ (−rē)	The Altar, A.
Aries (Arietis)	ār′ēz (ĕrī′etis)	The Ram, A.
Auriga (−ae)	awrī′gĕ (−jē)	The Charioteer, A.
Boötes (−is)	bōō′tēz (−is)	Boötes, A.
Caelum (−i)	sē′lem (−ī)	The Sculptor's Chisel, M.
Camelopardalis (is)	kamel′opah′dĕlis	The Giraffe, M.
Cancer (−cri)	kan′sĕ (kan̄g′krī)	The Crab, A.
Canes Venatici	kā′nēz venat′isī	The Hunting Dogs, M.
(−um−orum)	(−ĕm−aw′rem)	
Canis Major	kā′nis mā′jĕ	The Greater Dog, A.
(−is−oris)	(−is−aw′ris)	
Canis Minor	kā′nis mī′nĕ	The Lesser Dog, A.
(−is−oris)	(−is−aw′ris)	
Capricornus (−i)	kap′rikaw′nĕs (−ī)	The Goat, A.
Carina (−ae)	kĕrī′nĕ (−ē)	The Keel, M.
Cassiopeia (−ae)	kas′iōpē′yĕ (−ē)	Cassiopeia, A:
Centaurus (−i)	sentaw′rĕs (−ī)	The Centaur, A.
Cepheus (−ei)	sē′fēĕs (ēī)	Cepheus, A.
Cetus (−i)	sē′tĕs (−ī)	The Whale, A.
Chamaeleon (−eontis)	kĕmē′lēĕn (−ēon′tis)	The Chameleon, M.
Circinus (−i)	sēr′sinĕs (−ī)	The Compasses, M.
Columba (−ae)	kōlum′bĕ (−ē)	The Dove, M.
Coma Berenices	kō′mĕ ber′ēnī′sēz	Berenice's Hair, M.
(−ae−es)	(−ē−ēz)	
Corona Austrina	kōrō′nĕ ostrī′nĕ	The Southern Crown, A.
(−ae− ae)	(−ĕ −ē)	

Constellation	Pronunciation	Meaning
Corona Borealis (−ae −is)	kōrō'nĕ bōrēā'lis (−ē −is)	The Northern Crown, A.
Corvus (−i)	kaw'vĕs (−ī)	The Crow, A.
Crater (−eris)	krā'tĕ (−e'ris)	The Cup, A.
Crux (Crucis)	kruks (krōō'sis)	The Cross, M.
Cygnus (−i)	sig'nĕs (−ī)	The Swan, A.
Delphinus (−i)	delfī'nĕs (−ī)	The Dolphin, A.
Dorado (−us)	dōrah'do (−ōōs)	The Swordfish, M.
Draco (−onis)	drā'kō (drĕkō'nis)	The Dragon, A.
Equuleus (−ei)	ēkwōō'lĕĕs (−ēī)	The Little Horse, A.
Eridanus (−i)	ērid'ĕnĕs (−ī)	Eridanus, A.
Fornax (−acis)	faw'naks (fawnā'sis)	The Furnace, M.
Gemini (orum)	jem'inī (−ō'rĕm)	The Twins, A.
Grus (Gruis)	grus (grōō'is)	The Crane, M.
Hercules (−is)	hēr'kūlĕz (−is)	Hercules, A.
Horologium (−ii)	horōlō'jiĕm (−iī)	The Clock, M.
Hydra (−ae)	hī'drĕ (−ē)	The Water Snake, A.
Hydrus (−i)	hī'drĕs (−ī)	The Water Snake, M.
Indus (−i)	in'dĕs (−ī)	The Indian, M.
Lacerta (−ae)	lesēr'tĕ (−ē)	The Lizard, M.
Leo (−onis)	lē'ō (lēō'nis)	The Lion, A.
Leo Minor (−onis −oris)	lē'ō mī'nĕ (−ō'nis −aw'ris)	The Lesser Lion, M.
Lepus (−oris)	lē'pĕs (lep'ĕris)	The Hare, A.
Libra (−ae)	lī'brĕ (−ē)	The Balance, A.
Lupus (−i)	lū'pĕs (−ī)	The Wolf, A.
Lynx (Lyncis)	lĭngks (lin'sis)	The Lynx, M.
Lyra (−ae)	lī'rĕ (−ē)	The Lyre, A.
Mensa (−ae)	men'sĕ (−ē)	The Table, M.
Microscopium (−ii)	mīkrōskō'piĕm (−iī)	The Microscope, M.
Monoceros (−otis)	mĕnos'ĕros (−ō'tis)	The Unicorn, M.
Musca (−ae)	mus'kĕ (mus'sē)	The Fly, M.
Norma (−ae)	naw'mĕ (−ē)	The Square, M.
Octans (−antis)	ok'tanz (oktan'tis)	The Octant, M.
Ophiuchus (−i)	ofiū'kĕs (−ī)	The Serpent Bearer, A.
Orion (Orionis)	ōrī'ĕn (ō'riō'nis)	Orion, A.
Pavo (−onis)	pā'vō (pavō'nis)	The Peacock, M.
Pegasus (−i)	peg'ĕsĕs (−ī)	Pegasus, A.
Perseus (−ei)	pēr'sūs (pēr'sēī)	Perseus, A.
Phoenix (−icis)	fē'niks (fēnī'sis)	The Phoenix, M.
Pictor (−oris)	pik'tĕ (pictō'ris)	The Painter, M.
Pisces (−cium)	pis'ēs (pis'iĕm)	The Fishes, A.
Piscis Austrinus (−is −i)	pis'is ostrī'nĕs (−is −ī)	The Southern Fish, A.
Puppis (−is)	pup'is (−is)	The Poop, M.
Pyxis (−idis)	pik'sis (−idis)	The Compass, M.

Constellation	Pronunciation	Meaning
Reticulum (−i)	rētik′ūlĕm (−ī)	The Net, M.
Sagitta (−ae)	sajit′ĕ (−ē)	The Arrow, A.
Sagittarius (−ii)	sajitār′iĕs (−ii)	The Archer, A.
Scorpius (−ii)	skaw′piĕs (−ii)	The Scorpion, A.
Sculptor (−oris)	skulp′tĕ (−ō′ris)	The Sculptor, M.
Scutum (−i)	skū′tĕm (−ī)	The Shield, M.
Serpens (−entis)	sēr′penz (−en′tis)	The Serpent, A.
Sextans (−antis)	seks′tanz (−an′tis)	The Sextant, M.
Taurus (−i)	taw′rĕs (−ī)	The Bull, A.
Telescopium (−ii)	teleskō′piĕm (−ii)	The Telescope, M.
Triangulum (−i)	trīan͞g′gūlĕm (−ī)	The Triangle, A.
Triangulum Australe (−i −is)	trīan͞g′gūlĕm ostrā′lē (−ī −is)	The Southern Triangle, M.
Tucana (−ae)	to͞okā′nĕ (−ē)	The Toucan, M.
Ursa Major (−ae −oris)	ēr′sĕ mā′jĕ (ēr′sē mējaw′ris)	The Greater Bear, A.
Ursa Minor (−ae −oris)	ēr′sĕ mī′nĕ (−ē −aw′ris)	The Lesser Bear, A.
Vela (−orum)	vē′lĕ (vel ō′rĕm)	The Sails, M.
Virgo (−inis)	vēr′gō (vēr′jinis)	The Virgin, A.
Volans (−antis)	vō′lanz (−an′tis)	The Flying Fish, M.
Vulpecula (−ae)	vulpek′ūlĕ (−ē)	The Fox, M.

IMPORTANT STAR NAMES

Star Name	Pronunciation	Equivalent	
Achernar	ā′kĕnah	α	Eridani
Aldebaran	aldeb′ĕran	α	Tauri
Algol	al′gol	β	Persei
Altair	altār′	α	Aquilae
Antares	antār′rēs	α	Scorpii
Arcturus	ahktūr′us	α	Boötis
Betelgeuse	bet′eljo͞oz	α	Orionis
Canopus	kanō′pĕs	α	Carinae
Capella	kĕpel′ĕ	α	Aurigae
Castor	kah′stĕ	α	Geminorum
Fomalhaut	fō′malhawt	α	Piscis Austrini
Mira	mī′rĕ	o	Ceti
Polaris	pōlār′ris	α	Ursae Minoris
Pollux	pol′uks	β	Geminorum
Procyon	prō′sion	α	Canis Minoris
Regulus	reg′ūlĕs	α	Leonis
Rigel	rī′jel	β	Orionis
Sirius	sir′iĕs	α	Canis Majoris
Spica	spī′kĕ	α	Virginis
Vega	vē′gĕ	α	Lyrae

TABLE 1

Conversion of Mean Time to Sidereal Time

Date	6 p.m.	8 p.m.	10 p.m.	0 a.m. Midnight	2 a.m.	4 a.m.	6 a.m.
	h	h	h	h	h	h	h
Jan. 5	1	3	5	7	9	11	13
Jan. 21	2	4	6	8	10	12	14
Feb. 5	3	5	7	9	11	13	15
Feb. 20	4	6	8	10	12	14	16
Mar. 7	5	7	9	11	13	15	17
Mar. 22	6	8	10	12	14	16	18
Apr. 6	7	9	11	13	15	17	19
Apr. 22	8	10	12	14	16	18	20
May 7	9	11	13	15	17	19	21
May 22	10	12	14	16	18	20	22
June 6	11	13	15	17	19	21	23
June 22	12	14	16	18	20	22	24
July 7	13	15	17	19	21	23	1
July 22	14	16	18	20	22	24	2
Aug. 6	15	17	19	21	23	1	3
Aug. 22	16	18	20	22	24	2	4
Sep. 6	17	19	21	23	1	3	5
Sep. 21	18	20	22	24	2	4	6
Oct. 6	19	21	23	1	3	5	7
Oct. 21	20	22	24	2	4	6	8
Nov. 6	21	23	1	3	5	7	9
Nov. 21	22	24	2	4	6	8	10
Dec. 6	23	1	3	5	7	9	11
Dec. 21	24	2	4	6	8	10	12

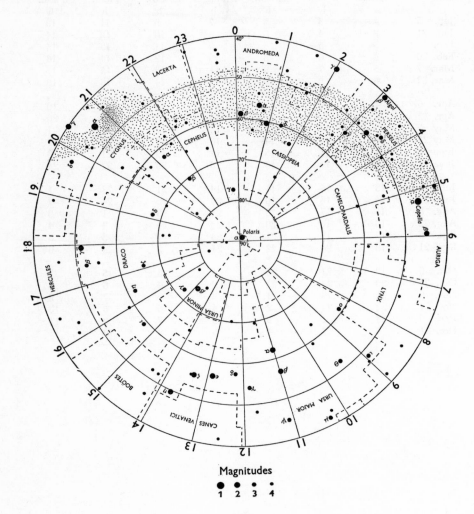

Map I.

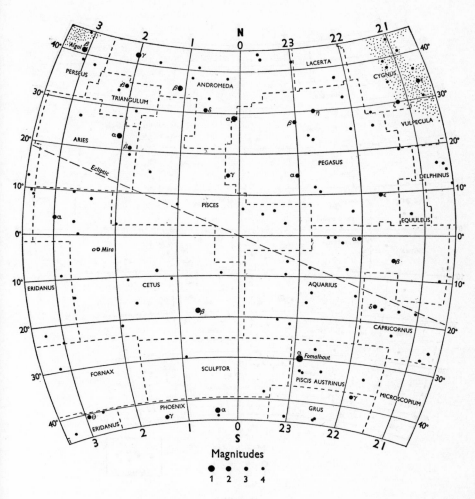

Magnitudes

● ● · ·
1 2 3 4

Map II.

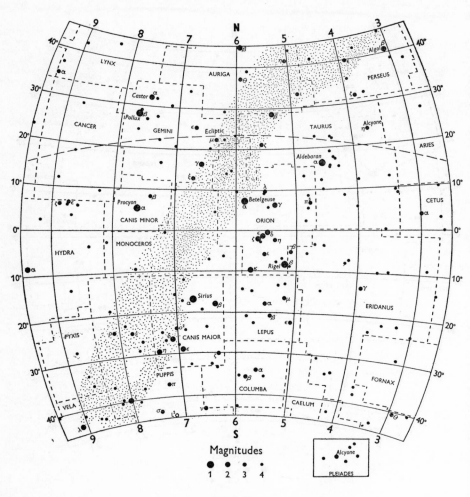

Map III.

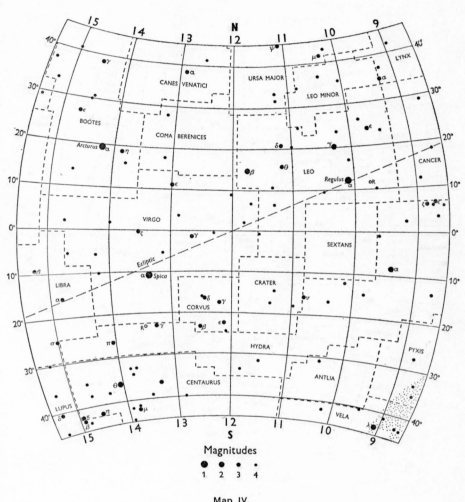

Map IV.

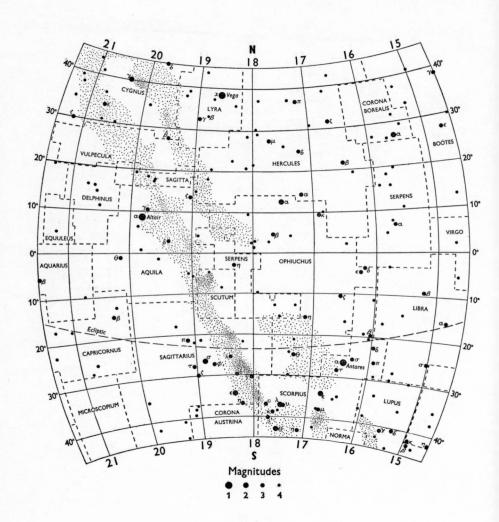

Map V.

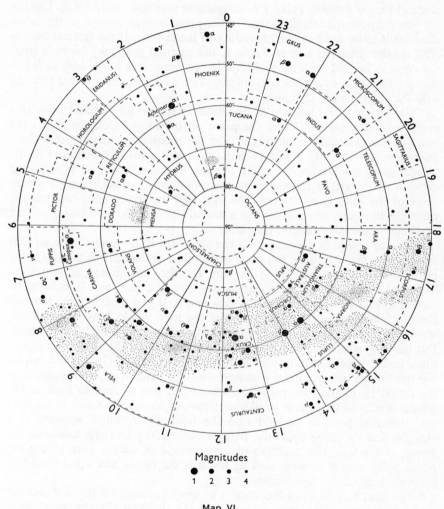

Magnitudes

1 2 3 4

Map VI.

HOW TO USE THE STAR MAPS

The maps are used by matching them to the sky. This may be done in several ways, but the first problem is to find the chart which represents the part of the sky which is at the moment visible. This is easy to do if the sidereal time is known. Table 1 is designed to give this information. Usually for this purpose the standard time of the place is near enough to the mean time for it to be used as corresponding to mean time. If the nearest date is read on the left hand side of Table 1, the sidereal time may be read from the column headed with time of day. If necessary it is fairly easy to interpolate times in between those tabulated. For example, the sidereal time on July 7th at 11 p.m. is 18 hours.

The approximate latitude of the observer is also needed and these two pieces of information indicate the place on the map which represents the point of the celestial sphere which is at the moment overhead. At Sydney latitude —34° on July 7th at 11 p.m. the point overhead would be in the constellation Saggitarius. The line towards the northern part of the map extends northward in the sky from this point with the higher right ascensions of the map lying towards the east and the lower ones towards the west. On the same day and time in a latitude 40° north, the point overhead would be in the constellation Hercules.

Now to compare the map with the sky, turn it in various ways so that the stars on the map have the same orientation as the part of the sky being examined. For example, at Sydney on the date mentioned, if you were looking towards the northern part of the sky, the map would need to be turned so that its northern end was downward. If you were looking towards the east, then the north-eastern part of the map would have to be downward. The rule is that the place of the zenith on the map must be uppermost. But the map which includes the zenith does not cover the whole sky at any time, and it is necessary to pass to neighbouring maps. This should not be too hard to do because there is always overlap between any two neighbouring maps. If, in the case used as an example, you wanted to look at the southern part of the sky, it would be necessary to use the South Polar map and it would have to be held with the hour circle, which appears as a straight line radiating from the pole corresponding to right ascension 18 hours, at the top. The northern observer would of course have to use the north polar map if he were looking towards the north, and again the same hour circle would be uppermost.

The best way to learn the stars is to work outward on the sky and the maps at the same time, from a part of the sky that you already know either through help of a friend or by a preliminary use of the maps. It is easiest to begin with a conspicuous constellation like Orion. Now suppose that you already know Orion on Map III. The Map indicates that, if you look along the line of the three stars near the centre of the constellation on the Celestial Equator about the distance equal to that between Betelgeuse and Rigel, Sirius is reached in one direction and Aldebaran in the other. By transferring the configuration of the Map to the sky in this way and making use of the brightness of the stars as indicated by the Map to help identification it is possible to extend the part of the sky with which you are acquainted. Once you have made a start, you will be surprised at the number of constellations and stars you will recognise after only a few short sessions.

If you have to commence without help, it is still easy. Just try, using the Map in the appropriate way, to recognise one or two of the first magnitude stars, and there are not many of them, or a conspicuous pattern of stars, and then begin making the correspondences between the Map and the sky as already suggested. When the correspondences begin to work out, you can be quite sure of being on the right track.

When you are able to make the correspondence between the maps and the sky, you may use the maps in several ways. Suppose you notice something in the sky which you want to identify. You can see where it is amongst the stars and, from this, where it should appear on the map. If it is a star, it may already be on the map and identified; if not, the right ascension and declination can be obtained from the map, and a further inquiry made. On the other hand, if the right ascension and declination of some object are known, its position can be noted on the map, and then by recognising surrounding stars it can be found in the sky. For example, the position of a double star Theta Eridani has right ascension 2 hours 56 minutes, declination —$40\frac{1}{2}°$. If you look at the map in this position, you will find that the star is marked as a third magnitude star. Or, supposing the position of the cluster of stars M41 is given as right ascension 6 hours 45 minutes, declination —$20.°7$, you could mark its position south of Sirius on Map III. If then you look at the sky represented at this point, you will see a hazy patch of light which in the telescope is revealed as a cluster of stars.

The naming of objects in the sky is complicated by the fact that there are far too many of them for the use of proper names that could be recorded or for the numbers of letters from alphabets. Hence many of the objects receive their names from the number that they have in some catalogue. The cluster M41 is so called because it is number 41 in a catalogue of nebulae and star clusters which was compiled by the French astronomer Messier in the eighteenth century. Many famous objects have Messier numbers or numbers from the New General Catalogue of Nebulae and Star Clusters which was published in 1888. Because this last Catalogue aimed at being complete, it included most of the objects in the Messier Catalogue, and NGC 2287 is the same object as M41. There are also catalogues dealing with positions of stars or their brightness, with double stars or variable stars. Each catalogue is capable of giving to each object it contains a further name which may be used in an appropriate context.

FINDING DIRECTION BY THE STARS

A familiarity with the stars gained in the way outlined can be very useful for finding direction at night. Recognition of a point in the sky near the pole which is above the horizon gives north or south and from this the remaining points of the compass. In the Northern Hemisphere, once the star Polaris is known it identifies the north, while in the Southern Hemisphere there are several ways of finding the South Celestial Pole. One way is to measure the length from Gamma to Alpha in Crux and then continue in the same direction for four times this length. Another way is to take the point half way between Achernar and Beta Centauri. It is easy to see other ways of finding south simply by looking at the South Polar Map. Of course, other parts of the sky can be used, too, for finding direction at night. If some stars such as the Orion stars which are known to be on the Celestial Equator are recognised near the horizon, their direction must be due east or due west. In former times using chiefly such aids to navigation long voyages were made out of sight of land.

3

TOOLS FOR DISCOVERY

THE tools used to extend our knowledge of the universe are of two kinds. First, there are the instrumental aids like telescopes or cameras with which observations are collected, and second, the theories with the help of which observations are interpreted. An established theory which forms part of the knowledge we have and affords means of enlarging our understanding or examining observations may be as much a tool for discovery as a telescope. One significant way of estimating the value of a theory is to consider the range of situations to which it can apply and the effectiveness with which, in association with observation and experiment, it leads to new knowledge. The theory of gravitation which will shortly be outlined is an outstanding example of this. It is an important part of our information about the physical universe, and it is, at the same time, a powerful means of extending our knowledge, whether the subject is the structure of the solar system, the constitution of a star, or the movement of a whole galaxy of stars.

Discoveries in astronomy are not made by magic but by examination of something which reaches our instruments, to be interpreted as a message from distant space. The most obvious and commonplace thing is light whose amount and colour may be measured and whose direction of arrival may be observed.

A short account of some of the properties of light is needed to show how it may be controlled in instruments, recorded and interpreted.

LIGHT AND ITS BEHAVIOUR

The most obvious thing about light is that if nothing comes in its way, it travels in straight lines. A small source of light throws behind any object a shadow which faithfully outlines the object. Our eyes could not define things clearly if light travelled in some confused manner rather than in straight lines. The velocity of light, which has been measured many times, is 186,000 miles per second.

When a ray of light strikes the surface of a transparent substance like glass some of the light is reflected and some goes through the glass, and in each case the path is bent. This is shown in Figure 9 in which a ray of light *AB* is supposed to reach the glass, indicated by stippling. Part of the light is *reflected* in the direction *BC*, and this ray after reflection makes the same angle with the surface as it did before. If the reflected ray is wanted, a reflecting substance like silver or aluminium is deposited on the surface. The ray *BD* in the glass is also bent, or *refracted*, to make a greater angle with the glass than before.

The amount by which the light is bent depends on the nature of the substances on either side of the surface through which it passes, and may be accurately calculated when their properties have been measured. If it passes in the reverse direction, it is bent towards the glass; that is, a ray of light in the glass moving in the direction *DB* would emerge in the direction *BA*. An important property of refraction is that different colours of light are bent by different amounts, and it is this which leads to the familiar phenomenon of a rainbow, visible as the range of colours from sunlight refracted and separated into its components by passage through rain drops. The order of the colours is red, orange, yellow, green, blue and violet, the red being bent least and the blue most.

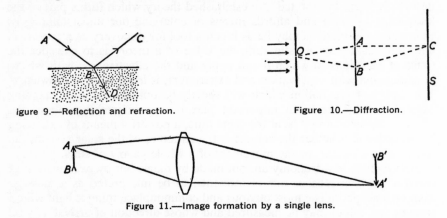

igure 9.—Reflection and refraction.   Figure 10.—Diffraction.

Figure 11.—Image formation by a single lens.

Wave Theory of Light

A ray of light has many of the characteristics of a succession of waves. This can be illustrated by arranging two beams of light to interact to cause alternating regions of light and darkness. Figure 10 represents an apparatus designed to do this. A bright source of light of one pure colour lies to the left of a slit, shown in section at *O*, from which it passes to two parallel narrow slits at *A* and *B*. Now the slits *A* and *B* act as sources of wave motion like the original arriving wave, and the light from them arrives at a screen *S* placed in the path of the light. The width of *O* should be small compared with its distance from *A* and *B* and the separation of *A* and *B* small compared with their distance from *S*. It is possible to calculate how the light varies at different places on the screen. At a point *C* the difference in length of the paths AC and BC might be equal to an exact number of wave lengths—in which case the crests and troughs of the waves from the two slits would arrive together and each would reinforce the other, so that at C it would be comparatively bright. At other places, where the difference in the paths from the slits to the screen amounted to an odd number of half wave-lengths, and the waves would consequently be arriving half a wave-length apart, the crests of the waves from A would occur when there was a trough in those from B and there would be a minimum of light on the screen. The light pattern is thus a series of parallel lines. Such a pattern would usually be so faint as to be difficult to see on a screen as described, but, if the screen is removed and the plane at S viewed from the right through an eyepiece, the bands would be observable.

The geometry of this apparatus, including the distance of the screen from the slits, the spacing of the slits and the wave-lengths of the light, would enable the pattern on the screen to be calculated or, if the pattern were measured, the same sort of calculation would enable an estimate to be made of the wave-length although in practice other methods would always be used. The length of the wave for yellow light is a little over 1/50,000 inch.

In dealing with wave-lengths of light it is convenient to introduce the micron as a unit of measurement. It is 1/1,000 millimetre or about 1/25,000 inch. The colour of light depends on its wave-length. If white light instead of light of one colour were used with the apparatus described above, the reinforcement of light for different wave-lengths would occur in different places, and the pattern would show coloured fringes. Red light has a wave length of $0\cdot7$ micron, yellow, such as is given by a sodium light, $0\cdot6$ micron and blue $0\cdot4$ micron.

An important piece of equipment for analysing light makes use of the principles involved in this experiment. Instead of just two slits there are many, very closely spaced, formed by ruling lines with a very accurate machine. The phenomenon described, that of *interference* between waves arriving by different paths from the same source, is called *diffraction*, and the system of rulings a *diffraction grating*. Such a grating might typically have about 14,000 lines per inch. Diffraction gratings have great practical importance because the different wave-lengths of light—that is, the different colours of light after passage through a grating—have their maxima in different places. A diffraction grating, therefore, may be used in an apparatus to analyse the light into its component colours as in the case of refraction. The explanation which has been given for alternate transparent and non-transparent lines would apply equally for alternate reflecting and non-reflecting lines, with the analysis into colours occurring after reflection. Reflection gratings are common.

Polarization

The existence of a wave implies the presence of an oscillation. The oscillation in the case of light is of an electrical character. The vibrations of a wave can be in the direction of travel of the wave or across its direction, but light exhibits properties which vary in different directions across its direction of travel, and so the oscillation must be of the transverse kind.

A common example of this occurs in the polarizing ("polaroid") spectacles that are sometimes used for protection against glare. Such a glass transmits the vibrations in only one plane when the light is said to be plane polarized or linearly polarized. If a second polarizing glass is placed in the path, it is found that in one orientation of the second glass for which the transmitted plane is perpendicular to the first, nearly all of the light is stopped, while in other orientations more is passed until a maximum is reached when the plane for transmission in the second glass is parallel to that in the first. Any lack of symmetry in the path of the light to the observer may give rise to *polarization*—that is, a favoured direction of oscillation.

The polarizing glass will facilitate observation of many examples of this in our everyday surroundings. Rotating it between the eye and the reflecting surface of a pool of water or sheet of glass causes a variation in the intensity of light received at the eye and shows that the reflected light is polarized. The vibrations are parallel to the reflecting surface. The blue light of the sky is polarized strongly if examined in directions at right angles to the direction of the Sun, but is less so towards the Sun or, if the Sun is low, in the direction away from the Sun. This characteristic of light is useful, on the one hand because it provides another way of manipulating light—for example, of controlling its brightness—and, on the other, because it affords another property that can be looked for to determine the kind of environment from which the light has come or, in astronomy, something of the history of its journey to the Earth.

If the light has originated from matter in a magnetic field we shall see later that it is affected in ways that may be revealed by passing it through a polarizing medium. This has enabled measurement to be made of the magnetism of the Sun and stars and will be referred to in discussion of the Sun. If light from a star has been reflected by a cloud of very small particles, it will be more polarized than if the particles are large. The light from stars in the Milky Way is polarized to some extent by the tenuous material it traverses on its way to us. Hence, something may be learnt about the material between the stars by observation of polarization of the arriving light.

OPTICAL INSTRUMENTS

Lenses and Mirrors

Commonly the first function of an optical instrument is to form an image of the object which is under examination. The image may be formed by a lens or a mirror. In Figure 11 a convex lens is shown, to the left of which is an object from which the light is gathered by the lens. Consider the point A of the object. A ray of light from this reaches the front surface of the lens and is bent inwards a little, and again bent inwards when it passes from the back surface of the lens. This happens for all of the area of the lens, and, if the lens has been properly shaped, all of the light from the point *A* will pass through the point on the right side of the lens marked *A'*. If the lens is ideal, the same thing happens for the light coming from any point of the object, and, when a white screen is placed at *A'B'*, the image of the object may be seen on it. With a small lens it is easy to form an image of the bars of a window on a sheet of paper. For a lens which is not too thick the distance from the lens of the image of a very distant object is called the *focal length* and the size of the image depends on this. For thicker and more complicated optical systems the same idea applies except that it is a more complex matter to decide from which point of the lens to measure.

So far the light passing through the lens has been taken to be one colour. If it is white light, composed of a variety of colours, the different colours will be bent by different amounts as they pass through the surfaces of the lens. The red light, being less bent, will form its image further away from the lens than the other rays, and blue, the more refracted ray, will come to a focus closer. An undesirable lack of clarity in the image arises in this way.

To overcome this *chromatic aberration* telescopic lenses are commonly made of two components as shown in Figure 12. The first of these bends the rays from the object inwards and the second one bends them outwards but not enough to prevent the image being formed. If the two types of glass of which the lens is made and the form of the surfaces are properly chosen, the second component will bend the blue light outwards more than the red in such a way that in the image they come very nearly together and there is a great improvement in the quality of the image.

There is another defect in a simple lens as depicted in Figure 11, in that the rays passing through the edge of the lens come to focus closer to the lens than those that pass through its centre. This defect is called *spherical aberration*, and it, too, may be largely removed if the components

Figure 12.—The achromatic lens.

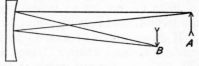

Figure 13.—Image formation by a concave mirror.

A. CORNEA
B. AQUEOUS HUMOUR
C. CRYSTALLINE LENS
D. VITREOUS HUMOUR
E. RETINA

Figure 14.—The human eye.

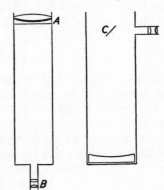

Figure 15.—The refracting and reflecting telescopes.

of the doublet lens are properly designed. There are other defects which may be important if the lens is required to cover a wide field such as is often the case with lenses designed for photography. In such cases more components have to be employed and it is common for a lens designed for photography to have four or more components.

The image of an optical system may also be formed by a mirror. This is shown in Figure 13 where we have an object at *A*, the light from which is reflected by the front surface of a concave mirror to form an image at *B*. In a mirror system rays of all colours are reflected in the same way and so come to focus at the same place. The mirror is still, of course, subject to the other aberrations. The shape of the surface of a mirror which has no spherical aberration and gives perfect images of a very distant object at one central point is called a *parabola*. More complicated systems are needed if good images are desired over a wide field, as in photography. It is usual to add a refracting element to the system. This correcting element may be placed just inside the plane of the focus of a parabola or where the light enters the telescope in the case of the Schmidt camera, where the correcting plate is designed to correct the defects of a spherical mirror.

The Eye

The most important optical instrument is the human eye—shown diagrammatically in Figure 14. The front surface is the cornea and a little below this there is a lens, called the crystalline lens, embedded in the fluids, aqueous humour and vitreous humour, of the eye ball. This system forms an image on the sensitive surface, the retina, at the rear of the eye. Muscles attached to the crystalline lens adjust its shape to bring into clear focus objects at different distances. From the retina impulses proceed to the brain by a system of nerve fibres and are there interpreted. The inclusion, as in the eye, of an image-forming device and the means to record and interpret what is imaged may be regarded as typical of an optical system. If an eye-piece or a small lens is placed before the eye, it is often possible to form an enlarged image of an object on the retina and see more detail. With age the eye usually loses its capacity to bring close objects to focus on the retina, and it becomes necessary for people to wear glasses to assist the eye to give a sharp image.

TELESCOPES

In the telescope the optical component which forms the image which is to be examined may be a lens, like that of Figure 12, or a mirror, as in Figure 13. In either case if it is to be used to see objects directly with the eye, the image is examined by means of an eyepiece. The optical parts must be mounted in a tube or rigid frame so that the relative positions of the optical components will be maintained. The refracting telescope, illustrated at the left in Figure 15, has its object lens *A* at the front and the eyepiece in position *B* just behind the image which it is examining. The reflecting telescope on the right of Figure 15 forms its image in front of the mirror, where the observer could not look at it without his head preventing the light from the star from reaching the mirror. Accordingly, at C inside the focus, a mirror is placed to send the image out of the side of the tube for examination by the eye-piece. This is the Newtonian form of the telescope, invented by Isaac Newton. There are other forms in which this secondary reflector is placed across the beam to send the light straight back down the tube through a hole in the centre of the main mirror, below which the eyepiece may then be mounted.

The Power of the Telescope

When you look through a telescope, you usually expect the object at which you look to appear larger than without the telescope—in other words, the image has a larger size on the retina of your eye and appears to subtend a larger angle. The ratio of the angles, with and without the telescope, is its *power* or *magnification.* If you look at a man 1,000 yards away with a small telescope of power 10, his apparent size matches that of a man of the same height 100 yards away viewed with the other, naked, eye. The power of a telescope may be calculated by dividing the focal length of the objective lens or mirror by the focal length of the eyepiece.

The power of a telescope can obviously be altered by changing its eyepiece and, depending on the object at which the astronomer is looking, he commonly does this to make best use of the conditions. However, it is of no use to increase the power indefinitely because the wave character of light implies that the image of a point source of light is not exactly a point, and thus the capacity of a telescope to resolve fine detail is limited. The smallest angular separation at which two stars can be seen as individuals, called the resolving power, is given in seconds of arc by the formula $250,000 \, L/D$, where L is the wave length of the light and D the diameter of the object lens or mirror of the telescope. For the wave length of green light this is about $5/D$ seconds, with D measured in inches.

The resolving power of the unaided eye varies a great deal with the individual, but it may, somewhat arbitrarily, be taken that two stars of favourable brightness can be resolved if they are two minutes of arc apart. It is useful to increase power only to the point where it is the limitation of the telescope rather than of the eye that prevents discrimination of fine detail. Beyond this we merely see more of the pattern necessarily associated with the formation of the telescopic image rather than features of the object being examined. In any case, the atmosphere which is part of the optical system often has a bad effect on the quality of the image. Thus the amount of magnification which may profitably be used is limited to about twenty-five times the diameter of the object glass, or mirror, in inches.

If a faint extended object is to be viewed, it may be a disadvantage to use a high power which spreads the available light over a wider angle, and if regions of the Milky Way are being viewed it may be better to use a low power which brings a bigger area of sky into view, thus providing a richer field of stars. To examine this situation we calculate the magnification in another way as the ratio of the diameter of the beam which enters the telescope, the diameter of the object glass, to that of the beam which leaves the telescope at the eyepiece. In order to enter the eye without possibility of loss the beam coming from the eyepiece should not exceed about a quarter of an inch, and so the lower limit of magnification normally useful is about four per inch of diameter of the object glass.

There is often a temptation, in obtaining a first telescope, to obtain powers which are too high. The limits are approximately set by the considerations outlined, and, if you can get two eyepieces, they should preferably give magnifications of about twenty times and five times the aperture in inches.

Telescopes in Use

The use of even a small telescope enables us to see many details quite beyond the reach of the eye alone. In small telescopes only two or three inches in aperture the mountains on the Moon are easily distinguished, some of the surface features of the planets Jupiter and Saturn may be seen, and the rings of Saturn, the satellites of Jupiter, the phases of Venus and magnificent views of the star clusters along the Milky Way all become visible.

The telescope can also be made into an accurate pointer for measuring the positions of the stars, just as the sights of a rifle are used to pinpoint the position of the target. A cross or more complicated pattern formed by thin thread is set up in the image plane of the objective and the position of the star may be ascertained by measuring the direction of the telescope when the star is brought on to these cross lines.

Large telescopes are sought not only because they are able to resolve finer detail but also because faint objects must be observed and it is necessary to gather light from an area as large as possible to supply the hungry recording and analysing accessories.

Most of the larger telescopes of the world are reflectors. The reasons for this are, that whereas a reflector requires only one large optical surface to be worked a refractor requires four, that the light passes through the glass of a refractor which must therefore be of a very high quality hard to achieve in large sizes, and, most important, that the glasses of a refractor must be supported around the edge and are therefore subject to bending under their own weight. This bending must change in the different positions of the telescope. With a reflector it is possible to arrange a complicated system of support for the whole of the underside of the mirror. The largest refracting telescope, at Yerkes Observatory near Chicago, is forty inches in diameter, whereas the largest reflector, at Mount Palomar in Southern California, is two hundred inches in diameter. If the images formed by an optical system are to be good compared with its resolving power, surfaces must be accurate compared with the lengths of the waves with which they are designed to deal. Errors of 1/100,000 inch in a mirror would not be tolerable and much better accuracy is usually sought. It is for this reason that so much care must be taken to guard against distortion of the optical parts arising from their own weight or from differences in expansion due to changes of temperature.

Many amateur astronomers make their own telescopes, mainly reflectors. There are several good books, listed in Chapter 12, which give directions for this work. Mirrors of six inches in diameter are satisfactory for a beginning, but larger sizes are made, up to the limit of the energy, patience and means of the amateur. Occasionally twenty inches are exceeded.

TELESCOPE MOUNTINGS

It is not easy to hold even binoculars in the hand so steadily that observation is not impaired by movement. Since the telescope magnifies so much more it is necessary to fix it on a very stable mounting and to provide it with facilities for pointing in a way which conforms with the purpose for which it is designed. The forms taken by mountings are very much influenced by their location on the rotating Earth.

The Transit Instrument

An important type of mounting in which the telescope is used as a pointer is the meridian transit telescope. This is illustrated in Figure 16. The telescope has only one mechanical axis AB, about which it turns in fixed Y's so that the axis is as nearly as possible to east and west and as nearly as possible to level. When the telescope is moved about this axis, it can be pointed only at stars which are on the meridian. It has cross wires at its eyepiece for pointing accurately at the stars. The axis of the Earth acts as the other axis of this telescope, and as the observer's meridian turns with the Earth, the telescope can, in time, point to every star which comes above the observer's horizon. If we know approximately the declination of a star, the telescope can be set at such an altitude that the star will pass through the field when it crosses the observer's meridian, that is, when the sidereal time is the same as the right ascension of the star. If the position of a star is known, the observation of its passage over the meridian tells the sidereal time at that instant, and so provides the means of setting the clock to correct sidereal time. If the clock shows sidereal time correctly, or if its error is known, then the observation gives the right ascension of the star. The declination of a star is found by measuring the altitude at which it crosses the meridian, by means of an accurately graduated circle, shown at C in the Figure, which is read by microscopes fixed to the pier.

This description implies that the observer has some way of finding the meridian for his instrument which, in accord with the definition of the meridian, means that he must be able to find the zenith and the Celestial Pole. The zenith is found by pointing the telescope directly down into a liquid surface, usually mercury. A ray of light directed down the telescope will make equal angles with the vertical before and after reflection, and by observing the reflected ray it is possible to estimate how the telescope would have to be pointed, to be directed vertically downwards or upwards. Then the axis of the telescope may be set so that the plane of its movement is the meridian, and passes through the pole, because three consecutive

passages by a circumpolar star across the meridian mark off two equal intervals of time. Deviation from this shows how the axis of rotation of the
telescope must be moved to run exactly east and west. The Celestial Pole
can be found in altitude because a star near it crosses the meridian at equal
distances above and below the pole. So the two reference points for the
meridian, the pole and the zenith, are made accessible to observation.

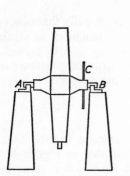

Figure 16.—The transit telescope.

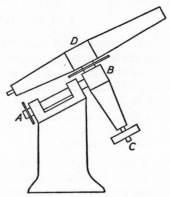

Figure 17.—The equatorial telescope.

The Equatorial Mounting

For general observing it is desirable to be able to point the telescope
at a selected object at any time, and the *equatorial* mounting is the one
almost universally adopted for this purpose. The equatorial telescope, illustrated in Figure 17, has two axes about which the telescope can move.
One *AB* on the Figure, is set parallel to the axis of the Earth and called the
polar axis, while the other one, *CD*, is at right angles to this. If the telescope
is moved around these axes, it can be pointed to any part of the sky. If it is
set on a star, it will then only need to be moved around the polar axis to
counteract the effect of the Earth's rotation. Furthermore, motion at the
correct rate—that is, one revolution in 24 hours—given to it by a mechanical drive enables it to track exactly on the star. The observer may then go
about his observing work with much less attention to the detail of guiding.
Most large telescopes are given equatorial mountings. Plate 2 shows the
74-inch telescope at Mount Stromlo Observatory. It is a reflecting telescope
with an equatorial mounting.

THE SPECTROSCOPE

The fact that light of different colours is sent in different directions after
passing through a refracting surface or after passing through or being reflected from a diffraction grating is made the basis of the *spectroscope*, an
extremely important accessory of the telescope. Suppose light of just one
pure colour, say red, passes through a slit represented at *A* in Figure 18.
Behind this a lens *C* makes the light coming from the slit parallel, that is,

the image of the slit formed by the lens is very distant towards the right. To simplify the Figure only the central ray is shown. If a lens D were placed into the beam of light, it would form an image of the slit at the point E; but if instead of this a prism is put after the lens C, the light in passing through the prism will be bent twice so that, if now the second lens is interposed in the beam at F after the prism, it will form an image of the slit at R.

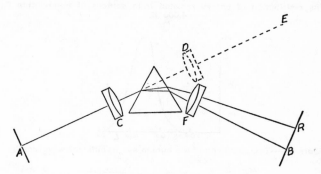

Figure 18.—The spectroscope.

If the light is bright enough and a white sheet is placed at this point, the red image of the slit may be seen on it or, if an eye-piece is placed behind R the slit may be examined visually. Now, if the original beam of single colour has another beam of single colour, blue, mixed in with it, the second colour will be bent through a different angle by the prism and the image of the slit in this new colour will be formed at a different place, B. For each new colour of just a single wave-length that may be introduced there will be a corresponding image of the slit. The pattern formed by the separation of the light in a spectroscope is called a *spectrum*.

The ability to separate out the various colours according to their various wave-lengths provides a means of analysing the light to deduce the kind of source from which it may have come and to tell much of its history on the way to us. It provides us with a language for describing completely the colour of the light, or the response to various colours of a device which may be used to record the light or the characteristics of any substance through which it may be passed. Some important examples are given in Figures 19, 20, and 21.

In Figure 19 is drawn a graph marked 6,000°K, which shows the analysis of the light from a source with about the temperature of the Sun. Along the bottom of the diagram are marked the wave-lengths of the light in microns and the vertical height of the curve represents the intensity of the light corresponding to the wave-length over which it appears. The maximum occurs at 0·5 micron. Such a diagram tells us all that can be known about the colour of the source from which the light has come. The graph marked 4,000°K shows the distribution for a source about as hot as some of the cooler stars.

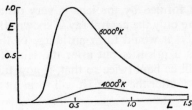

Figure 19.—The distribution of energy radiated from sources of temperature 6,000°K and 4,000°K.

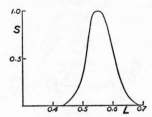

Figure 20.—The sensitivity of the human eye to different wave-lengths.

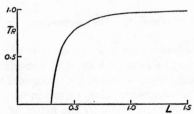

Figure 21.—The transmission curve of the Earth's atmosphere.

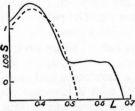

Figure 22.—The sensitivity curves of an orthochromatic plate (dashed curve) and a panchromatic plate.

Figure 20 is the same kind of diagram but shows the sensitivity of the light-adapted eye at different parts of the spectrum. Taking the maximum as 1, the response of the eye at various wave-lengths is represented by the height of the line in the graph. It can scarcely be an accident that the sensitivity of the eye is best for the kind of light that we receive from the Sun. The sensitivity to various colours of any other detectors of light can be shown in a similar way.

The next diagram, Figure 21, shows how much light is transmitted through the atmosphere of the Earth at various wave-lengths. Again, the atmosphere transmits the light in the brightest part of the solar spectrum to which the eye is most sensitive. Practically all radiation of wave-lengths shorter than $0 \cdot 3$ micron is stopped by the atmosphere, and in wave-lengths longer than on the diagram there is a complicated pattern of transmission and absorption.

RECORDING THE LIGHT

Photography

The image of an object in the telescope or a spectrum formed by a spectroscope has to be examined or recorded. Besides the eye, which has already been mentioned, there are other important ways. If a photographic plate is placed where the image has been formed, the light gradually builds up in the sensitive surface a change which can be developed to display the image. The exposure can be made very long and a suitable photographic plate then records the sum of the light received over a long period whereas the eye takes account only of the light received during a fraction of a second.

The sensitivity of two types of photographic plate is shown in Figure 22. The broken line shows the sensitivity to light of various wave-lengths of what is called an ordinary photographic plate, which was the only kind that existed until various dyes were applied to extend the range of sensitivity. The full line shows the sensitivity of a panchromatic plate which responds to all of the wave-lengths visible to the eye. It is valuable in ordinary photography, because it tends to show the light values in a scene in much the same way as they appear to the eye.

The existence of photographic plates with different characteristics which can be further modified by placing filters with different transmissions in front of the plate is extremely useful in astronomy. Supposing a star field is photographed with a combination of filter and photographic plate which records best at $0 \cdot 4$ micron and then with another one that records best at say $0 \cdot 5$ or $0 \cdot 7$ micron. The two pictures provide simultaneously samples of parts of the spectra of all of the stars which have been photographed, and give a very good idea of what the colour and the rest of the spectra of the stars might be.

Photo-electric Photometry

Another important way of recording the light from the celestial body is by means of the photo-electric cell. When light falls on some substances, electrically charged particles called *electrons* are ejected from the substance and these form a small electric current. The science of electronics has provided ways of amplifying such small currents and, if this is done, the current can be made to show on a meter or to move the pen of a recording device. In some cells used in astronomy, much of the amplification is done within the cell itself. The particles coming from the screen on which the light is falling are speeded up by the electric field and made to fall on a second screen where the speed is sufficient to make each particle knock several new ones from the second screen. If this process is repeated on 8 or 10 such screens, the final current is much larger than the one which started from the first screen.

A cell of this kind is called a *photo-multiplier*. It is very valuable in astronomy for measuring the amount of light reaching us from the stars because the current produced is very nearly proportional to the amount of light which falls on the original screen. Photo-multipliers can be made with high sensitivity in different parts of the spectrum, and in combination with filters they can be made to sample the spectrum of a star in the same way as was described for the photographic plate. The photo-electric method is the most accurate way known for measuring the amount of light which comes from a star.

Incidentally, photo-electricity—that is, the ejection of electric particles, electrons, by light when it falls on the substance—demonstrates a further important way in which light behaves. It is observed that when the light is kept the same colour but increased in intensity, the number of electrons which are released is increased proportionately but no difference is made to the speed with which they come from the surface. If, on the other hand, the wave-length of the light is made shorter, the speed of the electrons increases, and if it is made longer, the speed decreases until, if the wave-length is made longer than a critical wave-length, no particles are released. This suggests that waves of light carry their energy in small indivisible packets. If the energy of the packet is sufficient, it releases an electron and if not then no particle comes off. If the energy exceeds the minimum necessary to release electrons, the extra energy may give higher velocity to the particle. Increasing the intensity of the light while keeping the colour the same increases the number of packets but does not change the energy in each. This case of an indivisible packet of energy is one example of the *quantum theory*, which is needed to explain many of the reactions between light and atoms.

EXTENDING THE SPECTRUM

Energy may be radiated in wave-lengths on either side of the visible spectrum which is included in Figures 19 to 22. On the short wave-length side there is, first of all, the ultra violet light which is stopped, for the most part, by our atmosphere, but which is now being observed by apparatus carried above the atmosphere in rockets and satellites. Of very short wave-lengths are the X-rays used in medical diagnosis and in industry to examine opaque substances without destroying them. Radio-active substances emit radiations of even shorter wave-length. On the long wave-length side of the visible spectrum occur the waves which carry heat, and most of the energy from domestic radiators is in this part of the spectrum. The transmission of the atmosphere extends beyond the limit shown in Figure 21 to about 2 microns, and there is another "window" from 8 microns to 13 microns.

Radio Astronomy

At much longer wave-lengths occur the waves used in radio and television transmissions. In 1932 it was discovered that energy in these wave-lengths is coming to us from space, and a new branch of astronomy, radio astronomy is now of great importance. The atmosphere transmits radio waves between a few millimetres and 15 metres in length. Consequently, there is available for observation a new part of the spectrum in which energy reaches us from new kinds of formerly unsuspected sources. In some directions in space there are great clouds of gas and dust between the stars, and, since the radio waves penetrate these better than do the waves in the visible part of the spectrum, they make possible observation of radiation from great distances. Moreover, hydrogen is the most abundant element in the universe and much of it in interstellar space is in a state which does not give out energy observable by ordinary optical means. It does, however, do so in the radio spectrum in which observations of vital importance have been, and are being, made.

Much of the explanation of the behaviour of light waves applies equally to radio waves, where the radio astronomer has to control the energy in much the same way as the optical astronomer has been doing. He must have some system to collect the energy. The most common form for this is the large parabola which reflects the incoming radio waves into a receiver by which they are amplified and used to operate some sort of a recorder. Plate 3 shows the 210-foot radio telescope at Parkes, New South Wales.

The phenomena of interference and polarization are available for use in manipulating and interpreting the waves in the radio part of the spectrum as they are in the optical part. Since the radio waves are so much longer, the formula for resolving power shows that the limitation on the ability of the radio telescope to separate sources which are close together exists in a more acute form than with the optical telescope. To have a resolution equal only to that of the unaided human eye such a radio telescope operating on a wave-length of one metre would have to be more than two miles across, and the radio astronomers have used great ingenuity to devise aerial systems which have improved resolution but are nevertheless within the possibility of manufacture. These depend on the phenomenon of interference.

Let the analogy with the optical case serve as explanation. If in Figure 10 the geometry of the right hand section of the apparatus, that is the part marked *ABC*, is fixed and the arriving energy examined only at *C* the difference in phase of the waves reaching *C* varies with the path difference between *OA* and *OB*; that is the waves are received strongly at *C* only from certain directions. By arrangements which introduce further selection one among these directions may be made to predominate. Thus, since fortunately the radio telescope does not need a collecting area a mile across, it is not necessary to attempt the tremendous task of erecting so large an aerial. It is quite possible to design aerials which receive waves in only parts of such areas and still gain some of the benefits of increased ability to distinguish small detail or to point accurately.

The Mills Cross radio telescope, about 20 miles east of Canberra, A.C.T., is a good example of this. This has two cylindrical reflectors, each about a mile long and 40 feet wide. One which is aligned in an east-west direction collects the radio emission from a narrow strip of sky in the meridian while a north-south arm collects from a narrow strip aligned east-west. The electrical connections are arranged so that the radiation is recorded only when it is received by both arms and therefore comes from the very small area where the two strips of sky cross. By mechanical movement of the east-west arm and electrical adjustments in the north-south arm this area may be moved along the meridian. Thus this radio telescope works as a transit instrument with which, by the aid of the Earth's rotation, the whole of the sky may be surveyed and the positions of the radio sources found.

CONTINUOUS SPECTRA AND THEIR INTERPRETATION

A solid body, such as a piece of metal, when heated becomes red hot, then a pale orange-red and then white hot. If the light from it at the white hot stage is directed into the slit of a spectroscope, the resultant spectrum is a continuous band of colour covering the whole visible spectrum from violet to red. Such a spectrum is shown on Plate 22. In Figure 19 the distribution of the light for a source about as hot as the Sun was shown. For a cooler source the curve would have a similar shape but it would be lower because a cooler object radiates less heat, and its maximum would be further to the right, that is, towards the red or even infra-red.

In this context the best scale of temperature to use is the Kelvin scale, named after the great physicist Lord Kelvin. The freezing point of water is $273°K$ and the boiling point $373°K$. The temperature of liquid oxygen is $90°K$, a candle flame $1,900°K$, the filament of an incandescent lamp $2,500°K$ and of the surface of Sun $6,000°K$. The distribution of the energy for a source at temperature $4,000°K$ is also shown in Figure 19. The wave length where the maximum of the light occurs is given by the formula

$$L = \frac{2890}{T}, \qquad \text{(Wien's Law)}$$

where L is the wave length in microns and T the temperature in degrees Kelvin. For the Sun the maximum is about $0·48$ micron, for $4,000°$ the maximum lies at $0·7$ micron in the deep red.

The power of all of the radiation from a source for all wave-lengths in horsepower per square yard of the radiator is given by

$$H = 63 \left(\frac{T}{1,000}\right)^4. \qquad \text{(Stefan's Law)}$$

Max Planck found a more complicated formula which, for a given temperature defines the curve of which examples are given in Figure 19 for the distribution of the light with wave-length. Thus the measurement of the shape of this curve, or of enough of it to decide how it runs, gives the temperature of the body from which the radiation comes. If the area can be estimated, a measurement of the total radiation and hence the radiation per unit area yields, through the formula of Stefan's Law, a value of the *effective temperature* of the body.

ATOMS

Since much of the radiation of astronomical interest bears characteristics of the atoms in the place from which it was emitted or of the path through which it has travelled, some account must be given of the structure of atoms and the way in which they radiate. An atom is the smallest particle of a chemical element which retains the chemical characteristics of the element, and each atom of an element consists of a comparatively heavy *nucleus* about which revolve electrons whose number corresponds to what the element is. The electron is a very small particle carrying a negative electric charge, and the nucleus of an atom is built up of *protons* and *neutrons* each of which has a mass about 1,835 times as great as that of the electron. The proton has a charge equal in magnitude, but opposite in sign, to that of the electron. The neutron has no charge. The attraction of the nucleus holds the electrons in their movement around it unless there occurs some disturbance sufficient to remove them. Each atom in its normal condition has as a whole no electric charge since the number of positive protons in the nucleus equals the number of negative electrons about it.

The number of protons in the nucleus determines what the element is, but different forms of the same element may have different numbers of neutrons in the nucleus giving for the same chemical element different atoms, called *isotopes*, which have different masses. The lightest element is hydrogen which has one proton with one electron revolving about it although a heavier atom of hydrogen also exists in which a neutron is added to its nucleus giving the atom of heavy hydrogen a mass twice that of the ordinary variety. The next lightest of the elements is helium which has two nuclear protons and two electrons in the shells about it. The usual helium nucleus has two neutrons as well as the two protons but another isotope exists in which the number of neutrons is only one. Each atom is represented by an abbreviation of one or two letters to which may be added an index which gives the mass of the atom in terms of that of ordinary hydrogen. The atoms mentioned are written as H^1 and H^2 for hydrogen and He^4 and He^3 for helium.

ATOMIC SPECTRA

Experimental evidence and the quantum theory are in accord, concerning the arrangement of the electrons about a nucleus, that atoms can exist only in certain states in each of which the atom has a fixed internal energy. When the state of the atom changes, it can do so only to another state characteristic of the atom. Such a change leads to the release (or absorption) of a definite quantum of energy which appears usually in the form of radiation. As in the case of photo-electric release of particles by radia-

E

tion the wave-length correlates with the associated energy, high energy corresponding with short wave-length.

When the change of state of an atom decreases its internal energy radiation must be given off in a fixed amount and light of pure colour of the associated spectrum line appears. When the light from a glowing gas as in an advertising sign or a mercury street lamp is directed into the spectroscope, it is observed to consist mainly of a series of pure colours which appear as narrow bright lines in the spectrum. The colour of each line corresponds to a particular transition between two of the possible states of the atom. Since some of the energy transitions of an atom are more probable than others, the spectrum lines associated with energies given by these transitions are stronger than other lines which correspond to less probable transitions. The pattern of the spectrum lines from a particular atom is entirely characteristic of it and forms a kind of signature which leads to recognition of the presence of an element whenever its set of lines is present in a source of radiation which can be analysed in a spectroscope.

The same spectrum lines can occur in another form. Suppose a glowing body, giving a continuous spectrum, to be situated behind a mass of cooler gas through which the light must pass before it reaches the slit of the spectroscope. In this case an atom may absorb energy from the radiation and make a step to a higher energy state. Thus, narrow sections of the continuous spectrum of the hot body are absorbed by the gas and the spectrum is cut by a series of dark lines. These dark lines correspond exactly in position to the bright lines which the same gas would emit if it were glowing as the only source of the light, and they lead equally to recognition of the chemical substances present in the gas. Spectra of this kind arise in the atmospheres of the Sun and the stars. Plate 22 shows a bright line spectrum arising from a gaseous source and a spectrum of the Sun crossed by dark absorption lines.

One spectrum line must be singled out for special mention. It is associated with the lowest energy state of neutral hydrogen. The transitions to this state do not give spectrum lines observable by optical means at the surface of the Earth because the ones which occur are absorbed by the atmosphere. The observable line arises because the spin of the electron of the hydrogen atom may be in the same direction as or opposite to that of the nucleus. The atom has slightly more energy when the spin is in the same direction and so when a flip over occurs a quantum of energy is released and radiation of corresponding wave-length emitted. The spectrum line has a wave-length of 21 centimetres, observable by radio astronomical techniques, which therefore render accessible to observation much of the hydrogen in interstellar space.

Interpretation of Spectra

Study of the spectrum lines can yield a great deal of information about the physical conditions in the source in which they have originated. It is worthwhile to give examples of this. The higher states of an atom are usually unstable and change very quickly but some states are relatively stable so that the atom may exist in them for several seconds or even much longer. Since the atom is likely to make a collision with one of its neighbours or the walls of the container, with consequent change of energy, before a transition from such a state can occur the spectrum lines associated with these transitions are not usually observed and are called "forbidden" lines. However, they do occur when the atoms are in a very rare atmosphere, as in some of the gas in space and in the solar corona. This will be described later.

A consequence of the structure of the atom is that some of the electrons in the outer shell may be removed from the atom altogether if sufficient energy is absorbed by the atom either from radiation or as a result of a collision. An atom from which one electron has been removed is called a *singly ionized* atom, one with two removed is called doubly ionized, and so on. The spectrum lines of an atom are different for different stages of *ionization*. If the temperature is high, the atoms in the gas are moving more rapidly, collisions are more severe and many of the atoms have electrons removed. The lines of the ionized atoms appear in the spectrum. On the other hand, if the pressure is high, there will be more electrons present and consequently more encounters, which afford the possibility of recombination to keep up the normal supply of electrons of the neutral atom. Some atoms, like sodium, are easily ionized while others, like neon and helium, have their electrons firmly attached and require much more violent conditions to set an electron free.

Around us on the Earth the chemical elements commonly join together in more or less complicated combinations, called *molecules*. The molecules, too, have characteristic spectra by means of which they may be recognised. Molecules occur also in some celestial bodies although in the very hot environments in stars they are for the most part broken up.

The study of the spectrum of a star can thus be made to yield a great deal about the temperature and pressure of its atmosphere.

THE DOPPLER EFFECT

Careful measurement of wave-length of light in spectrum lines of light received from a star yields information on its motion. In Figure 23 is represented a source of light of one wave-length and a section through two con-

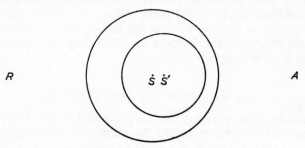

Figure 23.—The Doppler effect.

secutive waves coming from it. The source was at S when the first wave was emitted and supposed to be moving to the right, and so the second wave emitted when the source reached S' is displaced to the right relative to the first one. On the right hand side the distance between the waves is shortened and on the left it is lengthened. An observer to the right, towards whom the light is approaching, will observe the wave-length shorter—that is, displaced towards the blue—than it would be for a stationary source. An observer at the left, from whom the source is receding, would see the spectrum line displaced towards the red end of the spectrum. This is named the *Doppler effect* after the nineteenth century physicist.

Measurements of this kind are made by photographing alongside one another, under conditions carefully made the same, the spectra of the celestial source and of a terrestrial source. The positions and wave-lengths of the star can then be calibrated and an estimate formed of its motion in the line of sight between it and the observer. This use of change of wave-length to measure velocity, which also applies to the 21cm hydrogen line of radio astronomy, is of great use in studying motions of celestial sources and the structure of systems to which they belong.

THE THEORY OF GRAVITATION

The law of gravitation was discovered by Newton in the seventeenth century. The force of attraction that any two bodies mutually exert on one another is given by the formula GMm/r^2 where M and m are the masses of the two bodies, r the distance between them and G is the constant of gravitation, the numerical value of which depends on the units used to measure the masses and distances. The constant is found in the laboratory by measuring the attraction that bodies have for one another, the only difficulty lying in the smallness of the forces which need to be measured. The attraction between two bodies each one ton in mass and one yard apart would only be about one 1/35,000 ounce. If the masses and the force are measured in tons and the distance in yards $G = 8 \cdot 4 \times 10^{-9}$. The force may seem small, but the celestial bodies are enormously large and the forces are exerted relentlessly, without interruption. Thus the motions are inexorably determined by the forces of gravitation.

It may be deduced from this law of force that a body in the form of a sphere made of shells of constant density exerts its force as though all of its mass were concentrated at a point at the centre. This makes the calculations easier and is valuable because most of the bodies, for which the calculation is needed, are spherical. The formula for calculating the force of gravity is an extremely important one in astronomy.

THE LAW OF MOTION

The formula of the previous section provides for the calculation of the force experienced by a body due to the mutual attraction between it and another one. Another formula is needed to calculate the way in which the movement of the body is influenced by a force. The equation for this is:

$$F = ma$$

where **F** is the force acting on the body, *m* its mass and **a** the acceleration produced in the body by the force. **F** and **a** are printed in heavy type to indicate that they coincide in direction as well as being connected by the ratio *m*. This law of motion is one of the very greatest achievements of science. It enters into almost every aspect of science, from the movement of an electron in a magnetic field to the design of an automobile. We are sometimes apt to think overmuch of the scientific achievements of our own century, but it would be hard to name anything which has the importance of the law of motion which is now nearly 300 years old.

This law, with the law of gravitation, is constantly applied to assist in finding how bodies will behave in all sorts of circumstances. Together they determine how bodies fall towards the Earth, how a planet moves under the influence of the Sun and other planets, or a star under the influence of other stars, and how rocket propulsion may be used to launch a satellite or interplanetary probe.

4

THE EARTH AND THE MOON

THE EARTH

The Shape of the Earth

It seems natural to begin an account of the planets by considering, for our own Earth, the facts about its shape and size, constitution and motions which have relevance in astronomy. The Earth, as has been known for a long time, is nearly spherical in shape. If a ship is viewed sailing away from us, the hull disappears first and afterwards the higher parts of its superstructure. The obvious reason for this is that the surface of the sea is convex at the place where the observation is made, and, since the the result is the same wherever the observer stands, it is reasonable to regard the Earth as globular in shape. Then the fact that the Earth can be circumnavigated is evidence that anyone should be able to believe without actually carrying out the experiment himself.

Accurate measurement by methods of trigonometric survey refines the picture. This may be done by comparing the difference of latitude of places on the same meridian with the distances between them. Figure 24 represents a section, through the Earth by a plane through the poles, in which the departure from spherical shape is greatly exaggerated to make the description clearer. The line CA represents the Earth's Equator. At the point O on the Earth's surface OZ is the direction of the zenith and OE of the Celestial Equator.

The latitude is the angle ZOE, the declination of the zenith of the observer. It may be measured by observing the altitudes at which stars of known declination cross the meridian and hence deducing the declination an object would need to pass through the zenith. Now suppose the latitudes of two places on the same meridian to be determined and the distance between them measured by land survey methods. Let the difference in their latitudes be L degrees and the distance between them d miles. Then if the Earth were perfectly spherical it would be necessary to go a distance $360 \, d/L$ miles to circumnavigate it. The quantity d/L is the number of miles per degree of

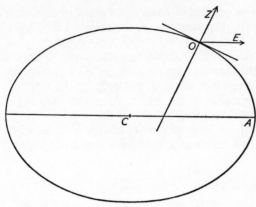

Figure 24.-

the circle which would best fit the meridian between the two places. When it is measured in various latitudes on the surface of the Earth it is found to be less near the Equator than at the poles. This is because, as represented in the Figure, the curvature is greater at the Equator. The equatorial diameter of the Earth is 7,926 miles and the diameter through the poles is 7,900 miles.

Because of the equatorial bulge of the Earth, the Sun and the Moon exert a force which on an average tends to pull the Equator towards the ecliptic. This produces an effect such as occurs in the case of a spinning top. The axis of the Earth keeps the same inclination to the ecliptic but moves around a direction perpendicular to the ecliptic. The complete circuit takes about 26,000 years. The motion, called precession, is the movement of the Equator mentioned in Chapter 1 as affecting the positions of the stars.

The distribution of the mass of the Earth affects the orbital movements of the artificial satellites and a study of their motion offers a clue to more details of the Earth's shape. It appears that the Equator is not quite circular and that sea level at the north pole is further, perhaps only by a score or so yards, than would be expected for a figure symmetrical about the Equator. In middle latitudes the average distance of the Earth's surface from its centre is slightly greater in the Southern Hemisphere than in the Northern.

The equatorial bulge of the Earth, its greater equatorial diameter, is explained by its rotation. The Earth is held together by gravitation, but a particle on its Equator is being carried around its axis by rotation with a velocity of about a thousand miles per hour, and part of the gravitational force on the particle is used in keeping it on its circular path in just the same way as a string must be pulled to keep an object tied to it whirling in a circle. Hence, at the Equator, all of the material presses a little less heavily on the supporting matter below than it would if the Earth were not rotating. Since the Earth is stable, the pressure at its centre must work out to be the same whether it is computed from the weight of matter lying towards the pole or towards the Equator where, the weight being less, the matter must extend further.

Similar considerations explain the equatorial bulges of other rotating planets. If careful measurements of the force of gravity are made at different latitudes, the result is affected, not only by the rotation, but also by the differences in the radius of the Earth. At places near the pole the observer is nearer the Earth's centre. Theory of this kind united with widely distributed measures of the force of gravity affords a means of deriving the shape of the Earth with a result in accord with that from trigonometric measurements.

The Mass of the Earth

The Earth's mass is found from the gravitational force it exerts. The equation in the last chapter may be used to express the force in tons on a mass of one ton, taking E as the mass of the Earth in tons and $6 \cdot 96 \times 10^6$ as the radius of the Earth in yards. The equation is then $1 = 8 \cdot 4 \times 10^{-9} E / (6 \cdot 96 \times 10^6)^2$, the solution of which gives the mass of the Earth as $5 \cdot 8 \times 10^{21}$ tons. With the mass and size of the Earth now known, its density is found by a straight-forward calculation to be $5 \cdot 5$ times that of water. Since the density of the rocks around us at the surface is only about half of this, it must be concluded that the material of much of the interior is of higher density.

The Earth's Interior

The physical conditions of the interior of the Earth can be examined by considering the behaviour of earthquake waves. Strains build up in the Earth's crust due to slow displacements until the stresses reach a point where rupture takes place. The potential energy developed before slipping occurs may be very great and a very large amount of energy may be released. When an earthquake occurs, a series of waves leaves the centre of the disturbance and, for an observing station some distance away, the waves, except for certain types which come round the surface, penetrate deeply into the Earth.

The waves travelling through the Earth, or any elastic solid, are of two kinds—those in which the vibration is along the line in which the wave is advancing (called P waves) and those in which the vibration is transverse to the direction of the motion of the wave (the S waves). The transverse waves are slower. The times that the waves take to travel from an earthquake to observing stations at different distances are used to derive the speeds. For greater distances the waves must have penetrated to deeper layers in the Earth. The speeds of the earthquake waves and the way that the Earth yields to the tidal forces from the Moon show that the Earth as a whole has a rigidity greater than that of steel. The speeds also tell something of the elastic properties and densities of the material at different depths through which the waves have to come. The speed of the P waves, which, near the surface of the Earth, is about five miles per second, increases with depth. By accurate timing of the arrival of the earthquake waves at observing stations distributed in various directions around it the centre of the disturbance may be located. Most earthquakes occur in well defined zones of the Earth. Most are within 45 miles of the surface although they may occur as deep at 400 miles.

When there is a change of properties of the material and consequent change in speed of the waves they may be reflected or refracted. Examination of earthquake records makes possible location of the discontinuities where the changes occur. The Mohorovičić (pronounced mōhō'rōvichich) discontinuity, which marks the lower limit of the Earth's *crust*, has a depth of about 20 or 30 miles beneath the continents and about half the thickness under the oceans. The smaller depth under the oceans is the reason why an ocean site has been chosen for the project of drilling a hole (the Mohole) to sample the material below the discontinuity.

Both the P and S waves are recorded to a distance of about 7,000 miles from an earthquake. Beyond this distance they disappear until the P wave is again observable at distances beyond 10,000 miles. The existence of this "shadow" zone and the derived travel times indicate a great discontinuity in the elastic behaviour of the material at a depth of about 1,800 miles. At this depth the speed of a longitudinal wave drops from about nine miles per second just outside the region to about five within it after which there is a gradual increase inward to the centre. If the observing station is so far from the origin of the earthquake that the waves coming to it penetrate to this discontinuity, the waves are refracted and reflected at the surface in such a way that the character of the recording is much changed. Since the transverse waves are not transmitted through the central part of the Earth the core is believed to be fluid for it is a property of fluids not to transmit transverse waves. The density of the core of the Earth is revealed as about twelve times that of water.

Thus, examination of the earthquake waves shows that the Earth may be divided into three layers, the thin outer crust only a few miles thick, a mantle, which may have the character of basaltic rocks of the kind that intrudes into the surface layers, and the core. Other less well displayed divisions exist. There is, for example, an inner core about 1,800 miles in diameter, where the material may again be solid. The core is thought to be composed largely of iron and nickel. The study of properties of solids at high pressure is consistent with this, but the evidence is confused. It may consist of other materials modified by the great pressure, which at the centre of the Earth must be over 20,000 tons per square inch, for it is known from laboratory experiments that the structure of matter may be altered by very high pressure.

In the part of the Earth's crust that can be examined the temperature increases with depth by about one degree Fahrenheit per hundred feet. This rate of increase probably does not continue since some of the heat being conducted outward is generated by radio-active substances in the outer layers and less heat is coming through the lower layers which, in addition, may conduct heat better. So, the rate of rise of temperature need be less even for the same heat flow. The temperature in the core must nevertheless be several thousands of degrees. The amount of heat flowing from inside the Earth is very much less than that arriving from the Sun which must therefore control the surface temperature.

Composition

The relative abundance of various elements has been determined in the outer part of the Earth's crust where they can be chemically examined. The element oxygen occupies first place with about 47 per cent by weight, silicon comes second with about 28 per cent, then come in order aluminium 8 per cent, iron 5 per cent, calcium 4 per cent. The composition of the whole Earth is uncertain but may be indicated by evidence from several parallel lines of enquiry. First, what substances would give the elastic properties which would account for the speeds of earthquake waves? Second, what composition would give the observed weight and density for the whole Earth? Third, what substances are found in other heavenly bodies, especially meteors? Some of these considerations suggest that iron may well be a much more important component of the Earth as a whole than it is for the crustal layers.

The Atmosphere

The Earth is made habitable by its atmosphere which consists chiefly of the gases nitrogen (about 75 per cent), oxygen (about 20 per cent), a variable amount of water vapour, and the remainder of argon, carbon dioxide and traces of some other gases. Beside providing an essential component for the chemical processes in living things the atmosphere serves as a blanket which gives protection from the heat of the direct sunshine and from the extreme cold which would occur in the shadow away from the Sun, as well as from the bombardment of undesirable radiations and missiles from space.

The water vapour plays a very important role in determining weather and climate. Whenever water melts or evaporates it absorbs heat and when it freezes or condenses from vapour it gives out heat. These processes play an enormous part in keeping the atmosphere in motion and distributing the heat received from the Sun to make the climates of the world more equable. Much of the Earth is normally covered by cloud in a layer which prevents radiation into space of the warmth of the Earth. It is the distribution of the water by the atmosphere which makes much of our world pleasant and fertile. For a place such as Sydney, by the sea, in the temperate zone of the Earth, the mean maximum temperature in the hottest month of the year differs from the mean minimum temperature in the coolest month by about 35° Fahrenheit. If there were no atmosphere, the highest and lowest temperatures of only one day might differ by 300° Fahrenheit.

The atmosphere extends outwards without any definite boundary, gradually thinning for several hundred miles above the Earth's surface. About half the mass of the atmosphere is below $3\frac{1}{2}$ miles—so the habitable portion does not extend far. On the tops of the highest mountains even a very fit person can live for only a short period after thorough preparation. The ionized layers from which are reflected radio waves occur at heights above 60 miles and there is sufficient atmosphere at 70 miles to cause a rapidly moving meteor particle to become incandescent. When an artificial satellite comes down to a height of 100 miles or so, the resistance of the atmosphere is sufficient to change its orbit quickly and bring it to the ground. The occurrence of aurorae, caused by the impact of particles from the Sun on the atoms of the upper atmosphere at heights of over 500 miles show that the atmosphere extends tenuously to these heights.

The Rotation of the Earth

The Earth's movements and its position in the solar system are astronomical factors important in determining its character. The rotation of the Earth was taken for granted in Chapter 1, and it is obviously more natural to ascribe the rising and setting and motion across the sky of all of the celestial bodies, some of which are much greater than the Earth and many billions of miles away, to a rotation of the Earth rather than to suppose the whole universe is revolving about the Earth. Apart from this there are several mechanical experiments which can be carried out independently of astronomical observation and which can be regarded as proof of the rotation of the Earth. If a pendulum which is free to swing in any direction (in this respect differing from an ordinary clock pendulum) is set swinging at a place away from the equator, it is found that the plane of its swing varies relative to the ground over which it is situated; at the pole the plane of the swing would vary through 360° in 24 hours—that is, just the period of rotation of the Earth. At any other latitude the component of the Earth's rotation around the vertical varies with the distance of the place from the Earth's Equator and the ground will rotate under the pendulum at this speed. Since the plane in which the pendulum moves is compelled by the force of gravity to remain vertical, but otherwise is free, it must appear to rotate in the opposite direction to the ground.

When a projectile is fired from a place on the Earth's surface, its velocity is composed of the velocity with which it is despatched added to that which its departure point has due to the rotation of the Earth. Since the motion is different at different places, fast at the Equator and slow at the poles, the movement of the Earth beneath the flying projectile is changing along its course and allowance must be made for an apparent deviation if the path is long. The gyro-compass, which consists essentially of a rapidly rotating flywheel mounted so that its axis is horizontal, derives its directional property from the rotation of the Earth.

The rotation of the Earth is an important fact in regulating its climate because it presents in turn various parts of the Earth's surface towards the Sun, the source of all our heat, making for much greater uniformity of temperature than would exist if one surface were always turned to the Sun or if the rate of rotation were very much slower.

The movements of the air are strongly influenced by the Earth's rotation which gives rise to cyclones and anti-cyclones. Any mass of air on the

Earth's surface partakes of the rotation of the Earth. If, as occurs with a
cyclone, the pressure is least in the centre of a region, the tendency will
be for the air to move inwards towards the centre. Since it will tend to
conserve its momentum, it has to speed up its rotation as it moves inwards.
Accordingly, relative to the solid surface of the Earth, it will begin to move
faster, as a ballet dancer does when she draws her arms in to her body.

To an observer looking down on the Northern Hemisphere its west to
east rotation would appear anti-clockwise, and so the wind of a cyclone
moves in an anti-clockwise direction around the centre. Similarly, in the
Southern Hemisphere, it moves in a clockwise direction. (Plate 10 shows a
cyclone photographed from the satellite Tiros I.) For an anti-cyclone the
pressure is highest at the centre, and the tendency for the air to move
outward produces winds in the opposite direction from that of the cyclone.
In this case the mass of air from a smaller area is extended so that the
velocity differences are dissipated, and the energy spread, more thinly over
a wider area, making for less energetic disturbances. Thus, anti-cyclones do
not produce the violent and destructive winds that cyclones sometimes do
if they have gathered their energy from a wide area.

Orbital Motion

The Earth, like the other planets, pursues an orbit around the Sun.
The curvature of the motion towards the Sun arises from the Sun's gravitational attraction. The orbit is approximately circular and the average distance from the Sun is 93 million miles. Again it is more natural to ascribe
the effects to a movement of the Earth rather than to attribute a complicated component of motion with a period of a year to the rest of the
universe. The Earth's movement in a plane gives rise to the apparent annual
movement of the Sun already described. The axis about which the Earth
rotates is not at right angles to the orbit in which it revolves and, except
for the exceedingly slow movement of precession, remains pointed in the
same direction, moving parallel to itself as the Earth goes round the Sun.
This motion is represented in Figure 25.

The latitude in which the Sun passes directly overhead varies during
the year. The limit to which it can reach is set by the angle between the
Equator and the plane of the Earth's orbit. During the half of the year from
March to September the Sun comes vertically overhead at a northern latitude and during the other half at a southern latitude. This apparent movement of the Sun alters greatly the amount of heat and light which is
delivered to the respective hemispheres and gives rise to the seasons, the
most important climatic phenomenon. When, for example, the Sun is at its
greatest southern declination about December 22, there are two factors
which give the Southern Hemisphere a greater amount of heat. In the first
place the portion of the Earth's surface in the Southern Hemisphere is more
nearly perpendicular to the Sun's rays and hence receives in a unit of time
more heat than when the Sun is low down in the winter. Figure 26 shows
how when the Sun is high in the sky, the bundle of rays of the same cross
section is delivered to a smaller area. Furthermore, as shown in Chapter 1,

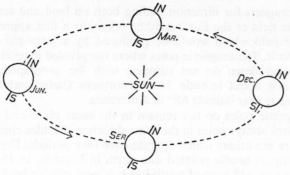

Figure 25.—The seasons.

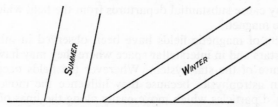

Figure 26.—The spread of sunlight in summer and winter.

places in the Southern Hemisphere then have the Sun above the horizon for a longer time during the day, so adding to the amount of heat received. Figure 25 shows that at this time in December there is a portion in the Southern Hemisphere near the pole on which the Sun does not set at all.

The same reasoning explains how this season of the year is the one when the Northern Hemisphere receives less energy from the Sun and has its winter while there is an area around the North Pole where the Sun does not rise. In June the two hemispheres exchange their circumstances giving summer in the north and winter in the south. Near the Equator where the factors vary less the seasons are much less marked.

The Earth's Magnetic Field

A bar magnet consisting of a small rod of steel or other metal which has been "magnetised" familiarly has an attraction for small pieces of iron. If a smaller magnet free to rotate in any direction is placed near the bar magnet, it tends to take a fixed orientation. One end of the smaller magnet is attracted towards one end of the bar magnet. It is evident that there are two kinds of *pole* at the ends of each magnet and that poles of unlike kind attract one another whereas like poles are repelled. The lines along which a small magnet tends to lie in the field of a larger one are the *magnetic lines of force.*

If a bar magnet is freely pivoted at the Earth's surface, it comes to rest in a preferred orientation which indicates the presence of a magnetic field around the Earth and shows the direction of the line of force at the place.

The use of magnets for direction finding both on land and sea is familiar. The magnetic field of the Earth may be taken, as a first approximation, to resemble the field which would be produced by a large bar magnet embedded within it. The magnetic poles where the pivoted magnet would point straight up and down do not coincide with the geographic poles. The northern one is about latitude 76° in northern Canada while the South Magnetic Pole is near latitude 68° in Antarctica.

The magnetic poles do not remain in the same place and the compass needle does not always point in the same direction. Besides changes of short duration there are others which operate over long periods. For example, in 1657 the compass needle pointed due north in London. In 1800 the compass pointing was 24° west of north but it is now moving back towards the northerly direction. The distribution of magnetic materials in the crust of the Earth may cause substantial departures from the field which would arise from a simple magnet.

The effects of magnetic fields have been observed in other planets, in the Sun and stars and in interstellar space where they may have an influence on the structure of the star system. Wherever the fields occur they are of importance in astrophysics because they influence the movement of electrically charged particles which move easily along the lines of force but are hindered in other directions. The interactions between radiation and energetically moving particles cause many of them to be electrically charged in many places in the universe.

Because of the mutual influence between a magnetic field and moving electrically charged particles the particles tend to carry the field with them. For this reason the outer part of the Earth's magnetic field has not the simple symmetrical form associated with a bar magnet. The Sun gives out a stream of charged particles which pass the Earth and blow the magnetic field out into a teardrop shape which has the tail directed away from the Sun.

The Age of the Earth

Ancient man had traditions about the origin and age of the Earth which have remained the subject of interest throughout history. Any estimate that can now be formed may be compared with the speculations on the age of the whole universe. The clearest results come from the estimates of ages of rocks by measurement of the ratio of the quantities of the elements uranium and lead in them. Naturally-occurring uranium, with atoms of weight 238 on a scale in which the weight of a hydrogen atom is $1 \cdot 008$, disintegrates slowly to yield new elements, which in turn disintegrate until there is reached a final product, lead, which is stable. The kind of lead remaining after these processes has an atom of weight 206. The law of the radio-active transformations is that the proportion of atoms which make a radio-active change in a particular length of time is a constant. In the series of reactions from uranium to lead the first change is slow but the remaining ones occur much more quickly so that once the changes are initiated the steps to reach lead, although some are long by the standard of human life, are short on a cosmic time scale. It takes 4,500 million years for half of the original uranium atoms to change. Once the law of the change is established the ratio of lead to uranium can be calculated for any period from a beginning with uranium only. Thus if the ratio of lead of atomic weight 206 to uranium of atomic weight 238 is measured, a time can be found to fit the ratio and an estimate formed for the age of the rocks, which have been analysed. The oldest rocks determined in this way are about 3,000 million years old.

There exist other series of radio-active transformations which may be used. In one, the radio-active element thorium gives as a final product lead of atomic weight about 208. The ratio of lead to thorium gives a result of the same order for the age of the Earth.

THE MOON

The Lunar Landscape

Even with the naked eye the Moon is attractive and, being the nearest to us of all heavenly bodies, it is the one on which, with any means available, we can see the most detail. Through a small telescope the main topographical features are plainly visible, and many of them contrast strongly with the shapes commonly seen on the Earth. Plate 4 is a photograph of the Moon about eight days after new Moon. The patterns may be interpreted by thinking of the Sun as shining in from the left with shadows of the mountains reaching away to the right. Plate 5 is a photograph on a larger scale taken with the 100-inch telescope on Mount Wilson, California.

The map of lunar features in Figure 27 will help the observer to identify some of the most prominent features of the Moon which are visible in a small telescope. The most remarkable characteristic is the presence of literally thousands of ring-shaped mountains which are called *craters* because they were considered to be similar in appearance to volcanic craters on the Earth. The craters are very nearly circular in outline. The surface inside the ring mountains may be lower or higher than the area in which the crater occurs. Often there is a smaller mountain at the centre of the crater. The heights of the mountains, estimated by measuring the lengths of their shadows, may reach more than twenty thousand feet above their surroundings. The largest volcanic craters on the Earth are much exceeded in size by those on the Moon, many of which are over fifty, and some over a hundred, miles in diameter.

The extensive plains on the Moon, seen as dark areas with the naked eye, are called *maria* because for some time after the invention of the telescope it was thought that they were seas. Independent of the craters there are also striking mountain ranges on the Moon. In one place there is a cliff face, the Straight Wall in the Mare Nubium, about eight hundred feet high and extending sixty miles. It apparently originated from faulting in the Moon's surface. There are also what appear to be narrow winding valleys, known as rilles, which cut through other features of the Moon's surface and extend for hundreds of miles. Again, most prominently seen near full

Moon, there extends on the Moon's surface from such craters as Tycho and Copernicus rays of lighter material about ten miles wide and hundreds of miles long.

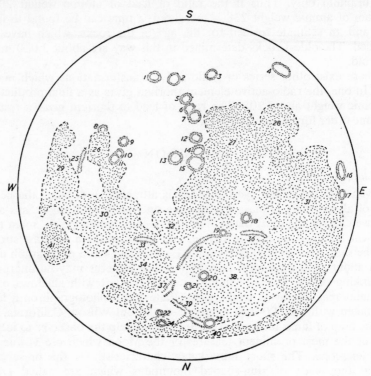

Figure 27.—Map of some lunar features.

TABLE 2

Craters

1	Maurolycus	13	Albategnius
2	Stöfler	14	Alphonsus
3	Tycho	15	Ptolemaeus
4	Schickard	16	Grimaldi
5	Walter	17	Hevel
6	Regiomontanus	18	Copernicus
7	Purbach	19	Eratosthenes
8	Fracastorius	20	Archimedes
9	Catharina	21	Aristillus
10	Cyrillus	22	Eudoxus
11	Theophilus	23	Plato
12	Arzachel	24	Aristoteles

Mountains and Maria

25	Pyrenees (Mountains)	34	Mare Serenitatis
26	Mare Nectaris	35	Apennines (Mountains)
27	Mare Nubium	36	Carpathian Mountains
28	Mare Humorum	37	Caucasus Mountains
29	Mare Foecunditatis	38	Mare Imbrium
30	Mare Tranquillitatis	39	Alps (Mountains)
31	Oceanus Procellarium	40	Mare Frigoris
32	Mare Vaporum	41	Mare Crisium
33	Haemus Mountains		

At the best phase for viewing it, about six to ten days after new Moon, when the mountains in the centre of the Moon's disc are throwing long shadows, the surface of the Moon looks rough and precipitous, but measurements of the way in which the brightness of the slopes varies as the Sun rises over the lunar landscape show that very steep slopes are by no means universal. In the Mare Imbrium for example, the crater Archimedes, which is about sixty miles in diameter with walls rising over six thousand feet above the floor, has "walls" of which the inner slope is only as much as 11° and outer slope 5°. An observer at the centre of the crater would see only tips of the range on his horizon and at the centre of some large craters the surrounding mountain would be invisible owing to the curvature of the Moon's surface.

The origin of the surface features of the Moon remains to be established. Some ordering of events is possible because it often happens that a crater deforms the shape of another which evidently was formed earlier or a crater has been drowned by a subsequent lava flow. The crater Copernicus must be later than the Mare Nubium in which it stands and than the crater Eratosthenes over which its rays pass. The photographs obtained by the Ranger space probes with a resolution not attainable from the Earth's surface show not only that the number of the craters increases as smaller sizes are observable but that many small ones are secondary, having been formed by the impact of material blasted from larger ones. Bombardment of the surface of the Moon by great meteors has probably played a major part, although the action of lunar volcanoes may have had an influence.

These questions should largely be settled in a few years when a landing is made there. Whatever theory has been tried, there appear to be formations which do not conform and it is likely that several agencies have been at work to produce the complexities of the lunar surface. The comparative absence of obvious similar features on the Earth has little bearing for here the weathering influences of the atmosphere make through the ages profound changes in the landscape, whereas on the Moon, in the absence of an atmosphere, the features would endure much better. A similar impacting mass would make a larger crater on the Moon than on the Earth, but some

F

craters such as those in Arizona or at Wolf Creek in Western Australia do exist, and remnants of more, larger ones are to be found on the older exposed surfaces of the Earth. When estimates are made of the number of craters formed in such places over geologically long periods of time, it is found to be of the same order as on the Moon.

The Moon's Motion around the Earth

Relative to the stars the Moon revolves about the Earth in a period of 27·3 days called its sidereal period. Since the Sun is moving among the stars in the same direction as the Moon, it takes a little longer than this for the Moon to overtake the Sun again, and the average period between consecutive conjunctions of the Moon with the Sun, 29·5 days, is the usual lunar month, the period from new Moon to new Moon. It is this motion of the Moon relative to the Sun as seen from the Earth that gives rise to the phases of the Moon. The Moon gives out no light of its own and is merely a huge ball 2,160 miles in diameter. The light we see is originally from the Sun. The Sun lights up one hemisphere of the Moon's surface and this is the part that appears light. As the Moon proceeds on its orbit we get different views of its lighted portion and its outline assumes different shapes.

A little experiment, with a lamp as the Sun, and a ball or piece of fruit as the Moon, shows quite clearly how the various phases occur. To represent the motion of the Moon in its orbit the ball may be moved around the experimenter's head which represents the Earth. When the Moon is in the direction opposite from the Sun, the whole of the illuminated half of the Moon is visible and the Moon is full. If the direction of the Moon is at right angles to the direction of the Sun only half of its visible surface is illuminated as it appears at first and last quarters. When the Moon is in the same direction as the Sun, the illuminated half is pointed away from the Earth and it cannot be seen. This stage is called new Moon. About a day or so after the Moon has passed the new, the edge of the illuminated portion begins to appear as a crescent. The motion of the Moon in the sky carries it eastwards relative to the Sun by over 12° each day; and so it rises each day, on an average, about fifty minutes earlier than on the previous one.

The experiment with the ball as the Moon shows how to make a rough estimate of the time of moonrise corresponding to its different phases. At full Moon when the direction of the Moon is opposite that of the Sun the Moon must rise at about the time of sunset and set at sunrise. At new Moon when the Moon is in the same direction as the Sun, it rises at sunrise and sets at sunset but, of course, being so close to the Sun, it cannot be seen. At first quarter the Moon is at right angles to the direction of the Sun and reaches its highest point in the sky—that is, it is near the meridian—at sunset. At last quarter it reaches its highest point at sunrise. This means that at first quarter it is moonlight through the first half of the night and at last quarter through the second half.

If, during the experiments with the lamp and ball, the ball comes directly between the observer and the lamp, it hides the lamp. This illustrates an eclipse of the Sun, which is caused by the cutting off of the light of the Sun at new Moon. If, at full Moon, the Earth comes directly into line between the Sun and the Moon, the light from the Sun does not reach the Moon and there is an eclipse of the Moon. An eclipse of the Sun does not take place at every new Moon nor an eclipse of the Moon at every full Moon because the orbit of the Moon is slightly tilted out of the ecliptic, the plane in which the Sun and the Earth always lie. Therefore, at new Moon the Moon more often passes by but not through the line which would give an eclipse and at full Moon does not enter the shadow of the Earth. It is only when the Moon is in the plane of the Earth's orbit just at the time of new Moon or full Moon that an eclipse occurs. When the Moon does not pass exactly in front of the Sun and so covers only part of it or when only part of the Moon comes into the Earth's shadow the eclipses are partial.

A remarkable feature of the Moon's motion is that the same face is always towards the Earth, and the part of the Moon which is turned away from us has never been seen except on photographs from artificial satellites. This feature means that the Moon rotates on an axis approximately perpendicular to the plane of its orbit in the same time that it takes to complete a circuit around the Earth. An observer away from the Earth, on another planet for example, would see all round the Moon in the course of the lunar month, whereas we see only the one side. This subject will be mentioned again in the discussion of tides.

The Moon's Distance and Size

This distance of the Moon is determined by a trigonometric process similar to that in which the distance of an inaccessible object on the Earth may be determined. Suppose, for example, that we have two observatories on the same meridian, one north of the Equator and the other south of it, and that the altitude of the Moon is measured when it crosses this meridian. This gives a triangle whose vertices are at the two observatories and the Moon, and whose base angles are given by the measurements. The solution of the triangle yields the distance of the Moon.

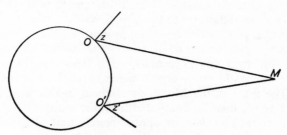

Figure 28.—Measuring the distance of the Moon.

Figure 29.—Measuring the diameter of the Moon.

As an example, let O and O' in Figure 28 represent two observatories on the same meridian at which the Moon is simultaneously observed. The latitude of O is 51° 28' north and of O' 33° 56' south. When the Moon was observed at the two places when it was on the meridian the zenith distance z at the first observatory was 75° 23' and at the second 11° 06'. The distance of the Moon in this case is calculated to be 61·3 times the radius of the Earth. A single observer may measure the position of the Moon when it is east of his meridian, then allow the rotation of the Earth to carry him away from his original place of observation, make the measurement with the Moon west of the meridian and, after allowing for motion of the Moon in the intervening hours, form an estimate of the way in which his own motion has influenced the Moon's position and hence calculate the distance of the Moon.

The difference in direction of a body as observed from two different places is due to *parallax* and for a member of the solar system the angle subtended at a body by the radius of the Earth is called its *horizontal parallax*. The Moon is the only celestial object near enough for its parallax to be seen with the naked eye and hence the only body whose distance was reasonably established in ancient times. The orbit of the Moon is not circular and its distance ranges from about 221,400 miles to about 252,700 miles.

If the distance of the Moon or a planet or any other object is known and angular diameter can be seen and measured, then its diameter in miles can be determined. Suppose, for example, in the above case (see Figure 29), that the Moon at the time of observation subtended an angle 31' 24" at the observatory O, then its linear diameter was 0·2727 that of the Earth —that is, 2,160 miles.

The mass of the Moon is determined as a by-product of accurate measurement of position of another body of the solar system to determine its distance in the way just explained. The body used has been the small planet Eros. Since the Earth and the Moon each exert a gravitational pull on the other both the Earth and the Moon are revolving about their common centre of gravity in a lunar month. The displacement of the Earth because of this makes a slight difference to the direction of the planet which is being observed. The change of direction being proportional to the distance of the Earth's centre from the centre of gravity of the Earth-Moon system yields a value of this distance. Then the mass of the Moon multiplied by its distance from the centre of gravity equals the mass of the Earth multiplied by its distance. The mass of the Moon, determined in this way, is 1/81 that of the Earth, and the density, computed from the mass and volume, is then about 2·6 times that of water, or approximately that of the surface rocks of the Earth.

Measurement of Lunar and Planetary Temperatures

As described in Chapter 3, measurement of the distribution of the energy in the spectrum of a body yields its temperature. The process can be adapted to give the temperature of cool bodies like the planets or the

Moon whose radiation arises partly from that of the Sun, reflected without change, and partly from the body's own heat, obtained by absorption of the radiation from the Sun. Figure 30 shows the curves for a body at the temperature of the Sun (about 6,000°K) and for one of temperature 293°K which occurs in our surroundings on the Earth. The latter curve, to prevent its being too insignificant on the diagram has its energy scale much enlarged—in fact, over three million times. On the same scale it would lie below the 6,000°K curve in the same part of the spectrum, but it has been raised to the same height. The significant thing is that the two curves have their maxima well separated. If the source being observed has two components of energy in this way and is examined first directly and then through a filter which absorbs one component but not the other, the change must be different from that which occurs for pure sunlight.

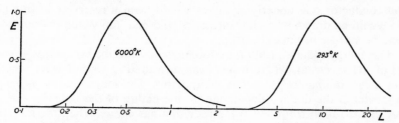

Figure 30.—Distribution of energy from bodies at 6,000°K and 293°K.

If the light is passed through a cell of water which transmits very little energy at the longer wave-lengths, only a small proportion of the unchanged sunlight but almost all of the radiation arising from the heat of the planet is absorbed. At the focus of the telescope the radiation falls upon and heats the junctions of two wires of dissimilar metals, producing an electric current proportional to the energy. The change in energy on placing the water cell in the beam is partly due to absorption of the solar radiation which may be calculated from the transmission of the cell measured in the laboratory, and partly to loss of the planetary radiation which is thereby measured. The whole of the planetary radiation P, by Stefan's Law given in Chapter 3, is in accord with the formula $P = kaT^4$, where a is the area from which the radiation is coming and k is a constant whose numerical value depends on the units employed. This formula may then be solved for the temperature. This measurement, because of the small energies that must be measured, is a difficult one but the appearance of T to the fourth power means that a large error in P leads to a much smaller error in T. For example, if P were in error by a factor of two, T would be out by only 20%.

Semiconductors, similar to the transistors used in small radio sets, are also used as detectors of radiation for temperature measurement. When the radiant energy falls on these their ability to carry electric current varies, so giving a measure of the radiation. Other filters also are used. Since, as in the case explained, these have different effects for sources with different energy distribution and different temperature, a measure of the temperature is provided. Refrigeration of the sensitive device, even down to the temperature of liquid hydrogen (20°K), reduces the unwanted effect from the immediate surroundings.

Physical Conditions on the Moon

At full Moon when we look straight towards the place on the surface where the Sun is shining at the middle of the lunar day, the temperature reaches about that of boiling water. When an eclipse of the Moon occurs, it is found that towards its end, which may be about two hours after the radiation of the Sun has been cut off, the temperature has fallen to —110°C, and it would fall even lower than this during the long lunar night. The rapidity with which the temperature changes shows that the material of the lunar surface conducts heat very poorly for, if it were a good conductor, the underlying layers would form a reservoir from which heat would be drawn when the surface is cold and into which it would flow when the surface becomes hot.

The energy radiated from the Moon extends into the radio-astronomical part of the spectrum, where it has been measured at several wave lengths, from a few millimetres to a few centimetres. The longer the wave length the greater is the depth—depending on the nature of the material—of the layer of the Moon from which the radiation has come. When the radiation has come from an inch or two below the Moon's surface, the variation during the month or during an eclipse of the Moon is very much less than for the optical part of the spectrum. This again is consistent with a very low conductivity of heat for the surface layer of the Moon.

The way in which light is reflected gives another clue to the nature of the Moon's surface. Only about seven per cent of the light is reflected. The way in which the reflection varies with the direction of the arrival of the Sun's rays and the direction in which the Moon is viewed leads to a sharp maximum of light at the time of full Moon, when both directions are perpendicular to the surface. From this it is inferred that the fine structure of the surface is rough, so that there is a large proportion of shadow when the Sun's light is arriving at an oblique angle. These observations combine with the low heat conductivity to indicate a very porous structure for the surface layer. It has at different times been suggested that it is made of a pumice-like rock which is pitted by bombardment of small particles from interplanetary space, or that it is a bed of dust. The close-up photographs taken by the space probe Luna 9 which made a soft landing on the Moon in February 1966 show no dust but do show the kind of surface which might be produced by age-long bombardment by small bodies of the sort that produce meteors in the Earth's atmosphere. More information must soon be forthcoming from further probes and possibly manned landings.

Some areas of the Moon cool more slowly when the Sun's light is cut off. These occur in crater areas, among which are Tycho and Copernicus. The insulating layer must be thinner at such places which may have been more recently exposed by the crater-forming processes.

Although around the Moon there is most probably a slight increase in the density of the interplanetary gases and it is possible that the body of the Moon gives off a little gas, the situation is best described by saying that the Moon has no atmosphere for it is of such tenuous character that it cannot be detected. As the Moon proceeds in its orbit it occasionally covers a star and, when this happens, the star appears to approach the very edge of the Moon without any diminution in brightness or displacement of position and to disappear with startling suddenness when it reaches that edge. From a theoretical point of view it is not surprising that the Moon has not an appreciable atmosphere. Any mass at the surface of a celestial body, or particle of a gas surrounding it, is held to the body by its gravitational attraction. If the mass is given an upward velocity, it will usually fall back but, if the velocity is sufficiently high, it will escape altogether from the gravitational field of the body. The least velocity which will take the mass completely away is called the *escape velocity*, which is seven miles per second for the Earth—as has been well publicised in connection with rocket and satellite experiments. For the Moon the escape velocity is 1·5 miles per second. The particles of a gas have a wide range of velocities, which are greater at higher temperatures. A small proportion of the particles of a gas on the Moon would have a velocity higher than that for escape and an atmosphere would leak away into space in a time long by standards of human life but short in terms of a cosmic time scale.

TIDES

The tides of the ocean are due to the gravitational pull of the Moon and, to a lesser extent, of the Sun. Every particle of matter in the Earth, including the waters of the sea, is attracted to the Moon and Sun, but it is the differences between the forces that produce the tides. In Figure 31 the Earth is represented at E and the Moon at M. The average force of the Moon on each pound of the Earth is represented by the dotted line from E and the force per pound on the water at a place P by the dotted line from P. The difference between these two is shown by the full line from P, and this is the force tending to move the water, relative to the Earth. The part of the force in the direction perpendicular to the Earth's surface has no chance

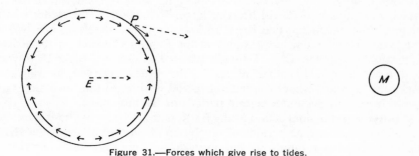

Figure 31.—Forces which give rise to tides.

to move the water which, however, is influenced by the horizontal part of the force represented at *P* by the full line inside the circle. The corresponding horizontal components of the tidal forces, which may be similarly found for other places, are shown by the arrows around the circle which represents the Earth. These forces tend to cause a flow of the water, which would raise the water on the side of the Earth toward the Moon and also on that away from it. As the Earth rotates relative to the pattern of the tidal forces, the tides progress around the Earth. The average interval between passages of the meridian by the Moon is 24 hours 51 minutes, and so the average time between successive high tides is 12 hours 25½ minutes.

Similar tidal forces must be exerted by the Sun, but, because of its much greater distance, the forces originating from the Sun are only about forty per cent of those from the Moon.

Changes in the distance of the Moon, changes in its declination and changes in the declination of the Sun alter the magnitude and direction of the tidal forces, and the full theory of tides is complex. When the Sun and Moon are together in the sky at new Moon or opposite at full Moon, the tidal forces of the two bodies reinforce one another and the tides have a large range. Such tides are called *spring tides*. At first and last quarters of the Moon occur the *neap tides*, which have a smaller range.

The rotation of the Earth makes it impossible for the water ever to attain the shape it would take if the same forces were acting on a non-rotating Earth and the high tides do not correspond to the time when the Moon is on the meridian. Besides this, any body of water in the ocean will have periods associated with it in which the water tends to vibrate more naturally. If some particular component of the tidal force corresponds nearly with this natural period, the oscillation due to this particular component will be exaggerated. The same sort of thing can be observed by rocking a dish of water. If the rocking is done with the natural period of vibration the amplitude of the motion is much greater than for other periods. So important is the part played by these natural periods in determining the character of the tide at a particular place that the astronomical theory is used merely to indicate the periods of the components of the tidal force, and actual observations at the place are analysed to see how each component contributes to the tide there.

In places where the natural period corresponds approximately to the half of a lunar day, the tide corresponding with the main tidal forces which have this period will become large. Reduction in the width of the channel into which the tide is advancing also tends to raise the height of the tide. These circumstances apply in the English Channel, in the Bristol Channel, and in the Bay of Fundy which lies between New Brunswick and Nova Scotia. In other places in the world—Darwin, in northern Australia, is one—where the natural period is close to the lunar day only one tide per day occurs at certain periods of the month.

It has been the tidal action of the Earth that has brought about the exact equality of the average periods of revolution of the Moon about the Earth and the period of rotation, so that, even during long ages, the same face is always presented towards us. If the Moon were rotating more quickly than it does relative to the line between it and the Earth it would also be rotating relative to the tide raised on it by the Earth. This would act as a brake on the rotation until the periods of rotation and revolution became equal as they are now.

THE CALENDAR

The day—to which our lives are regulated—is the most important of all units of time. When the days have to be counted out into longer periods to form a calendar, use is made of natural measures provided by the apparent motions of the Sun and Moon.

In early times calendars were based on the movement of the Moon, the months corresponding to the ordinary lunar month. There are still peoples who regulate their calendars in this way, a new month starting for them when the crescent Moon is first sighted in the sky.

The year which corresponds to the motion of the Sun must be recognised as a much more important unit of time since to this corresponds the cycle of the seasons which regulate the important agricultural activities of the planting and harvesting of crops. Even in ancient times, the Egyptians used astronomical means to determine the length of the year, for regulation of their calendar.

The length of the year most natural to use for a calendar is that which corresponds to the interval between successive passages of the Sun in the same direction across the equator. This is the year which corresponds to the progress of the seasons. Its average length is 365·2422 days. An important reform of the calendar was made by Julius Caesar in 45 B.C. when he sought the advice of the astronomer Sosigenes and decided to base the calendar entirely upon the motion of the Sun, abandoning the lunar reckoning altogether. In this calendar the average length of the year was made 365·25 days, close to its true value, by having a leap year with an extra day in it once in every four years. However, even with this average length the calendar dates of the seasons began in the course of centuries to drift away from their original values.

This showed itself most obviously when the rules for fixing Easter gave a date which was gradually drifting away from the vernal equinox, the astronomical phenomenon with which it was originally connected. Pope Gregory XIII accordingly introduced a reform which would bring back the dates to their original place in the year and change the calendar to make the mean length of the calendar year so close to its proper length that it would be satisfactory for several thousands of years. In the year 1588 ten days were dropped from the reckoning. It was decided that, for years divisible by 100, the leap years should be observed only if the years were divisible also by 400. This leads to a mean length for the year of 365·2425 days, in error by an amount equivalent to a day in every three thousand years or so. This calendar was finally adopted by all European countries and countries of predominantly European civilization.

A DISTANT VIEW OF THE EARTH

While discussing the Earth and Moon it is of interest to consider what their appearance would be from a distance comparable with those at which other planets are seen. If some observer were able to see the Earth from Venus (at a distance of 30,000,000 miles) he would have before him a spectacle more magnificent than that which any of the planets provides for us. The Moon which, relative to the size of the Earth, is larger than any other satellite of the solar system compared with its planet, would be plainly visible to the naked eye and about equal in brightness to the brightest star. The Earth would be, in opposition to the Sun, a magnificent object with magnitude approximately -7, a good deal brighter than Venus ever looks to us. In the telescope this observer—at present imaginary, but possibly real in the not very distant future—would not find it easy to examine the details of the surface of the Earth because of the great areas of cloud and because of the haze of the atmosphere. These clouds add greatly to the *albedo* or reflecting power of the Earth which reflects back into space about $0 \cdot 3$ of the light falling on it; whereas the Moon has an albedo of only $0 \cdot 07$, similar to that of rather dark-coloured rock.

When the relative positions of the Earth and the observer were right, he would be able to see a brilliant reflection of the Sun in the ocean, a phenomenon which has no observed counterpart on any of the planets. The extensive snow caps at the poles would be a prominent feature. No doubt, by patient observing, it would be possible for him to map approximately the areas of land, which would be revealed by contrast with the surrounding darker oceans. The movements of the great areas of cloud associated with cyclones would give him material for the study of terrestrial meteorology. Some areas would no doubt be observed to have characteristic colouration, the Sahara Desert differing from the tropical forests of the Amazon region, but small scale markings of the kind made by man would not be likely to come within range of observation. From the outer planets of the solar system the Earth would appear somewhat fainter than Venus.

ARTIFICIAL SATELLITES

Launching a Satellite

The Earth's first artificial satellite, weighing 180 pounds, was launched in October 1957. Since then scores of satellites have been placed in orbit, the heaviest up to July 1965 weighing 12 tons.

Rocket propulsion, similar to that used in firework skyrockets, must be used to launch a satellite—for a body cannot be placed in orbit around the Earth by firing it from a gun at the surface of the Earth. If the projectile were fired from a gun as at P in Figure 32, its motion would be controlled by the law of gravity to follow an orbit which would nearly repeat itself and pass through P again in the same direction. Since it cannot do this without striking the Earth it could not continue in orbit. If the velocity

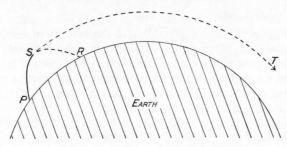

Figure 32.—Launching an artificial satellite.

were greater than the velocity of escape the body would, of course, leave the Earth altogether.

The situation is different if the body can be launched nearly horizontally from *S*, a great height above the Earth's atmosphere. For fairly small velocities it will follow a curved path and be pulled back to the Earth's surface as at *R*. With increased velocity of launching the range is increased until the projectile altogether misses the Earth, whose pull is enough only to make it follow a curved path above the Earth's surface and, after a complete circuit, return to *S*. This situation can be achieved with rockets that can still be made to exert a thrust after leaving the launching site. Such a rocket can reach the point *S* with thrust still available and, if everything has gone according to the plan, the thrust can be applied at this point to give a velocity sufficient to place the satellite in orbit. The orbits calculated by using the law of gravity and Newton's law of motion (Chapter 3) represent the motion very well, except that the part of the force due to interaction with the atmosphere is not predictable.

The time that a satellite takes to complete a circuit of the Earth depends on its average distance. This is shown in Table 3 which gives, for various average heights of travel above the Earth's surface, the corresponding periods to complete a circuit of the Earth, neglecting any effect of the atmosphere. The table shows, incidentally, that Puck, in "A Midsummer Night's Dream", unless he could defy the laws of nature was offering to do the impossible when he said he would "put a girdle around the earth in forty minutes". If he were to travel at the necessary speed, he would leave the Earth altogether!

TABLE 3

Periods and Heights of Satellites

Period Minutes	Height Miles	Period Minutes	Height Miles
86	46	100	470
88	108	110	760
90	169	120	1,042
92	230	130	1,316

Observations from Satellites

Observations which are not possible at the surface of the Earth can be made from satellites. The radiation, including the ultraviolet and even X-rays, which cannot penetrate the atmosphere is available for observation and will be mentioned when the sources from which they come are being described. The character of the orbits has already been referred to as giving a clue to the shape of the Earth.

Unless a satellite is very high, some of its energy must be lost in passing through the parts of the atmosphere. If velocity at *S*, the point from which it is launched, is greater than that needed to send it in a circular orbit, it will move outside the circle and be further from the Earth on the other side; and the lowest point, the *perigee*, of its path will be near *S*. When the satellite is in the low part of its orbit in each passage around the Earth, it may brush into the atmosphere so that at each return it loses a little velocity and the distance to which it recedes on the other side is reduced. In consequence the orbit becomes more nearly circular and shrinks, and the period becomes shorter as shown in Table 3. When the period comes down to 90 minutes, the interaction with the atmosphere is so great that the satellite is soon brought down.

The changes in the orbit brought about by interaction with the atmosphere yield information about the density of the high, previously almost unexplored, zones. The density, although greater than was thought in pre-satellite days, continues to fall off at increasing heights and by 200 miles above the Earth's surface is only 10^{-10} of its value at sea level. The outer parts of the atmosphere have been shown to be very sensitive to changes on the Sun and there are very large variations of density associated with sunspots and other disturbances on the Sun.

The Van Allen Belts

Some of the early satellites carried radiation detecting instruments for observations directed by United States physicist J. A. van Allen. These detected a layer of high velocity particles above the Earth. The particles owe their origin to the presence in interstellar space of highly energetic particles, mostly the positively charged hydrogen nuclei, and to the existence of a stream of particles from the Sun. The interstellar particles, or *cosmic rays*, are so energetic that they may produce many more when they collide with and smash an atom belonging to the atmosphere. The motion of charged particles is controlled when they are near the Earth by the Earth's magnetic field within which they become trapped. This field extends from the magnetic poles, widening out over the magnetic equator, and so the belt surrounds the Earth, somewhat in doughnut form, with the openings over the magnetic poles.

There are two belts, centred respectively on heights about 2,000 miles and 10,000 miles, where the population of the particles is much higher. The trapped particles are mostly electrons and protons, and in the inner zone many of them are moving with very high velocities such as would be obtained if they had been accelerated through an electric field of from

50,000 to hundreds of millions of volts. The strength of the radiation and the thickness of the belts change with the incidence of disturbances on the Sun which vary the discharge of particles into interplanetary space.

The Growth of Space Science

The satellite field is one of enormous activity in which new well-publicised events are sure to occur in the near future even before this book is published. In October 1959, and again in 1965, the far side of the Moon was photographed from a satellite that passed around it, and the pictures were telecast back to the Earth. In 1964 and the beginning of 1965 three Ranger satellites sent back magnificent, close-up pictures of the near side of the Moon which gave a resolution a thousand times better than previously obtained from the Earth's surface. These space probes crashed on the Moon when their work was done. Plates 6 to 9 show photographs from Ranger IX as it approached the Moon.

It seems desirable to make further soft landings and place instruments on the Moon, to examine the nature of its surface, and earthquake —or should it be moonquake?—recording apparatus which would give data for investigating the structure of the interior. The structure of the surface of the Moon and the nature of the large scale features, the craters and maria, should give information of great importance for unravelling the history of the solar system. With the slow rate of erosion on the Moon, it may be possible to decipher events that occurred a thousand million years ago. The erosive action of wind and water effectively prevents this on the Earth.

Other space probes have been sent further afield. In 1962 Mariner II sent back useful information about the interplanetary space through which it travelled and about Venus after its close approach to that planet. In the middle of July 1965 Mariner IV provided observations from the vicinity of Mars, and sent back a series of photographs which have a resolution many times what was possible from Earth-based telescopes.

The success of these launchings has naturally given prominence to the idea of interplanetary travel. The first satellite to carry a human passenger performed an orbit on 12 April 1961, and by the middle of 1965 nineteen people had been in orbit. One completed 64 circuits of the Earth, twice astronauts ventured outside their craft in space suits, and one space ship carried three men. Plans are going ahead for a landing on the Moon within a few years.

There remain problems in medicine and in rocket propulsion before the interplanetary traveller will be able to venture far into space in an environment not previously encountered by man. One problem, not realized in pre-satellite days, is protection against the radiation, including the particle radiation, which must be encountered. In the Van Allen belts this reaches a level which would be a danger to human life. This danger might not only be from the particles themselves but from the more penetrating X-rays which they might generate when they encounter the body of a space-craft. The probe Pioneer III showed in the inner belt radiation which would penetrate a $\frac{1}{4}$ inch of lead. The launching, it appears, must be made so that the passage through the Van Allen layers would be quick or else take place in a polar area where the layers have their opening. On the other hand, the results from observations by past probes show that the danger from small pieces of material like those seen as meteors in the Earth's atmosphere is less than had previously been feared.

The rockets for launching space vehicles have to be very large for, in order to achieve a velocity several times the exhaust velocity, the weight of fuel at take off must be many times that of the final vehicle and its contents. This cannot be small since, besides the mass of the travellers themselves, it will be necessary to take all of their needs with them, including oxygen to breathe, as it is impossible to rely on gathering any of their needs from space. Space travel still includes planning the orbits to economize energy, by choosing the most appropriate starting time for the intended destination and placing the vehicle in the right orbit with high accuracy. Until the traveller can leave with a large reserve of energy, interplanetary travel must remain hazardous. When the space vehicle can take a great supply of energy, say several times what is needed for take-off from the Earth, interplanetary travel will be more practical. Then the traveller will be able to change his mind and repair errors to which both man and machine have proved only too prone.

One vital experiment was carried out in December 1965 when the spacecraft Gemini 6 succeeded in making a rendezvous with Gemini 7. This was most valuable because it shows how it would be possible to establish a base outside the atmosphere by several flights from the Earth. It would partly solve the energy problem, for less energy would be needed for further progress from such a base.

5

THE OTHER PLANETS

THE SOLAR SYSTEM

The Motions of the Planets

The paths of the planets are controlled mainly by the gravitational attraction of the Sun which is far more massive than any of them. For this reason the planets all move around the Sun in a way suggested by Copernicus in 1643. The actual motions of the solar system are worked out by mathematical processes which make use of two laws discovered by Newton, the law of gravitation and the law of motion. The latter states that the acceleration of a body is proportional to the force acting on it. If the motion of a planet is to be computed with accuracy over a long period, it is necessary to take into account the attractions of the other planets, and it becomes a complex problem which has occupied some of the finest mathematicians. Because of the predominance of the Sun the main features of the movements may be described without allowing for the influence of the planets.

In Figure 33, *S* represents the Sun and *P* the position of a planet at a particular instant. If there were no relative motion between them, the body would fall straight towards the Sun and eventually would strike it. Now suppose that the planet is given a small motion at right angles to the direction of the Sun from it. As it moves, its path will be continually bent towards the Sun by the gravitational force and the orbit will take a form somewhat as shown by the curve *R* in the diagram. The point *P* where the planet is furthest from the Sun is called *aphelion*, and point *Q* where it is nearest the Sun is called *perihelion*. If the body is given a higher velocity at *P*, the *ellipse* will spread out, and there is a velocity for which the planet will move around the Sun in precisely a circle. For a still greater velocity the orbit again becomes an ellipse, but *P* is then perihelion, and with increasing velocity the aphelion recedes into the distance to the left. For a sufficient velocity the Sun's gravitation is insufficient to make it return. When the velocity is

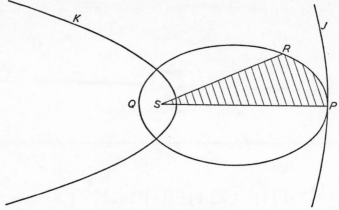

Figure 33.—Possible paths of bodies moving under gravitational attraction of a central body.

just enough to carry the body right away, the motion is in a *parabola* which is illustrated by the curve *J*. To show better the form of the parabolic orbit the curve *K* is drawn for the case when the perihelion distance is small. Beyond the velocity necessary for parabolic motion the curve is called a *hyperbola*.

These curves have been studied by mathematicians from ancient times, but it was only about 350 years ago that Kepler discovered that the planets move in elliptical orbits. The ellipse is the shape which is drawn by sticking two pins into a board with a thread extending around them and tracing the curve with a pencil within the loop which is kept tight by pulling the pencil outward as far as the length of the thread allows. The sum of the distances of the pencil point from the pins is constant, and the position of each pin is said to be a *focus* of the ellipse.

The laws of planetary motion discovered by Kepler are:—

1. Each planet moves about the Sun in an ellipse of which the Sun occupies one focus.
2. The line joining the Sun to a planet passes over equal areas in equal times; that is, if, in Figure 33, *P* and *R* are two positions of the planet, the area of the sector *PSR* is proportional to the time that the planet takes to go from *P* to *R*.
3. The square of the period taken by the planet to complete one circuit around the Sun is proportional to the cube of its mean distance from the Sun. That is, for two planets of periods *T* and *t* and mean distances respectively *A* and *a*, the relation would be

$$\frac{T^2}{t^2} = \frac{A^3}{a^3}.$$

Since the period increases more quickly than the radius of the orbit, the velocities of the distant planets are slower than those of the planets near the Sun.

It is striking that all, except Pluto, of the large and massive bodies of the solar system move in nearly the same plane, and all perform their revolutions about the Sun in the same direction in nearly circular orbits.

Distances within the Solar System

By means of a long series of observations or by measuring the periods and using Kepler's third law, the relative sizes of the orbits of the planets can be found and a scale diagram of the solar system may be drawn without measuring any distance. When just one distance is measured, the scale of the diagram is set and all of the distances become known.

Until recent years the most direct method of setting the scale was to measure the distance of the minor planet Eros by the method described for the Moon in Chapter 4. This body was used because its image is small like that of a star, and so its position can be measured accurately; and, because it comes near to the Earth, the apparent change in its position from different points of the Earth is greater and so easier to measure. An extensive series of observations of this kind was made in 1931 when Eros came within 16 million miles of the Earth.

Since 1962 the distance of Venus has been measured several times by the radar method. Clearly defined echoes of transmitted signals have been received and the time interval between transmission and reception used to find the distance of the planet. This method supersedes all others in accuracy. The mean distance of the Sun, thus found to be 92,956,000 miles, is taken as the astronomical unit of distance within the solar system.

The Planetary Motions as Seen from the Earth

The orbits of the four planets nearest the Sun are represented on Figure 34, where the solar system is supposed to be viewed from the northern side, from which the motions of the planets and the rotation of the Earth are anti-clockwise in direction. The motions appear more complicated when they are viewed from the Earth which is the third planet out from the Sun. This complexity is the reason why it took mankind so long to become convinced of the geometry of the motions expounded by Copernicus and Kepler.

Venus, our nearest planetary neighbour, is closer to the Sun and moves more quickly than the Earth. Consider the situation when Venus is at position *V1* with the Earth at *E1*. Because the Earth's rotation is anti-clockwise, the horizon first reaches the Sun which therefore sets first, and Venus would be an evening star at the furthest angular distance from the Sun in the evening sky. As it overtakes the Earth, Venus would appear closer to the Sun, and set a shorter time after it, until the positions *V2* and *E2* are reached with Venus in *conjunction* with the Sun. After passing the Sun it becomes a morning star and reaches its greatest angular distance west of the Sun when the two planets are in positions *V4* and *E4*. As the half of Venus towards the Sun is the illuminated portion of the planet, it shows crescent phases in the telescope, similar in appearance to those of the Moon. After the position *V4* it again approaches the Sun but passes on

G

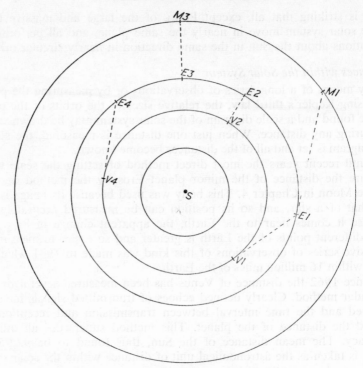

Figure 34.—Planetary orbits.

the opposite side of it. Venus never reaches the part of the sky opposite to the Sun.

The same description applies to Mercury except that Mercury does not go as far away from the Sun as Venus does. It appears in the twilight sky where it is likely to be seen only by people who look for it. When they go between the Earth and the Sun, Venus and Mercury occasionally pass directly in front of the Sun and may be seen as a black dot on it. This happens fairly often for Mercury, but rather rarely for Venus. It was to observe a transit of Venus from Tahiti in 1769 that James Cook made the voyage in which he discovered the east coast of Australia. Transits of Venus over the Sun occurred in 1874 and 1882 and the next one will be in 2004.

The outer planets such as Mars may reach a part of the sky opposite to the Sun, but suppose that Mars is in the position M1 with the Earth at E1 moving more quickly than it and overtaking it. At this time Mars is west of the Sun and rising about 6 hours before it. As the Earth overtakes the planet, Mars rises earlier each evening, and finally, when it reaches the position M3 it is in the opposite part of the sky from the Sun and on the meridian about midnight.

It is interesting to consider the changes in the apparent motion of Mars relative to the background of the stars. In the position M1, and indeed for most of the orbit, the line joining the Earth to Mars moves in the sky in the same direction as the Earth and Mars themselves are moving, and the planet's right ascension increases. However, when the two planets reach the positions *M3* and *E3*, the Earth is moving more quickly than Mars and the line from *E3* to *M3* rotates in the opposite direction, so that Mars appears to move backwards among the stars. This period of so called *retrograde* motion is a feature of the movement of the outer planets which always regress for a period when they are in *opposition* to the Sun. In Figure 35 is drawn a portion of the star map, showing the apparent path of Mars from October 1964 to July 1965, to illustrate the kind of motion that may occur. These apparently complicated motions of the planets led

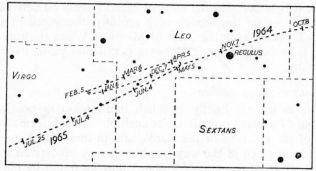

Figure 35.—Motion of Mars from October 1964 to July 1965.

to great complexity in the theories of the planetary system invented by ancient astronomers. The outer planets do not show phases to anything like the same extent that the inner ones do although the dark side does encroach a little on to the side of the planet turned towards the Earth, for example, in positions like that represented at *M1* in Figure 34.

The Masses of the Planets

The size of a planet in miles is determined by measuring its diameter in angle and making a computation in the same way as was described for the Moon in Chapter 4. The distance of a satellite of a planet from its primary is also found in this way by measuring the angular distance. The mass of a planet may readily be found if it has a satellite. The motion of the satellite is governed by the theory of gravitation which furnishes a relation which is simple if the mass of the satellite is neglected when compared with that of the planet. This is often justifiable to a good approximation. Taking the distance of the satellite from its primary as *a* astronomical units and its period of revolution as *T* years, the mass, *M*, of the planet in terms of that of the Sun, is given by

$$M = \frac{a^3}{T^2}.$$

T and *a* are found by observation.

For example, when it is known that the period of Jupiter's fourth satellite is 0·04569 years and its mean distance from Jupiter 0·012586 astronomical units, the formula gives the mass of Jupiter as 0·000955 of that of the Sun which agrees with the value given in Table 4. Several of the planets have more than one satellite from each of which a result may be obtained. The masses of the planets like Mercury and Venus which are not accompanied by satellites must also be found from their gravitational effects, in this case on the movement of other planets. The mass of Venus disturbs the motion of the Earth and Mars, and study of the departure of the orbits of these planets from what it would be if Venus were not present can be made to yield a mass of Venus. Mercury, however, is less massive than Venus and more distant from other planets; so its mass is rather less well determined. It is hoped that the mass of Mercury may be derived from the effects it produces on the motion of a recently discovered minor planet, Icarus, which passes near the orbit of Mercury. When the size and mass of a planet is available, a straightforward calculation yields its volume and average density.

Table of Planetary Information

In order to present briefly as much information as possible on the planets Table 4 has been prepared. For each planet the information is listed at the top of the columns of the Table, and in most cases some account has already been given of the way in which it may be derived from observation. The period of rotation of a planet may be found by observing the returns of some well-defined feature on its surface. (Venus has no such observable features.)

The detection of the chemical components of the atmosphere of a planet needs a little further comment. In the part of the spectrum which comes through our own Earth's atmosphere and is available for observation some gases have lines which are strong and readily observable. Such gases are carbon dioxide (CO_2), carbon monoxide (CO) and nitrous oxide (NO_2). Water (H_2O) and oxygen are rather more difficult to observe, partly because their accessible lines are not very strong and partly because they are plentiful in our own atmosphere for which allowance must be made. Two gases, hydrogen and nitrogen, which are certainly plentiful in the universe cannot be observed spectroscopically because their usual spectrum lines are not accessible.

The temperatures are those measured in the way described for the Moon. As the radiation comes from various layers in the atmosphere, the use of a single figure is an over simplification. For the layers of the atmospheres accessible to measurement by optical methods the temperatures quoted are representative of the warmer parts of the planets. Values found in the radio part of the spectrum may apply to different levels and are given in some cases under the sections devoted to the particular planets.

In the following discussion of the planets—in their order outwards from the Sun—reference will be necessary to the information in Table 4 and further information not suited to tabulation will be added. The planets down to Saturn, which have been known since prehistoric times, are bright

TABLE 4

Planet	Distance, from Sun, Millions of miles	Orbital period, years	Orbital velocity, miles per sec.	Diameter of equator, miles	Rotation period	Brightest mag.
Mercury	36·0	0·241	30	3,100	59 days	−1·9
Venus	67·2	0·615	22	7,700	247 days	−4·4
Earth	93·0	1·000	18·5	7,927	23h56m	
Mars	141	1·881	15·0	4,200	24 37	−2·8
Jupiter	483	11·86	8·1	88,700	9 50	−2·5
Saturn	886	29·5	6·0	75,100	10 14	−0·4
Uranus	1782	84·0	4·2	29,300	10 49	5·6
Neptune	2792	165	3·4	27,700	14	7·9
Pluto	3664	248	2·9	4,900		14·9

Diameter through poles: Earth, 7900 miles; Jupiter 82,800; Saturn 67,200

Planet	Mass, Earth =1	Density— Water =1	Velocity of escape miles per sec.	Detected parts of atmosphere	Surface temp. degrees K	No. of satellites
Mercury	0·054	5·6	2·6	—	610	—
Venus	0·815	5·0	6·4	CO_2, H_2O	230	—
Earth	1·000	5·5	6·9	N_2, O_2	295	1
Mars	0·108	3·9	3·1	CO_2, H_2O	283	2
Jupiter	318·4	1·3	37	CH_4, NH_3	135	12
Saturn	95·2	0·7	22	CH_4, NH_3	120	9
Uranus	14·6	1·6	14	CH_4	—	5
Neptune	17·3	2·2	15	CH_4	—	2

The Mass of the Sun on this scale is 333,400 and of the Moon 0·0123

Atmosphere: N_2 is nitrogen, O_2 oxygen, CO_2 carbon dioxide, CH_4 methane and NH_3 ammonia. The atmosphere of the Earth contains also water, H_2O, carbon dioxide and small amounts of other gases. Jupiter, Saturn, Uranus and Neptune must have hydrogen, helium and nitrogen.

Temperatures are at the visible surface by infra-red measurements.

and, in fact, as the Table shows, four out of five of them are, at maximum, brighter than any star. These planets were associated by the ancient peoples with the deities who are famed in their myths and legends.

MERCURY

Although Mercury is quite bright, its nearness to the Sun means that, as far as the naked eye is concerned, it appears in the twilight sky of the morning or evening. With the telescope, however, it is usually better to observe Mercury when it is higher in the sky even though it must be in daytime when observing conditions are poor. The small size of the planet makes it a difficult object.

The rate of rotation of Mercury, and of Venus also, has been measured by radar methods. A short pulse of radiation is emitted and examined on its return after reflection from the surface of the planet. The first part of the returning pulse is that reflected from the nearest part of the surface of the planet. By choosing a particular time interval after this, the radiation returned from a zone of constant distance from the disc centre is isolated. If the planet is rotating relative to the Earth, different parts of this zone will have different velocities in the line of sight from the observer, and these will give different Doppler shifts in the wave-length of the returning radiation. By analysis of these the rate of rotation may be estimated. By observing the value at different times, from different directions, and in different combinations with the motion of the Earth the direction of the axis of rotation and the sense of the rotation may be obtained.

For Mercury this method of observation gives the rotation period of 59 days which is entered in Table 4. Visual observations had previously suggested the period of rotation of Mercury as 88 days, the same as its orbital period. Now the time intervals between drawings with duplication of marking has also given a rotation period of 59 days. It was formerly believed that the tidal action of the Sun would necessarily cause Mercury to present always the same face to the Sun as the Moon does to the Earth. Now, however, it is thought that since the orbit of Mercury departs a good deal from circular shape, the much greater tidal influence when the planet is nearest and moving more rapidly around the Sun predominates and gives the more rapid rotation.

The temperature on the sunward side of Mercury is above the melting point of lead and the point directly beneath the Sun may have a temperature over 1,000°K. Radio measurements at short wave-length indicate that the dark side of Mercury may not be so cold as previously thought. This may indicate a small amount of atmosphere, which would transport the heat from the side towards the Sun to the dark side. Observation of polarization of the light from Mercury also points to a tenuous atmosphere. If there is an atmosphere, it must be very thin. No sign of it is detectable when Mercury transits across the face of the Sun as it does about twelve times per century. The low mass and velocity of escape and high temperature give small expectation of Mercury's retaining an atmosphere.

VENUS

Venus is the planet which comes nearest to the Earth being at its closest approach 26 million miles away. The brightness of Venus is so striking that when you know where to look it is not hard to see it with the naked eye in full daylight. Just by chance many people do see Venus in the daytime, especially when the Moon, in its monthly journey around the Earth, is close to Venus and draws attention to it. In the evening it is so bright that shadows cast by it can be seen. The entries in Table 4 show that in size, mass and density Venus is very nearly a twin planet with the Earth. Very probably its internal structure is similar to that of the Earth.

The solid surface of Venus is not seen because of the permanent layer of cloud in its atmosphere. The high reflectivity of these clouds is a reason for the great brightness of Venus, and the lack of enduring visible features made it impossible to find a reliable period of rotation for the planet. Attempts have also been made to determine the speed of rotation by spectroscopic examination of the disc of Venus. If it were rotating with appreciable speed, Doppler shift of the spectrum lines would reveal the direction and speed of rotation. These attempts were successful only in showing that the period of rotation must be more than a few days. On the other hand, there is no very great contrast in temperature between the dark and bright sides of the planet. It is thus clearly unlikely that it always presents the same face to the Sun. The radar method gave a result for Venus before it was applied to Mercury. This was described in the discussion on Mercury. The rotation period derived is about 247 days. The remarkable thing about the result is that the motion is retrograde, that is clockwise if we look at Venus from the north side of the solar system as we did in Figure 34. Retrograde motions are unusual in the solar system.

As Venus approaches the edge of the Sun during a transit, it is surrounded by a bright ring of light which is another indication of the existence of an atmosphere. The atmosphere of Venus has yielded only a little to spectroscopic examination. Carbon dioxide, which is in our own atmosphere, is produced by burning coal or wood, and is in the exhaled breath of all animals, has been detected as present in great quantity. Venus has vastly more than is in our atmosphere. If all of the carbon dioxide in the Earth's atmosphere were stowed at the base of the atmosphere, it would form a layer seven feet thick. For Venus a layer at the same pressure would be six miles thick.

The gas nitrogen which makes up the bulk of our earth's atmosphere is thought to be plentiful in the atmosphere of Venus, but the test for this is not available. Water has recently been detected by spectrographic observations from balloons, which have carried the spectrograph above most of the confusing water vapour of our own atmosphere. The composition of the clouds had long been the subject of discussion while the water defied detection. Now the cloud spectrum has been found to fit that of ice crystals. It seems, then, that the tops of the clouds are composed of ice crystals, as are the high level clouds of the Earth. The difficulty in detecting the water vapour occurs because there is so little of it above the high level of the clouds. Oxygen could be detected, if present in appreciable proportions, but has not been revealed and therefore, if present, must be so only in very small amounts in the limited part of the atmosphere that can be examined above the clouds.

At the top of the clouds temperatures well below freezing point have been measured by infra-red observations, but radiation of longer wavelengths, which are observed by radio techniques, penetrates the cloud from a lower layer and shows that the temperature is higher for deeper layers. The energy received at wave-lengths of several centimetres, probably coming from the surface at the base of the atmosphere, indicates a temperature about 600°K. This high temperature is no doubt due to the blanket of cloud which stops the infra-red rays from leaving the planet as they would do if it were bare.

On 27 August 1962 the Mariner II space probe was launched to make observations of Venus and of interplanetary space during its flight. It was within 22,000 miles of Venus on December 14. Measurements were made of the temperature of the planet. These verify the above results which were then somewhat uncertain and show little difference in the values of the surface temperature for the bright and dark sides of Venus. Observations were made to reveal a magnetic field or belts of trapped particles such as exist around the Earth, but neither the magnetic field nor the count of particles was greater than in interplanetary space. The magnetic field, if it exists at all, must be very much less than that of the Earth. The effect of the approach to Venus on the path of Mariner II indicated a mass of $0 \cdot 81485$ of that of the Earth.

MARS

Observations of Surface Markings

The orbit of Mars departs somewhat from being circular and so, when the Earth comes between it and the Sun, it may, on different occasions, be at very different distances. The closest distance to which it can come on such an occasion is about 34 million miles, and, as we then look straight down on the side of the planet illuminated by the Sun, a good view of the planet is obtained. In the telescope, the solid surface of the planet can usually be seen, and many permanent features have been recognised and mapped by keen-eyed, patient observers. Some of these are shown in Plate 2.

The time of rotation of the planet, revealed by long series of observations of the markings, is not very far from the rotational period of the Earth. In another respect, Mars resembles the Earth, in that its axis of rotation is inclined to its orbit, so that the Sun is overhead at different latitudes of Mars at different times in the 687 day Martian year. This gives rise to seasons on Mars which parallel those we have on the Earth and to the changes in the white polar caps which vary in size according to the season and which, in the telescope, are the most conspicuous features on the planet. The one in the winter hemisphere is very extensive and may spread to over 3,000 miles in diameter at its greatest extent towards the end of winter. When spring comes it shrinks and in the summertime becomes relatively small and on several occasions the southern polar cap has completely disappeared. As the cap contracts its edge is indented, since the melting advances more quickly in some places than others. This is no doubt due to the lingering of the frost in the higher localities as is the tendency on the Earth. As the regions emerge from the shrinking cap, the ground markings are darker than usual, giving rise to the appearance of a dark belt around the cap.

Much of the area of the planet has a pink colour, and this is why it appears red to the naked eye. These portions and the major dark markings are permanent and appear on the maps of the surface of Mars. The dark areas are subject to changes in shape and intensity, some of which are seasonal. There is a tendency for the darkness that appears at the edge of the shrinking polar cap in spring to progress towards the equator as a kind of seasonal wave. There are, too, more erratic and long term changes which may affect the smaller dark markings that occur in the lighter areas of the planet. The seasonal changes suggest to some that a plant life may exist on the planet and some observers have seen a green colouring. However, as the features of the chlorophyll of plant life of the kind we have on the Earth do not appear in the spectrum of Mars, the seasonal changes, if correctly attributed to some form of life, may arise from the presence on Mars of something akin to moss on the Earth.

Atmosphere

Mars has an extensive atmosphere in which not infrequently there are observed clouds which may at times be dense enough to hide large areas of the planet. There are yellow clouds, which may well be dust raised by wind from desert-like areas. Other clouds are white and may be like the cirrus clouds which in the Earth's atmosphere are due to ice crystals. Morning mists are often observable in the winter hemisphere. Measurements of the drift of these clouds have given some information on the Martian winds which have generally lower velocities than the winds on the Earth.

The amount of gas in the atmosphere of Mars can be estimated by measuring how the absorption of light from features on the surface of the planet varies during the Martian day and by observing the polarization of the light from the planet and its atmosphere. The amount of gas over an area of Mars is estimated to be much less than that which would appear above the same area on the Earth but because Mars is so much smaller, its mass exerts less pull in its atmosphere. Hence the pressure of the atmosphere at the surface of the planet is probably about a fortieth of the value at the surface of the Earth. Because of the lower gravitational pull of Mars its atmosphere, being less tightly packed, nevertheless reaches to a high level above the surface of the planet.

Analysis by spectroscopic means has revealed that carbon dioxide exists in the atmosphere of Mars in an amount which, if packed at the pressure and temperature at the base of our atmosphere, would form a layer about 160 feet thick, twenty times that on the Earth. Unsuccessful attempts to reveal oxygen show that it cannot be present except in very small amounts beyond the limit of detection. There is water present on Mars. The polar caps reflect in the infra red, and polarize light, in the same way as frost deposits that have been produced in vessels in which the conditions of temperature and pressure on Mars can be simulated. The polarization of the white Martian clouds is like that of terrestrial cirrus cloud, and finally traces of water vapour have been found in the spectrum of the planet. The total amount of water in the atmosphere, it appears, would form a layer only about a fiftieth of an inch thick if deposited on the surface of the planet. It is clear that nothing like rain could occur on Mars, that there could not possibly be permanent bodies of free water, and that the polar caps must be very thin as is borne out by the rate at which they evaporate with the approach of spring. It is possible that nitrogen is a component in the atmosphere of Mars, but nitrogen does not leave its trace on the part of the spectrum that can be examined after the light has come through the atmosphere of the Earth.

Temperature

Because of the greater distance from the Sun Mars naturally has a lower temperature than the Earth. Measurements in the infra-red give values of surface temperature about 300°K (or near 80°F) for dark areas at noon near the equator but owing to the more tenuous atmosphere the variation during the day is much greater than we experience. The temperature falls off quickly in the Martian afternoon and night so that by early morning it is about —100°F. Observation by radio methods gives results which fall within the range set by the infra-red measurements. The radio measures are in the low part of the range and less subject to diurnal variation because the source of the radiation would be a little below the surface from which the infra-red radiation comes.

Satellites

Mars has two interesting satellites. Deimos, about five miles in diameter, travels 13,000 miles above the surface of the planet, while Phobos, ten miles in diameter, is only 4,000 miles up and travels so quickly that to an observer on the surface of Mars it would appear to rise in the west and set in the east as do most of the artificial satellites so far launched from the Earth. The sizes are, of course, too small for a measurable disc to be seen and must in each case be estimated from a measurement of the brightness.

Mariner IV

On 28 November 1964 the Mariner IV space probe was launched and on December 5 some correction to its orbital motion around the Sun was made by operation of the jets built into it for the purpose. This led to an approach to within less than 7,000 miles of Mars on 14 July 1965. At that time observations were made of the surroundings of Mars and a series of photographs taken of the surface of the planet. These observations and photographs, made when our distance from Mars was 134 million miles, were then, over some days, transmitted back to the Earth. It was reported that no magnetic field or accompanying radiation belts such as surround the Earth were observable. The low estimate for the density of the Martian atmosphere was reinforced by observation of the way in which the transmission from Mariner IV died away as the space probe passed behind the planet. The density seems not enough to provide for braking when a spacecraft comes to land on Mars.

The most remarkable discovery was that Mars has a crater-pocked landscape similar to that of the Moon and some of the photographs, for example Plate 12, could easily be taken for photographs of the surface of the Moon shown under similar difficulties of transmission and printing.

JUPITER

Telescopic Appearance

Jupiter is the giant planet of the solar system. Even in a small telescope it is a magnificent sight. Plate 13 is a drawing of Jupiter. The great system of cloud belts which is clearly visible divides the surface into alternate dark and bright bands running parallel to the equator. Although, as would be expected from a cloud structure, they do vary somewhat, the bands have sufficient permanence to make it worth while to give to the various zones names such as South Equatorial Belt or North Tropical Zone which are indicative of their places on the planet. The belts, besides having a certain amount of fine structure, frequently exhibit coarser spots, either darker or lighter than their surroundings. These changes, being visible in a small telescope from a distance of several hundred million miles, are really on a large scale by terrestrial standards. By timing the movement of these spots the rotation period of the planet is measured, as a little under ten hours. The areas near the equator rotate more rapidly taking about five minutes less time to complete the rotation than those in the higher latitudes. Even in the one zone the rotation periods do not remain constant. The shortest period which has been noted is 9 hours 48 minutes, and the longest 9 hours 58½ minutes. Currents flow within the belts, and a relative motion of over 300 miles per hour has been observed between neighbouring parts of Jupiter's atmosphere.

A noteworthy marking is a spot about 26,000 miles in length and 10,000 miles in width that occurs in the South Tropical Zone. It varies in size and in colour, sometimes being quite reddish—hence being called the "Great Red Spot"—and sometimes less intense or even grey so that it almost merges into the background. A variation of about 10 seconds in its period of rotation appears to indicate that it is an atmospheric feature so that its very long life of at least a hundred years, or much longer if some observations of the seventeenth century are correctly ascribed to it, is remarkable.

Temperature

Because of the great activity visible on the surface of Jupiter it was for many years thought to be hot, but it was pointed out that if the surface were hot, it would, during the lifetime of the planet, have radiated away more heat than it could ever have started with, and that the temperature must be such that the heat radiated by the planet equals that received from the Sun. The radiation from a body of temperature $T°$K is, with C a constant, $R = CT^4$ and that received from the Sun on unit area at distance d is, with D a constant, D/d^2. Equating these two formulae shows that for the condition of equilibrium T varies inversely as the square root of the distance. Now taking the mean temperature of the Earth's surface as 283°K and Jupiter as 5·2 times as distant from the Sun would make the calculated temperature of Jupiter 120°K. This is approximately confirmed by observation, for measurements of the temperature in the infra-red yield a value of 130°K; while measurements at radio wave-lengths of about 3 centimetres, where the radiation is presumed to be of thermal origin, indicates a temperature of 145°K.

Composition of the Atmosphere

The components of the atmosphere of Jupiter which have been clearly revealed by the spectroscope are methane and ammonia. Methane, the chief component of natural gases tapped from underground sources, occurs naturally in marshy areas and hence is called marsh gas, while ammonia is the same substance which, dissolved in water, is used for household purposes. Jupiter is so massive, and the velocity that gas particles would have to reach to escape from the planet is so high, that it must have retained its original components. It is likely that the gases hydrogen and helium are predominant, and the question has been tested by observing how a star is dimmed when Jupiter in its motion passes between the Earth and the star. If the particles of the gas are heavy, the pressure increases more quickly with depth in the atmosphere than if they are less massive and the star is dimmed more quickly. This observation has shown that the gas particles in Jupiter are less in mass than would be the case if gases like ammonia or methane or nitrogen were the chief components present. The clouds of Jupiter are probably frozen ammonia.

Internal Constitution

Although Jupiter is so massive, its average density is only 1·3 times that of water. To decide what composition for the body of the planet best fits the data, trial has been made of possible materials with the conclusion that Jupiter is composed mainly of hydrogen. Physicists tell us that at very high pressures hydrogen has a change of state, taking on the character of a metal, and in a body of Jupiter's size most of the hydrogen would be in the metallic phase. If the distribution of mass of the planet with depth is taken as known then the gravitational force and the pressures at all depths are calculable and must give densities of the matter which fit again with the masses.

In investigating anything so completely inaccessible as the interior of a planet every possible clue must be used, and an additional one is provided by the shape of Jupiter which is flattened by rotation as is easily observed, so that the polar diameter is 6,000 miles less than the equatorial. This external shape, for a particular rate of rotation, also depends on the way in which the mass of the planet is distributed. The calculations with hydrogen as the main chemical component of Jupiter, and with helium as the next most abundant element, fit the observed values of radius, mean density and ellipticity.

Radio Observations

Apart from the radiation of about 3-cm wave-length from which a temperature of Jupiter was derived there are radiations at longer wave-lengths which are too intense to be thermal in origin. When a rapidly moving electron is situated in a magnetic field its path is bent and its motion accelerated so that it radiates. Light originating in this way was first observed in the great machines, called synchrotrons, designed for accelerating particles for experiments in atomic physics. Hence radiation of this kind is called *synchrotron radiation*. The radiation from Jupiter at wave-length about 10 cm to 70cm is thought to be synchrotron radiation. The source of this radiation has a diameter several times that of the planet. Evidently Jupiter has belts of particle radiation, like the Van Allen belts of the Earth trapped by a magnetic field of the planet. The magnetic field of Jupiter must be vastly more powerful than that of the Earth. As would be expected the radiation from this source is polarized and the direction of the polarization oscillates through about 20° with a period of just under 10 hours. This suggests that the magnetic axis is inclined at 10° to the axis of the rotation and is carried around by the rotation of the planet.

At still longer wave-lengths, in the region of 8 to 50 metres, there is another component of the radiation. This is extremely variable. Individual bursts may last only a few seconds or endure for a good many minutes. The regularity that is noticed about this kind of radiation is the tendency for the bursts to recur after a period of 9 hours 55 minutes 29 seconds, which is within the range of rotation periods, but attempts to make a correlation with optically observed features of the planet have failed.

Satellites

Of Jupiter's twelve satellites four which are easy to see with a small telescope or good binoculars were discovered in 1610 when the newly invented telescope was turned on the planet. They make a fine sight spread out parallel to the planet's equator and would be bright enough for naked-eye visibility if their light were not swamped by that of the planet. The fifth satellite was discovered in the middle of last century, and seven more have been found during this century. The fifth one is close to the planet, but the remaining newly discovered ones are outside the orbits of the original four. The most distant one from the planet is about 14 million miles from it. Their positions change quickly, and, in the case of the four bright satellites, their eclipses when they pass into the shadow of Jupiter, their disappearances behind the planet, and their passages across it are a constant source of interest.

The velocity of light was first clearly demonstrated in 1676, by observation of eclipses of Jupiter's satellites. The eclipses happen about eight minutes earlier than average when the Earth lies between the Sun and Jupiter and, when Jupiter is beyond the Sun from us, about eight minutes later. In the latter case the light has to travel a distance greater by the diameter of the Earth's orbit. The delay corresponds to a speed of 186,000 miles per second.

SATURN

A little study of the entries in Table 4 shows that Saturn resembles Jupiter in many ways. It is large in size and mass. Its temperature, as would be expected from its greater distance from the Sun is lower. Like Jupiter it is cloud-covered with bands of cloud stretching out parallel to the equator. The belts seem to be less sharply defined, and, in any case, the greater distance would make detail more difficult to see. However, spots are occasionally seen, and observation of these indicates a rotation period which is 10 hours 14 minutes at the equator—not very different from that of Jupiter. The detected components of the atmosphere, methane and ammonia, are the same, although the lower temperature causes more of the ammonia which solidifies at a higher temperature than methane to be frozen out of the atmosphere leaving a greater proportion of methane in the part of the planet from which the light comes to us. The low density is even more striking in the case of Saturn than it was for Jupiter. Saturn has a mass 95 times that of the Earth, but its density is less than three-quarters that of water. The predominance of hydrogen as a component of Saturn would explain this. Because the planet is slightly smaller than Jupiter, there would be a smaller volume at very high pressure near its centre and so a lower proportion of the hydrogen in its high density metallic form.

Satellites

Saturn has nine satellites, and the largest of these, Titan, has been shown to have an atmosphere which, like the atmosphere of the planet itself, contains methane. This is the only satellite which is known to have an atmosphere. Phoebe, the outermost satellite of Saturn's system, revolves from east to west about the planet. This is somewhat remarkable because most of the rotations and revolutions throughout the solar system are from west to east. Four of the more distant satellites of Jupiter revolve in this out of step manner and this argues a different history for such bodies. It may be that such satellites were revolving around the Sun as independent bodies until being captured and held by the gravitational field of the planet to which they are now attached.

The Ring System

The most striking feature about Saturn is the system of rings which make a beautiful sight in the telescope. The rings are well shown on Plate 14. Their various aspects help to sustain interest in them. The ring system has an overall diameter of 169,000 miles. There are two divisions in the system and a clear space of about 9,000 miles between the inside diameter of the system and the surface of the planet. As Saturn goes around the Sun, this flat system is carried along parallel to itself, and twice in the period of the planet, that is, about every fifteen years, the Earth is near the plane of the ring system. The rings must be exactly edge-on at least once at such times. Seven years after this the ring system opens out to maximum breadth and brightness. The system is so thin that, when it goes through its edge-on position, it disappears for a short time, even in a large telescope.

The rings must consist of myriads of small bodies revolving about the planet for they could not be stable if they had any other structure. If such bodies were not moving in one plane, collisions would occur and damp out motion perpendicular to the plane. Consequently, the rings must be very thin—possibly only a few inches, depending on the size of the bodies. In accordance with this idea it has been shown that the outer edge of the ring is moving more slowly than the inner edge. This conforms to the way that individual bodies move under the law of gravity. As a parallel case it should be remembered that Mercury, the nearest planet to the Sun, is also the most quick moving, its speed being 30 miles per second, whereas Saturn moves at only 6 miles per second. When Saturn passes in front of a star, the particles of the ring system are shown to be sufficiently far apart for a star to be visible through the rings, although somewhat dimmed. The divisions between the rings are due to the influence of the satellites. One division is in a place where the period of the particles would be half of that of Mimas, the innermost satellite, the continued gravitational action of which on the particles keeps the gap swept clear of them. Similar relations occur for the other division.

Saturn is one of the show pieces of the sky, a source of wonder and interest to the casual viewer, and of pleasure for even the most hardened professional astronomer.

URANUS, NEPTUNE AND PLUTO

The planets so far discussed had been known during the whole of the history of mankind. The story of the discovery of the outer ones is of interest. When William Herschel, in 1781, observed in his telescope an object which moved relative to the stars, it was natural for him to announce his discovery as that of a comet. New comets were not unusual, and before this the only object added by observation to the list of bodies orbiting the Sun was Halley's Comet whose first predicted return had occurred in 1759. After a few months the orbit of the new object and further telescopic exam-ination of it showed that it was really a new planet moving beyond the orbit of Saturn. This is the planet Uranus, the first planet whose discovery is recorded.

It soon became evident that observations of the positions of Uranus could not be made to conform to any calculated orbit, and as time went on this tendency became more marked and more certain. It was natural then that several astronomers speculated that there might be, beyond Uranus, another planet whose attraction was having an influence on the movement of Uranus. This idea was successfully examined by two mathematicians, U. J. Leverrier and J. C. Adams; and so, purely as a result of calculation, the new planet was discovered at the Observatory in Berlin very near to the place indicated by Leverrier. It was called Neptune, and, arising from con-sideration of its orbit, the search was eventually begun for a planet beyond it. A systematic and laborious search was carried on for some years at the Lowell Observatory in Arizona, and in February 1930 the search was re-warded by the discovery of a new planet which has been called Pluto. The values in Table 4 indicate that these new planets are much fainter than the ancient ones although Uranus is just bright enough to be seen by the naked eye—it is, perhaps, surprising that it was not recognised earlier. Although no rotation period for Pluto is given in Table 4, it may be about $6 \cdot 4$ days as its light has a cycle of variation with this period.

Taking into account their size and place in the solar system the known properties of Uranus and Neptune are not unexpected as compared with what is known of Jupiter and Saturn. The gas methane has been detected on Uranus and Neptune and both planets are, like Jupiter and Saturn, giants of low density. However, their lower mass and higher density indicate that they cannot be composed mainly of hydrogen as are Jupiter and Saturn. At the pressures inside Uranus and Neptune, ammonia (NH_3) and hydrogen would combine to form ammonium metal (NH_4). The properties of these two remote planets may be accounted for if much of their mass is ammonium and they include a central core of heavier material.

If we could travel to these outermost regions of the solar system, we would have a very different view of it. The Sun would be a small object in the sky, and, although it would give ample light for visual purposes, it would be very deficient as a supplier of heat. The heat would be enough to keep Pluto at a temperature of about $50°K$ at which oxygen and nitrogen, the chief components of our life giving atmosphere, would be frozen. The other planets would be fairly insignificant among the stars, even Jupiter being out-shone by many of them, and Saturn would be just visible to the naked eye. None of the others would be visible.

THE ORIGIN OF THE SOLAR SYSTEM

Several theories have been suggested for the origin of the solar system. It is an interesting subject to think about although it may well be that no theory yet comes really near to the actual story. To be satisfactory the theory must explain the most obvious regularities in the system, the revolution of the major components in one direction about the Sun and very nearly in a common plane, the revolution of most satellites and the rotation of most planets in a similar direction. The theory must also account for details such as the existence of minor planets and for the composition of various bodies of the system and it must be compatible with an age of about 5×10^9 years for the Earth. The exceptions must not be forgotten though some at least of these may have come about in the later history of the system. The distant retrograde satellites may have been captured, the high inclination of the orbit of Pluto may be due to an ancient perturbation in a close approach to Neptune—or perhaps Pluto was a satellite of Neptune.

A factor of great significance in considering the theories is the way in which the momentum of the system is distributed. The angular momentum of a planet about the Sun is the product of its mass, orbital velocity and distance from the Sun. The angular momentum of the Sun itself about its axis of rotation may be estimated by adding together the results, calculated in the same way, for its separate parts. It is a law of nature that the total momentum of a body or a system like the solar system is constant unless external forces act on it. When these calculations are carried out for the bodies in the solar system, it is found that 98 per cent of the momentum of the whole system resides in the four great planets although they contain only about one thousandth of the mass of the Sun. This must be accounted for in any theory of the origin of the system.

The theories are broadly of two kinds, one in which the material which forms the planets was drawn from a star and the other in which the bodies of the system have condensed from diffusely spread primeval matter in space. In order to meet the difficulty presented by the distribution of matter and momentum in the first of these theories it was suggested that the Sun was a component of a double star and that a third star came near enough to the system for tidal action to draw from the companion star material from which the planets were later formed. The encounter removed the companion but left the filament to form the planets. A difficulty is that in such an event the gaseous filament would probably be hot enough merely to evaporate into space rather than form a series of discrete bodies like the planets.

Formation of the system by the contraction of material of a nebula was suggested by Kant and Laplace. The difficulty of transferring so much of the angular momentum to so small a proportion of the mass made this theory lose favour, but in recent years modifications show the possibilities of theories of this kind. The discrete massive bodies like stars or planets are not likely to be much influenced by the electric and magnetic fields which exist in space and their motions are mainly influenced by gravitational forces. The diffuse matter not yet condensed would however probably carry electric charges and therefore be subject to electrical and magnetic forces. So possibly a magnetic field of the Sun rotating with it could transfer momentum to the surrounding cloud of material from which the planets were being formed and slow down the rotation of the Sun. The planets, and the Sun too, might have originated in knots of higher density in the diffuse material of space. Magnetic fields would be instrumental in maintaining permanent condensations until by collisions and accretion of matter the masses became large enough for gravitational forces to hold them together. The knots with small angular momentum would be likely to meet and coalesce into a larger mass, eventually forming the Sun, while knots with larger motions would be left to form planets and satellites. If, as it is natural to think, the original nebula had a composition—largely hydrogen—similar to that of the Sun, a much greater mass than the mass of the Earth was needed to supply the proportion of heavy elements in the Earth.

If some process exists for forming a system of planets with much of the angular momentum removed from the central star, then it would be expected that stars of space with accompanying planets would rotate more slowly than others. This can be tested by the spectroscope. One side of a rapidly rotating star may be approaching and shifting the wave-lengths towards shorter wave-lengths, while the other side recedes and shifts wave-lengths towards the red. So when the light from the whole star is considered,

H

each spectrum line is broadened by an amount corresponding with the velocity of rotation of the star. Measurements of rotation in this way show that most hot stars are rotating rapidly while stars like the Sun for the most part rotate more slowly. This may be because much of their momentum has been given to a group of planets. Since so many of the stars resemble the Sun in the properties we can observe, it seems likely that at least a proportion have retinues of planets.

LIFE ON OTHER PLANETS

Astronomers are often asked whether they believe that life exists on other places than the Earth, and it would be pleasing to be able to give a satisfactory answer. A brief review of the properties of the planets of the solar system does not offer much hope. Mercury, with at most only a small atmosphere, is so hot on the side towards the Sun and so cold on the side away from it as to be out of the question, the surface of Venus is so hot, and the planets beyond Mars have such great cold atmospheres of uninviting composition that they could have no life on them. This leaves only Mars.

The atmosphere of Mars is so deficient in oxygen and water and so low in pressure that the higher living forms of the Earth would appear to have no chance of surviving if they were transferred to Mars. However, the seasonal changes in colour of some parts of the planet may indicate some lowly form of plant life. The failure to identify the components needed for animal life is not reassuring. There seems to be no attractive place to lure the prospective space traveller. Even the Moon, where the temperature on the sunward side or not far below the surface would be tolerable, and where the landscape would be strange and interesting, offers us only a vacuum in place of an atmosphere. Space travellers who may in future venture on the Moon or Mars must certainly do so on the assumption that every physical need must be taken with them from the Earth. It is not at all impossible that there are some cold, sunless places on Mars where deposits of ice might be found. If so, they would form an extremely precious find, for by suitable processes they might become sources of oxygen as well as water.

The task of finding life, if it exists in places remote from the Earth, is difficult. One characteristic of life is purposive action. Some radio telescopes have been set to look for signals having order and repetition which might imply artificial emission. If a structure or sign of order could be found this would be evidence of the existence of life. The presence of large molecules particularly ones, like the chlorophyll of terrestrial plants, which absorb energy from radiation or ones which can act as catalysts would be indicative of life. Some meteorites contain carbonaceous material which has properties similar to material produced only by life on the Earth and this has been taken to suggest that the minerals of the meteorite may have been derived from living organisms as the fuel deposits of the Earth have been.

Of course life may exist in forms not yet envisaged. To illustrate this imagine a race of men living away from the sea and knowing nothing of living forms under water. If a man of this race were presented with a view of the sea, it would surely tax his imagination considerably to believe that anything could live under its surface. Knowing even less of the nature of the environment elsewhere in space we Earth dwellers may be in an even worse position for estimating whether some hypothetical form of life may exist.

If we think of places beyond the solar system and if the process which formed the solar system is one likely to occur many times there would be among the stars of the Milky Way and of other similar systems, hundreds of thousands of stars surrounded, like our Sun, by bands of planets. Among these there would probably be some like the Earth, and possibly some of these might bear highly developed living forms.

6

MINOR PLANETS, COMETS AND METEORS

APART from the planets mentioned in Chapters 4 and 5 the solar system has several interesting minor components, some of which may appear to the naked eye. These are the minor planets, the comets, and the meteors, which arise from small bodies entering the atmosphere where they are seen to end their lives in a short burst of light.

MINOR PLANETS

Discovery and Numbers

In the eighteenth century a simple arithmetical rule, the Bode-Titius Law, was noticed connecting the distances of the planets from the Sun. The distances were found to be approximately proportional to the numbers obtained by adding 4 to 0, 3, 6, 12, 24, 48 and so on, but no planet was known corresponding to the number 24. This was the subject of a good deal of interest and conjecture, and the rule seemed to be justified when, on 1st January 1801, a new planet was discovered approximately conforming to it. (I doubt if anyone now attaches physical significance to the "Law" —certainly Neptune and Pluto do not conform to it at all.) The new planet was named Ceres after a divinity associated with Sicily where its discoverer, Piazzi, was working. It is interesting that because Ceres was observed for only a short period there was danger of losing it, for astronomers were not used to dealing with new members of the solar system. The great astronomer-mathematician C. F. Gauss, who had developed a new method of orbit calculation, was able to calculate an orbit which led to re-observation of the object when it came again into a position where it could be seen. In the next year a new small planet Pallas was discovered, followed by Juno in 1804 and Vesta in 1807. In 1845 a fifth was discovered and three more in 1847, since when the number has grown yearly, until there are now more than 1600 with calculated orbits.

These *minor planets* or *asteroids* are all comparatively small bodies. The largest one is Ceres whose diameter is about 480 miles. Then follow Pallas 300 miles, Vesta 240 miles, and Juno 120 miles. There are possibly about 150 of them with diameter greater than 50 miles. The number increases rapidly for smaller sizes and additional small ones are being continually discovered on photographs. It is not likely that any more with diameter greater than 50 miles will be found, but it is estimated that there are possibly 100,000 within reach of the most powerful telescope. Even though there are so many of them their total mass must be low, only a very small fraction of that of the Earth. The brightest minor planet is Vesta which at times comes just within reach of the naked eye. The brightness of Vesta is interesting for it is only about half the size of Ceres and must therefore be of lighter colour to reflect more light.

The Orbits

The great majority of the orbits of the minor planets lie between those of Mars and Jupiter. The study of their orbits is of interest. Many of them are disturbed away from the nearly simple ellipses, such as are followed by the large planets, because of the attraction of their giant neighbour Jupiter. A list of the minor planets in order of period shows that there are very few of them with periods which bear simple ratios to the period of Jupiter. Minor planets with a period of four years, one-third that of Jupiter, or of six years, half that of Jupiter, are rare. The reason for this is that such minor planets would return repeatedly to the same position relative to Jupiter and be subjected to perturbations of the same kind. Such perturbations would soon increase and alter the orbits of these minor planets. An example of this has occurred in the last few years. In 1943 the minor planet Griqua had a period of $5 \cdot 93$ years, half of that of Jupiter. This leads to such enormous changes in the orbit that, if its position were computed from its motion in 1935, and only the attraction of the Sun taken into account, its place as seen from the Earth in 1971 would be in error by $61°$. Careful analysis of these orbital changes will yield a mass of Jupiter independent of the usual method which uses the satellites.

There are other interesting examples of minor planet orbits. Eros, which comes close to the Earth, has already been mentioned in connection with its use in determining distances in the solar system and the mass of the Moon. Of the minor planets to come near the Earth the closest one has been Hermes, which came within half-a-million miles of the Earth in 1937. Another asteroid which has a very elongated orbit passes near the orbit of Mercury, and the way in which its path is affected by the attraction of Mercury should lead to an improved estimate of the mass of Mercury. Because, of the known asteroids, this is the one which passes closest to the Sun, it is appropriately called Icarus—from the mythological character who, after his father had fastened wings to him with wax, flew so close to the Sun that the wax melted and he fell to his death.

The Trojan asteroids form a group of minor planets whose orbits have an interesting relation with the orbit of Jupiter. Each member of this group moves around the Sun, so that its position makes nearly an equilateral triangle with the positions of the Sun and Jupiter. That such orbits would be stable was discovered by the mathematician Lagrange in the eighteenth century, but the first such body was found only in 1906. Since then over a dozen more have been discovered. They are named after Achilles, Priam, Agamemnon and other heroes of the Trojan War. Under the influence of perturbations of other planets, chiefly Saturn, they can depart widely from the position equidistant from the Sun and Jupiter without leaving it permanently and the study of their orbital motions presents some involved problems.

Constitution

The minor planets are all so small, and the velocity of escape from them consequently is so low that none would retain an atmosphere. Even Ceres whose velocity of escape is about 1,500 feet per second could not attract back a bullet fired from a rifle.

Many of them show variations in light, doubtless arising from their rotation which presents to us different aspects of their irregular shapes at different times. For example, Eros, which appears to have an irregular shape (glimpsed during the approach in 1931) about 26 miles long and perhaps 10 miles wide, rotates with a period of about 5¼ hours. It is not known how minor planets originated, but it could well have been from the break up of a larger body. Perturbations of the orbits and subsequent collisions would be sufficient to alter the paths so much that their original orbits would be hard to ascertain.

COMETS

The Appearance of Comets

There is always much interest in the appearance of a comet visible to the naked eye. As this occurs rather seldom most people have the impression that comets are very rare objects. However, this is not really so, if those observable telescopically are included. In thirty years, from the beginning of 1923 to the end of 1952, 194 comets, including returns of periodic comets, were observed, an average of more than six per year. The interest and discussion aroused when a bright comet appears accustoms astronomers to inquiries from people who had seen Halley's Comet during its visit in 1910 or have heard an older generation speak of the great comet of 1882 which was bright enough to be seen near the Sun in daylight.

In the telescope bright comets usually show a point of light at the centre of the head. This is the *nucleus* which is the source of the diffuse gas and dust forming the bulk of the comet. The nucleus may be some tens of miles in diameter. At a distance of about 250,000,000 miles from the Sun the diffuse more or less spherical envelope, the *coma*, expands, and the *tail* may develop at about 150,000,000 miles distance. For a bright comet visible to the naked eye the coma may be several hundred thousand miles in diameter and the tail 30- or 40-million miles or more long, covering at its most favourable aspect many degrees of the sky. The tail is almost always directed away from the Sun, and so if the comet is near the Sun its tail may stand up from the horizon before dawn or after sunset. On some occasions a comet may approach the Sun from a part of the sky where it cannot be seen and then suddenly appear, as one did during an eclipse of the Sun in 1948. Though some naked-eye comets may remain bright enough to be visible for several months, most are visible for only short periods. The bright southern comet of 1947 appeared suddenly on December 7, but began to fade immediately, and was beyond the reach of the naked eye in about ten days. The comet appears brighter as it approaches the Sun or the Earth. There is a formula which is designed to represent the changes, but a comet's brightness may depart much from this, with large irregular variations. The general appearance of comets is shown by Plates 17, 18 and 19.

A new comet is generally given the name of its discoverer although sometimes it may be the name of someone associated with it in another way as is the case with Comets Halley and Encke. The comets are also given as preliminary names the year of discovery with a letter in the order of discovery: 1964a, 1964b, and so on. Finally, when their orbits are known, the year is used with a Roman numeral, in order of their nearest approach to the Sun: 1964I, 1964II, etc. If the comet is periodic, it is given a P as prefix. For example, Comet P/Encke at one apparition was given also the designations 1960i and 1961I.

The Orbits

The orbit of a comet may be either an ellipse or very nearly a parabola. The preliminary orbit of an unexpected comet is computed as soon as possible so that its path may be predicted for the period of its visit. This is usually satisfactory as a parabola and then, after the comet has gone, a final orbit has to be prepared. The path near the Sun where the comet is observable is often so small a part of the orbit that an extremely elongated ellipse such as many comets follow is scarcely, or perhaps not at all, distinguishable from a parabola and must be so listed. Some orbits have been observed to depart slightly from the parabolic towards the hyperbolic which is the shape that the path would have if the comet had come to us from outer space and was not really a member of the solar system. In the cases that have been carefully investigated, however, it has always been shown that the motion of the comet has been altered by the attraction of the planets and that the path before its visit was actually elliptical or very nearly parabolic. There is therefore no clearly proved case of a comet arriving from outer space. Of course, once its orbit has become hyperbolic, unless it is again turned back by the planetary attractions it will be permanently lost from the solar system.

The orbit of a new comet sometimes resembles strikingly the orbit of an earlier comet and a number of pairs and groups have been listed. Comet Ikeya-Seki, which was prominent in the morning sky in 1965 and the great comet of 1882 were members of a group of six comets whose orbits are very similar and take them very close to the Sun. This is the "sun grazing" group of comets.

The extremely elongated elliptical orbits have periods of thousands of years, and the small uncertainty in the departure from being a parabola makes for such very large uncertainty in the period that in many cases it is clear only that the period must be extremely long. This necessarily means that with comets of this kind which have not visited us during historic time the appearances are unexpected and not predictable.

There are however comets with periods short enough to make their visits accessible to prediction. The first comet to have an orbit assigned so that its return could be foreseen was the famous one for which Halley calculated the orbit. He noticed similarities between the paths of the comets which had appeared in 1531, 1607, and 1682 and predicted that it would appear again about 1758. Since then it has appeared in 1835 and 1910. Careful examination of historical records at the times of calculated previous returns to the vicinity of the Sun has revealed that it was observed on every apparition for over 2,000 years. Its appearance in 1066 is an example of the terrible significance formerly attached to comets, for the success of the Norman invasion was attributed to it and it appears on the Bayeux tapestry on which the events are recorded. On its last visit it was first observed in September 1909. It was a naked-eye object between the latter half of April 1910 and towards the end of June, being brightest about May 12. On May 19 its tail was over 100° long. Halley's Comet will next appear in 1986.

Since Halley's time about 70 comets have been shown to have periods of less than 100 years. About two-thirds of these have a period of about six or seven years and have their furthest distances from the Sun not far from the orbit of Jupiter. They go around the Sun in the same direction as the planets, whereas the comets of very long period appear to be orientated at random and may go in either direction. It seems likely that these short period comets have been captured because of perturbations of their original orbits by the planets, chiefly by the great mass of Jupiter. Several comets which have been investigated show the great changes that an approach to Jupiter can make in the orbit of a comet. Comet Oterma had a period of 18 years in 1936, 8 years in 1938, and in 1964 it was lengthened again. Comet Brooks had its period changed from 29 years to 7 years in 1886.

Constitution

Despite their enormous dimensions comets are not massive. When they pass over a star it is not dimmed and on two occasions, those of the great comet of 1882 and Halley's in 1910, when comets passed between the Earth and the Sun with their heads projected on the visible disc of the Sun, nothing whatever was seen. Moreover, although comets have several times passed near other objects, in one case among the satellites of Jupiter, the orbits of these bodies have not shown observable perturbations by a comet. On the other hand, the nucleus must contain enough material to serve as a supply for the dust and gases which are evolved at each visit to the Sun's vicinity. Perhaps a hundred-millionth of the mass of the Earth might be of the right order for the mass of a bright comet.

Comets have been examined by the spectroscope. In the head, particularly while the comet is, distant, much of the light is merely the sunlight reflected with a continuous spectrum and the dark lines characteristic of the Sun. This is so also for the light of the nucleus. However, as the comet comes closer, there is an increase in the importance of emission lines and bands in the spectra which reveal molecules containing ordinary atoms like carbon, hydrogen, and nitrogen. Near the head some of the molecules observed are CN, OH, CH, NH and C_2. The strongest emissions are those of CN and C_2. It seems most likely that the nucleus contains frozen compounds such as CH_4, NH_3, H_2O and $(CN)_2$ which are sufficiently volatile to become gaseous when they absorb some warmth in approaching the Sun. These are dissociated by the radiation of the Sun to give the observed compounds which can exist in the rare cometary atmospheres but are unfamiliar on the Earth, where they would quickly meet neighbouring atoms with which they would combine. The energy radiated from the cometary compounds is gained by absorption of the radiation from the Sun. This is very nicely confirmed because the observed strengths of the lines in the spectra are affected by the presence of dark lines in the Sun's spectrum in a way which accords with calculation. If the comet goes quite close to the Sun some less volatile substances may be evaporated from the nucleus, and the spectrum of sodium has been seen in such cases. In some cases other metals may appear, as iron did in the spectra of the great comet of 1882 and Comet Ikeya-Seki in 1965 which went very close to the Sun.

The molecules detected in the tail are characterized by ionization. The emissions of ionized CO (the strongest and most extensive), N_2, CO_2, and CH and NH are among those observed. The complex processes which lead to the tail formation are not well understood but observation of the shape of the gas tails and of the movement of identifiable patches of gas in them show that the particles are repelled from the Sun by forces many times the gravitational attraction. The combined effect of the wind of particles from the Sun and the magnetic fields of interplanetary space appears to be responsible. The tails are nearly straight, directed nearly away from the Sun and may have intricate, rapidly changing streamers.

Violent events on the Sun appear to affect the gas tails. Since the comets move so widely in the solar system astronomers look forward to a time when the processes are better understood and the comets may be used as probes to measure the radiations of the Sun and physical conditions in otherwise inaccessible parts of space. A comet may have several tails. There is a tail form due to small solid particles expelled from the nucleus. The outward acceleration of particles of these dust tails, which are shorter and more curved, is much less, and explicable in terms of the pressure of radiation of the Sun. The dust tails show the reflected continuous spectrum of the Sun. The photographs of Plate 19 show the gas and dust tails of Comet Mrkos, 1957.

The material which streams away from the head of a comet at each of its visits to the vicinity of the Sun can never return to it and so it is natural to look for its eventual disappearance. Biela's Comet, which had a period of 6·8 years and was seen on several visits in the first half of last century, was observed to break into two parts in 1846. These were seen in 1852, but have not since been observed despite every effort. Other comets have been recorded with decreasing brightness. Even Halley's Comet can be expected to have a life of only some thousands of years.

Speculation often occurs as to the result of the collision of a comet with the Earth. The Earth passed through the tail of the great comet of 1861, and probably through the tail of Halley's Comet in 1910, with no observable effect, and even collision with the nucleus might produce serious effects only around the area of fall.

METEORS AND METEORITES

Number and Appearance of Meteors

Even casual observation soon reveals occasional star-like objects which appear suddenly, move rapidly across the sky in an undeviating path and disappear. They are due to small bodies which have been following a path around the Sun, and, when they strike the Earth's atmosphere, the energy of their rapid motion is transformed to heat and light. These are *meteors* or, if we wish to emphasize their character as orbiting bodies before they reach the Earth, *meteoroids*. Greater numbers appear in the morning owing to the fact that the observer's location is then facing in the direction towards which the Earth is moving, and naturally more meteoroids are swept up by the Earth. A careful watch reveals about eight meteors per hour in the evening and about twice as many in the early morning sky. Tens of millions of meteors bright enough to be seen by the naked eye arrive in the Earth's atmosphere each day. Most of them are faint, but an occasional one gives a great flash which lights up the landscape for hundreds of miles and attracts universal attention.

The Observation of Meteors

If a meteor is seen by one observer, he can tell only the direction in which it lies at a given instant, and, for its whole path, the plane in which it moves. In the case of careful observation made by two observers some 20 or 30 miles apart, the intersection of the directions in which they see a meteor must be its actual place, and, if either of the observers is equipped to measure the time it takes to follow its path, its speed may be determined. When the path of the meteor is being observed photographically, the timing may be done by rotating a sector in front of the camera lens. This breaks the trace of the meteor in the photograph at intervals of time according to the speed of rotation of the sector. To time the visual observation the meteor may be viewed in a rocking mirror so that the observer sees the path with a series of loops, the separation of which depends on the angular velocity. The heat produced by a meteor in its passage through the atmosphere breaks up some of the atoms to form an ionized track from which a radio wave may be reflected. The maximum echo is returned from the place where the meteor track is perpendicular to the radio beam. The time taken for a reflected radio pulse to return gives the distance of the meteor, and the pattern of the echo may be made to yield the velocity. Fainter meteors can be observed by radio than either visually or photographically. This important method, which does not depend on a dark or cloud-free sky, has revealed for the first time the showers of meteors which arrive by day.

The observations show that meteors appear at a height of about 60 or 70 miles. The fainter ones disappear at about 50 miles while the brighter ones endure a little longer and may remain visible down to about 40 miles or even lower. The velocities are from 8 to 44 miles per second. Morning meteors which meet the Earth in its motion are faster than those which arrive during the evening hours and have to overtake the Earth. The faster ones have a greater average height and brightness. Some meteors leave a luminous train which endures for a short time after their disappearance. Fast bright ones are more likely to do this.

When careful observation of a meteor gives its speed and direction of travel it is possible, after allowance for the attraction and motion of the Earth, to calculate what its path around the Sun must have been before it became a meteor within our atmosphere. As with comets the orbits may theoretically be elliptical, parabolic, or hyperbolic, but, although visual observations have sometimes indicated hyperbolic paths, photographic and radar observations of the most reliable kind exhibit no definitely hyperbolic orbits, and it seems unlikely that any meteors reach the Earth from space beyond the solar system.

Meteor Showers

It often happens that several meteors are following parallel paths in space and that their apparent tracks across the sky, plotted on a star map and traced backward, cut at one point of the heavens. A group of meteors of this kind is called a *shower* or stream, and the point in the sky from which the tracks appear to radiate is called a *radiant*. This appearance is a perspective effect, for parallel paths appear to converge and meet in the distance as railway tracks do. When the Earth is passing through a meteor stream, there are frequently two or three times as many meteors as at other times, and just occasionally a great shower occurs in which the rate of appearance of meteors is increased several hundred times. The orbits followed by shower meteors are similar to those followed by the periodic comets.

Sometimes a shower appears to be associated with a comet and the pieces of which it consists may in fact be fragments shed by a comet. An outstanding example of this is the case of the relation of the Giacobinid meteor stream with the Comet Giacobini-Zinner. In 1933 this meteor shower gave a display during which an observer could see over 300 meteors each minute. It was found that these meteors were coming from a radiant in the constellation Draco (right ascension 17 hours 30 minutes, declination $+ 54°$) consistent with movement in the same orbit as Comet Giacobini-Zinner which was discovered in 1900 and has a period of $6\frac{1}{2}$ years. At the time the Earth was passing through a place which had been occupied by the comet about eighty days earlier. An association of this kind between a comet and a meteor stream was first noticed in the case of Biela's Comet, the disappearance of which has been mentioned. Two streams are associated with Halley's Comet.

The accompanying Table gives particulars of a few notable meteor showers which are named after the constellation in which their radiants are situated. When the radiant comes well above the horizon it is worthwhile looking for meteors of a shower during the period of the year mentioned in the Table.

TABLE 5

Meteor Showers

Period of Visibility	Name of Shower	Radiant		Associated Comet
		R.A.	Dec.	
Jan. 3–Jan. 4	Quadrantids	15h 30m	$+50°$	
Jul. 18–Aug. 18	Capricornids	20 10	$-10°$	1948n
Jul. 25–Jul. 30	Delta Aquarids	22 35	$-14°$	
Jul. 27–Aug. 17	Perseids	3 10	$+58°$	1862III
Dec. 9–Dec. 14	Geminids	7 30	$+32°$	

Size and Constitution of Meteors

Although meteors may be bright enough to be seen from a distance of more than a hundred miles, the particles producing them turn out to be quite small. The energy necessary to give the light can be estimated from observation and then, using the observed velocity, it is possible to calculate the mass which would have the required amount of energy. The calculation shows that an object only as large as a grain of sand would be large enough to produce a visible meteor and a particle the size of a grain of wheat would produce a bright one. Strikingly bright meteors are called *fireballs*. They require more massive bodies, and a meteoroid of mass 200 pounds would produce a fireball as bright as the Moon, illuminating the countryside for many hundreds of miles.

The spectra of meteors which have been obtained on a few occasions show the presence of iron, calcium, magnesium and other elements common in the rocks of the Earth and indicate a composition broadly corresponding with that of the meteorites.

Meteorites

Although most of the meteoric particles are so small that they are entirely dispersed before they come through the atmosphere, there are some that are large enough to survive and reach the ground. There must be each year several thousands of these of which about a dozen are recovered, and they provide, so far, the only way in which material from space actually comes into our laboratories. These *meteorites*, as they are called when they fall and become mineral on the Earth's surface, have a variety of composition but may usually be grouped into one of two main classes. First, there are the stones in which are minerals similar in composition to those of the rocks around us on the Earth; and second, the irons in which the main component is metallic iron with a fairly large proportion, up to 30 per cent of nickel. There are intermediate types in which a mixture of these two kinds of component is present. About 1,500 meteorite finds are known. No meteorite is thought to have come from a meteor shower.

When a meteorite is broken up and heated, it gives off gases which contain hydrogen, nitrogen, and compounds of carbon. These components are in fact somewhat parallel to those which are observed in comets. However, the main components of meteorites, allowing for the greater abundance of stones, are in order iron, oxygen, silicon and magnesium. Radioactive age determinations on meteorites, similar to work described on terrestrial rocks, give ages of the same order as that of the Earth.

Most of the meteorites which are recovered after they have been seen to fall are stones and it is believed that this must represent an indication of their much greater actual frequency. However, most of the samples in museums are iron. The reason for this is doubtless that the stone meteorites are not easy for a layman to distinguish from the ordinary stones on the Earth's surface, whereas irons are unusual objects which are likely to stimulate inquiry on the part of almost everyone who finds one. The internal structure of either kind of meteorite differs from that of terrestrial materials, and they are readily identified by a competent mineralogist. The presence of microscopic diamonds and of various crystal structures in meteorites indicates that they have come from within a large body in which they could have been subject to high pressure and slow cooling from a high temperature. It is therefore believed that they, like the minor planets, may have originated in a comparatively large body.

Meteorite Craters

When a meteorite is very large, it may come through the atmosphere with nearly all of its original velocity to strike the Earth with a speed greater than that of any waves which could travel through the rocks to relieve the pressure. So the rocks and the meteorite become subject to a compression released by an explosion which is increasingly great according to the size of the body and its velocity. At the velocities normal for meteors the energy associated with the motion is many times the explosive energy of the same mass of high explosive. In a few places on the Earth's surface there are large craters which have evidently been formed in this way.

The best known meteorite crater is in Arizona. It is over 4,000 feet in diameter, has a rim which rises about 160 feet above the surrounding plain and a depth of 570 feet from rim to floor. There is evidence of a great deal of material having been thrown from the crater, and many fragments of metallic meteoritic material have been recovered around it. The crater is geologically quite young with an estimated age of not more than 50,000 years. Various calculations have been made of the size of the meteorite which gave rise to it, with 110 feet diameter as a recent estimate.

Other meteorite craters are located at Henbury in South Australia and Wolf Creek in Western Australia. The Wolf Creek Crater is shown on Plate 16; and a formation which may have originated as a meteorite crater appears in Plate 20, a photograph taken from the Gemini 4 spacecraft. At Henbury about 2,700 pounds of iron meteoritic material has been found around the craters. The Deep Bay Crater in northern Canada has a diameter of about 7 miles and present depth of 720 feet, but it is estimated that the original depth from rim to floor was over 3,000 feet. Its age is thought to be about 150 million years. The 17 mile diameter Ries Kessel basin in south-western Germany is also thought to be an ancient meteorite crater.

A parallel has already been drawn between craters like these and those that occur on the Moon. A plot of the relation of diameter to depth of craters arising from explosions, including those of atomic bombs, from terrestrial meteorite craters and from the craters on the Moon yields points which lie near the same smooth curve. This is consistent with a similar origin. There may well be many more fossil craters to be detected on the Earth, for the techniques for recognising them are not well developed and, allowing for the amount of country that can be seen at a time by an observer, a very large crater in a much eroded location may be very hard to observe.

On several occasions minor planets have come near the Earth. Hermes came within half-a-million miles in 1937. Such an object if it were to strike the Earth or the Moon, would make a very large crater. A minor planet such as Eros would probably produce one like the giants we see on the Moon.

Interplanetary Material

In this chapter the material which lies between the planets has been considered, but the census is not complete without considering the components of smaller size. Space vehicles equipped with microphones or other micrometeorite detectors have shown the existence in interplanetary space of particles too small to make a flash of light when they come into the atmosphere. Such particles which have percolated through the atmosphere have been found in rain water and in the ooze of the ocean floors. The Earth must gain much more material from these than from the visible meteors.

Before sunrise and after sunset there is a glow seen along the ecliptic. This is the *zodiacal light*. The polarization and spectrum of the zodiacal light is consistent with its being sunlight scattered by a mixture of the interplanetary dust and electrons arising from ionization by the Sun's radiation of the gases which lie in space. There is also a faint glow—called the *gegenschein*—of interplanetary material in a direction opposite to that of the Sun. The region between the planets with its gas, dust and magnetic field is at present the subject of much investigation by the methods of space science.

7

THE SUN

THE SUN is as essential for human life as the Earth itself. Besides being the source of light it is the source of all of the energy we use (excepting atomic energy). The vital energy of all animals is derived ultimately from plant life, which depends in turn on the energy received from the Sun. The energy of coal was received from the Sun ages ago by plants, absorbed to support the chemical processes necessary for their growth, and stored in the Earth until mined and used. It is the warmth of the Sun which evaporates the water into the atmosphere, whence it can fall as rain to feed the rivers which may be harnessed by hydro-electric power stations. Without the light and heat received from the Sun there could be no life on the Earth; it would quickly become a frozen inert body. It is unlikely that human life could make the necessary adjustment if the Sun in a short period were to change so as to give twice or half its present heat.

The study of the Sun would be important even if there were no other stars but to the astronomer it is all the more significant because among the innumerable stars the Sun is the only one near enough to display a surface which can be examined in detail. The tremendous surging activity of the Sun is an example of forces which are dwarfed by the explosive action of many of the stars. Although complete interpretation of the observations is usually difficult a great deal of interesting, detailed information is available about the Sun.

Dimensions and Energy Output of the Sun

The determination of the scale of the solar system, described in Chapter 5, sets the mean distance of the Sun at 93,000,000 miles. The angular diameter of just over half a degree yields 864,000 miles as the diameter, which is 109 times that of the Earth. This diameter corresponds to the boundary visible in the telescope, although tenuous extensions of the Sun reach out even beyond the Earth.

The force exerted by the Sun to maintain the Earth, or any other planet, in its orbit can be calculated and this, using the law of gravitation, yields the mass of the Sun in the same way that the mass of a planet with a satellite may be found. The result is that the Sun's mass is 333,000 times that of the Earth. The mass and the volume, calculated from the size, show that the average density of the Sun is a quarter of that of the Earth, 1·4 times that of water.

The radiation given out by the Sun is enormous. The energy in a beam of sunlight of known area at the Earth's surface may be measured by observing, in a carefully controlled experiment, how it would raise the temperature of a mass of water. At the distance of the Earth a surface facing the Sun receives enough energy to raise a layer of ice cold water one inch thick to boiling point in 131 minutes. This is equivalent to 1½ horse-power per square yard. The ratio of the Earth's distance from the Sun to the Sun's radius is 215 so that the ratio of the area of a sphere of radius equal to the distance of the Earth to the area of the Sun is 46,200. As all of the energy reaching as far as the Earth must pass through the Sun's surface, it must be radiating energy at the rate of 69,300 horsepower per square yard. To show what this means in terms of brilliance the radiation may be expressed otherwise as 400 watts per square of side one tenth of an inch, and as the Sun, on account of its high temperature, gives at least four times as much visible light per unit of radiation as a good filament lamp it can be seen how extremely bright its surface is. The Sun is so brilliant that it must never be looked at with the naked eye or with a telescope which is not specially equipped for its examination. People who have been tempted to look at the Sun near the time of an eclipse have often, unfortunately, suffered permanent damage to their eyes by the bright image of the Sun formed on the sensitive surface of the retina.

The Appearance of the Sun's Surface

The first observations of spots on the Sun were made in the time of Galileo some of whose scholarly contemporaries found it hard to believe that they really existed. Since then the spots have been observed in detail and a great variety of activity has been revealed on the surging surface of the Sun. Plate 21 is a photograph of the Sun's surface.

The visible surface of the Sun is called the *photosphere*. The edge of the Sun's disc is sharp in the telescope because of a rapid increase with depth in the opacity of the gases of this part of the Sun—which sharply limits the depth to which we can see. As explained in Chapter 3, a gas usually absorbs narrow sections from a continuous spectrum passing through it. In this case the absorption is due to the distribution in the gas of a small proportion of negative hydrogen ions, that is, hydrogen atoms to each of which an electron is attached. This electron is removable by only a small amount of energy. Hence, light waves shorter in wave-length than that corresponding to this energy can be absorbed, giving rise to continuous absorption.

As observed visually in a telescope or, even more obviously, on a photograph, the brightness of the Sun becomes less towards its edge or *limb*. This is because at the centre we look straight down into the photo-

1. Four-hour star trails around the South Celestial Pole. The horizontal trace arose from the passage of the satellite Echo I.

2. The 74-inch telescope at Mount Stromlo Observatory.

3. The 210-foot radio telescope at Parkes, New South Wales.

4. The Moon, 8·3 days after new Moon.

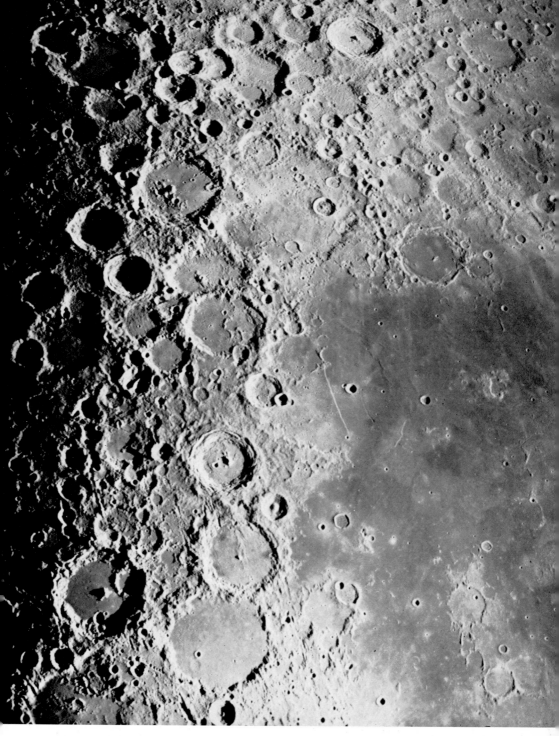

5. Portion of the Moon from Ptolemaeus to Tycho. Photographed at last quarter by the 100-inch telescope. The crater Alphonsus is in the lower part of the picture.

7. Ranger IX photograph from a height of 35 miles. The Ranger
   IX flight occurred in March 1965.

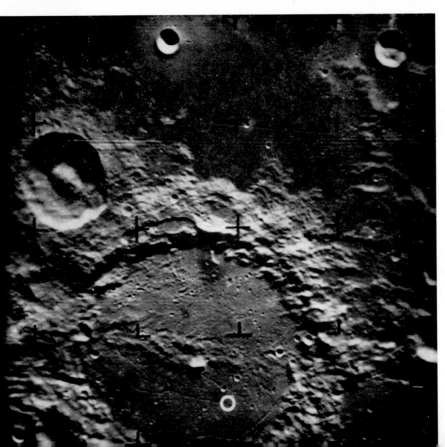

6. The crater Alphonsus photographed by the space probe Ranger
   IX from a height of 265 miles. The impact point is marked by the
   white circle on each picture.

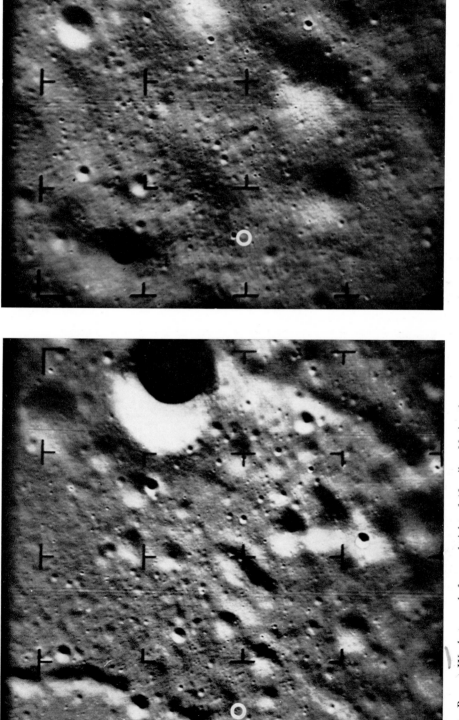

9. Ranger IX photograph from a height of 4·5 miles above the lunar surface. The smallest craters visible are about 40 feet in diameter.

8. Ranger IX photograph from a height of 12 miles. Notice that the rille through the impact circle of the first Ranger picture is resolved as a chain of craters.

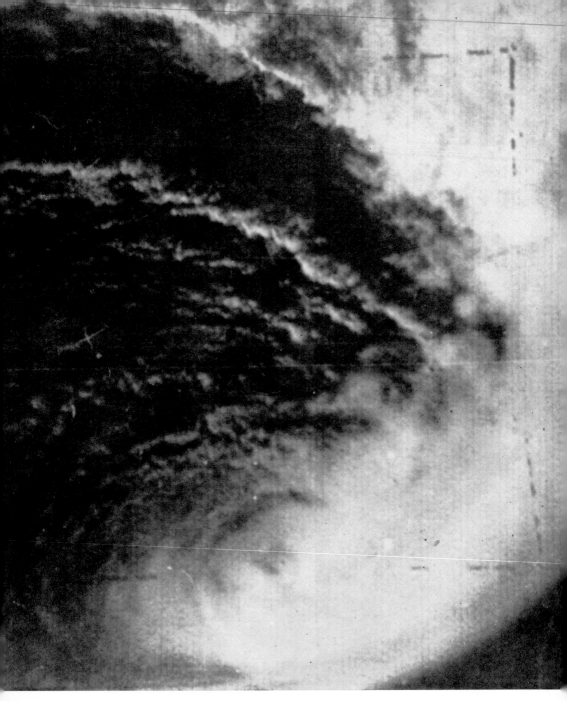

10. Storm in the South Pacific Ocean photographed by the U.S. meteorological satellite Tiros I.

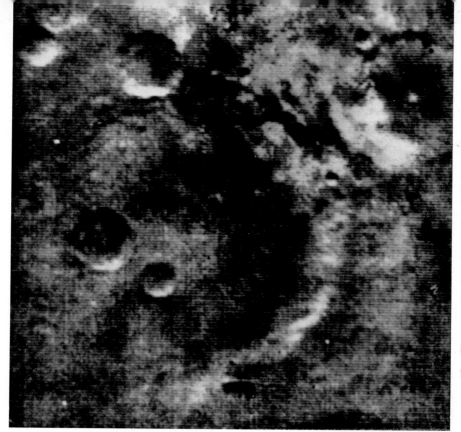

12. Close-up photograph of Mars in July 1955 by the Mariner IV spacecraft.

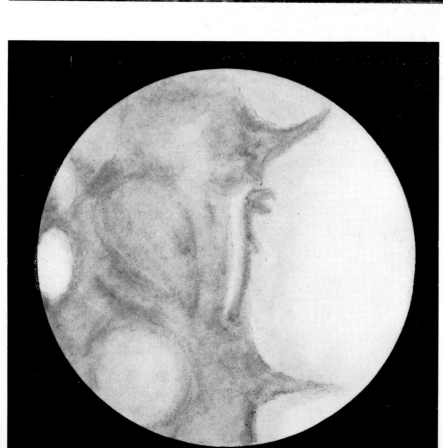

11. Mars on 18 August 1956.

13. Jupiter on 25 March 1957.

14. Saturn and its ring system photographed with the 100-inch telescope.

15. Two-hour exposure showing the movement of the bright asteroid Hebe.

16. Wolf Creek Meteorite Crater, longitude E 127° 46′, latitude S 19° 18′.

17. Comet Morehouse 29 September 1908.

18. Comet Ikeya-Seki photographed at Narrabri Observatory, 31 October 1965.

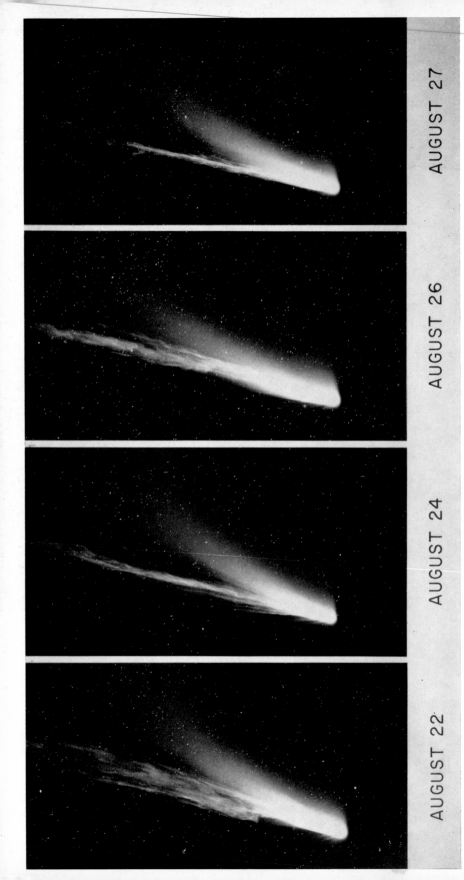

AUGUST 22   AUGUST 24   AUGUST 26   AUGUST 27

19. Comet Mrkos, 1957d. Four views taken with the 48-inch Schmidt telescope at Mount Palomar. These pictures show the dust tail, on the right, and the gas tail which underwent marked changes in a few days.

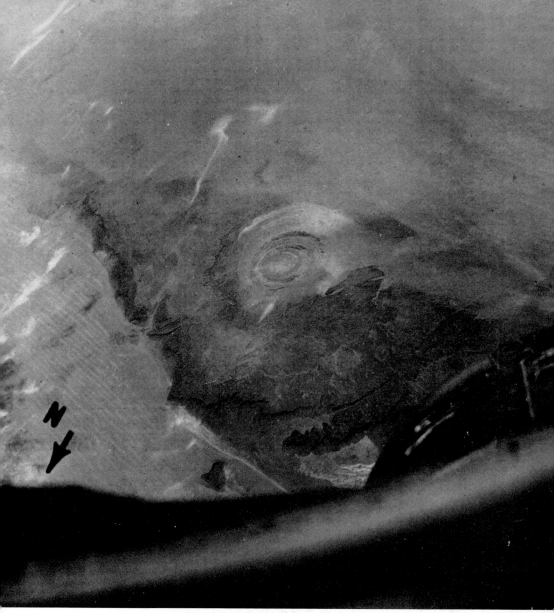

20. View of Mauretania taken from Gemini 4 spacecraft in June 1965. The circular structures may have originated in a meteoritic impact.

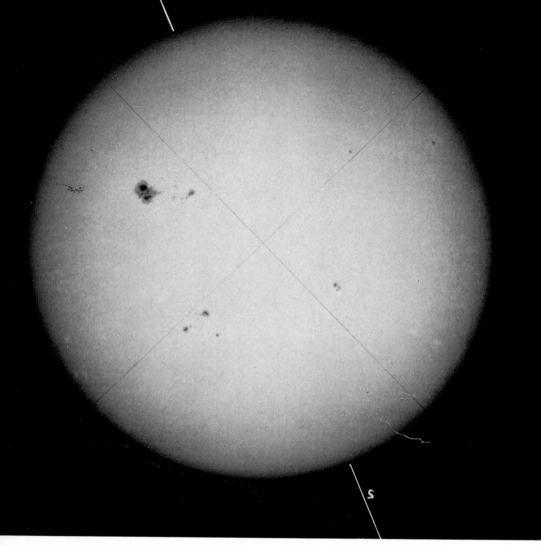

21. The Sun photographed in white light, 10 November 1960.

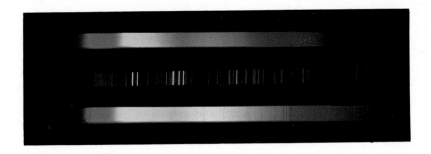

22. *Top*: The Crab Nebula, photographed in colour with the 200-inch telescope. *Bottom*: Spectra of an incandescent lamp (continuous spectrum), a cadmium arc (line spectrum), and the sun.

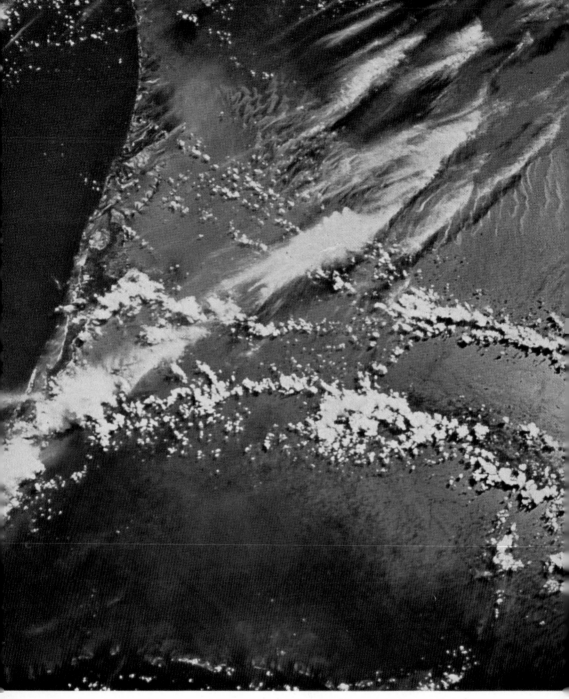

23. Portion of the Bahama Islands and the Great Bahama Bank
from Gemini 4 in June, 1965.

24. The Great Nebula in Orion.

25. The Great Galaxy in Andromeda (M31). The outer portions appear blue because of the presence of hot blue population I stars; the inner parts, where the older stars predominate, is reddish.

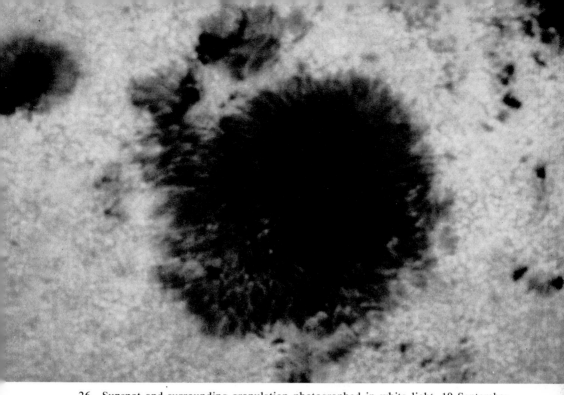

26. Sunspot and surrounding granulation photographed in white light, 19 September 1958.

27. A large active prominence, 140,000 miles high, photographed in calcium light on 9 July 1917.

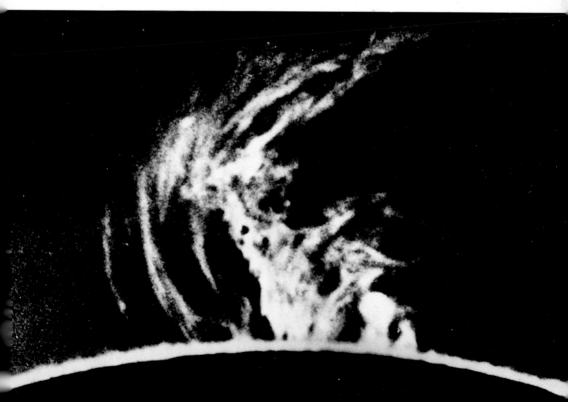

28. The solar corona of 15 February 1961.

29. The globular cluster 47 Toucanae.

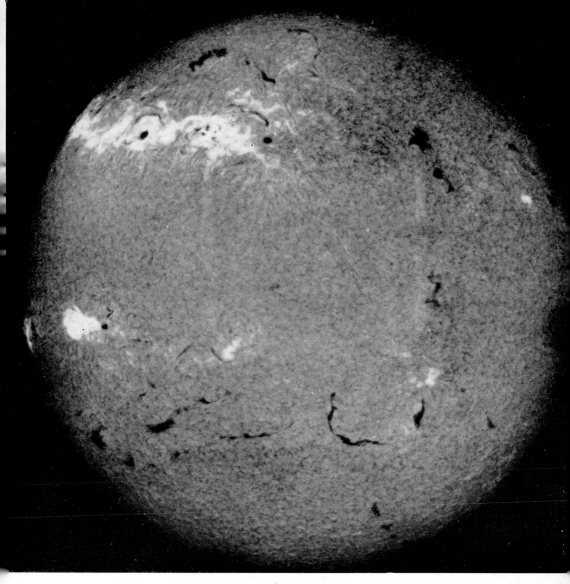

30. The Sun photographed in Hα light.

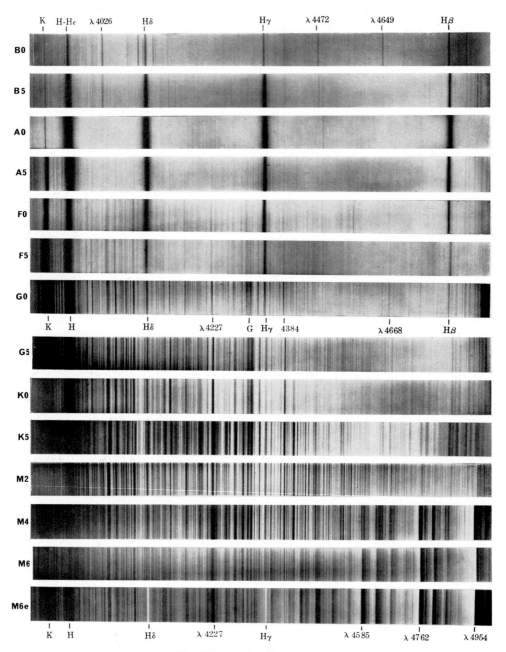

31. Classes of stellar spectra.

32. The open cluster △ 289 (NGC 3766).

33. The type S*c* spiral galaxy M101 (NGC 5457).

34. Star clouds in Sagittarius.

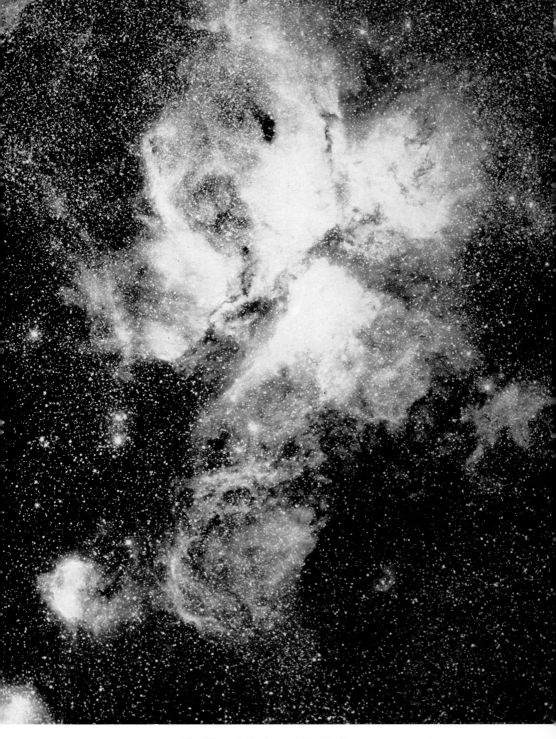

35. The nebula around Eta Carinae.

36. The Horsehead Nebula south of Zeta Orionis photographed in red light with the
200-inch telescope.

37. A field of star clusters and obscuring matter in the eastern end of the Large Magellanic Cloud, photographed with 74-inch telescope.

38. The 30 Doradus Nebula in the Large Magellanic Cloud, photographed with the 74-inch telescope at Mount Stromlo.

EO NGC 3379

E2 NGC 221 (M 32)

E5 NGC 4621 (M 59)

E7 NGC 3115

NGC 3034 (M 82)

NGC 4449

39. Types of galaxies—elliptical, and irregular—photographed with the 60-inch telescope.

40. The edge-on spiral galaxy NGC 891 photographed with the 60-inch telescope.

44. Po[...] of the cluster of galaxies in Coma Berenices, distance 200,000,000 light-years, photographed with the 200-inch telescope.

RELATION BETWEEN RED-SHIFT AND DISTANCE
FOR EXTRAGALACTIC NEBULAE

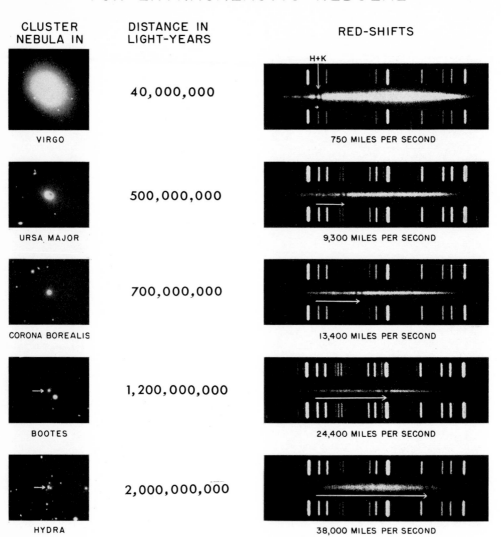

CLUSTER NEBULA IN	DISTANCE IN LIGHT-YEARS	RED-SHIFTS
VIRGO	40,000,000	750 MILES PER SECOND
URSA MAJOR	500,000,000	9,300 MILES PER SECOND
CORONA BOREALIS	700,000,000	13,400 MILES PER SECOND
BOOTES	1,200,000,000	24,400 MILES PER SECOND
HYDRA	2,000,000,000	38,000 MILES PER SECOND

45. The relation between red-shift and distance for galaxies.

sphere and see into deeper and therefore hotter and more luminous layers, while near the edge of the disc the radiation from the deeper layers is absorbed by the greater path through the Sun's atmosphere in our direction, light being received only from the outer cooler levels. Near the Sun's limb there are bright areas named *faculae*. They are usually, though not always, in spotted areas of the Sun. Their elevation above the photosphere helps to make them more readily visible near the limb where the photospheric brightness appears lower.

Under good conditions, a fine structure is visible, consisting of many small bright grains. These are best seen near the Sun's centre. The granulation is not uniform in pattern and individual grains have a life of only a few minutes. The small size of the grains and their constantly changing patterns make the granulation hard to observe, but improving techniques and the desire to extend solar observation to finer details has brought greater attention to it. Photographs with apparatus designed to take advantage of instants of good atmospheric conditions, and others taken during unmanned balloon flights organised for this purpose, show a representative diameter of 400 miles for the granules. It appears that this turbulent layer plays an important part in the processes which convey energy into the higher layers of the Sun's atmosphere.

The rotation of the Sun may be estimated by observing the apparent movement of the sunspots. The Sun does not rotate like a solid body. At the Sun's equator the rotation is fastest with period 25 days, at latitude 20° it is 25·7 days and at 40° 27·4 days. Other methods of determining the rotation confirm the trend of these figures and show that the rotation period is even longer nearer to the Sun's pole.

The Sunspots

The most conspicuous features on the Sun are the spots which have been observed since the first telescopic examination of the Sun. The active areas of the Sun, of which the spots are one manifestation, are centres of events of great energy and complexity. The spots range in size from bare visibility to huge areas up to 30,000 miles across. Typically they have a dark central area, called the *umbra*, which occupies about a sixth of the spot area.

Plate 26 shows a large sunspot. In most photographs, with exposure suitable for showing details of the surrounding photosphere, the umbra appears uniformly dark, but a photograph designed for the umbra reveals that it contains varied structure. The *penumbra*, the less dark area around the umbra, has a pattern of more-or-less radial filaments leading out into the surrounding brightness of the photosphere. Usually, as the spot is carried around by the Sun's rotation, it changes appearance as though it were a depression with the penumbral region sloping inward towards the centre. Accordingly, when the spot is towards the limb of the Sun, the edge of the penumbra towards the observer appears narrower than the one nearer the limb.

The development and history of sunspots or sunspot groups exhibit

I

great variety. Many have lifetimes of less than a day while others may persist for several months. Usually, though not invariably, a large long-lived spotted area develops over only a few days and then declines more slowly. Soon after its first appearance it shows a duality consisting of two spots or two groups of spots separated in an east west direction. The two components separate in the direction of the Sun's rotation so that the spread in longitude becomes much greater than that in the direction perpendicular to the Sun's equator.

Although, by contrast with the neighbouring surface of the Sun, the spots appear dark, they are really bright and hot, and methods outlined in Chapter 3 reveal their temperature to be about 1,500°K cooler than the surrounding photosphere. The movements of the gases in the Sun's atmosphere may be examined by measuring Doppler shifts of the spectrum lines. The observations are difficult because the details are small in size and the motions complicated. However, recent views are that the gases flow out of the sunspot along the bright, and therefore hotter, penumbral filaments while, side by side, gases flow into the sunspot along the dark penumbral filaments. A sunspot group is the most obvious manifestation of a vast centre of activity around which many of the most interesting and violent happenings on the Sun tend to occur.

The number of spots or their total area, varies in an approximately regular pattern with a period which averages about eleven years. Sunspot maxima occurred in 1928, 1937, 1947 and 1958. The period may vary a little for different cycles and the number of spots occurring around maximum or minimum may differ for different occasions, but the Sun often has twenty times as many spots during a period near maximum as compared with a similar period near minimum. The spottedness of the Sun from 1930 to 1960 is shown in Figure 36.

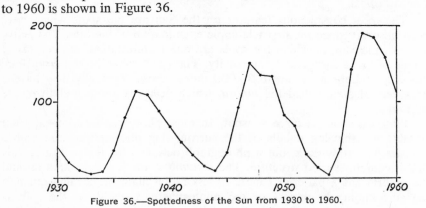

Figure 36.—Spottedness of the Sun from 1930 to 1960.

The spots do not occur at random places on the Sun's surface. Nearly all are distributed between latitudes 5° and 40°, either north or south. The last spots of a cycle occur near the Sun's equator at about the same time that the first spots of the new cycle are beginning to appear around latitudes 30° to 35°. As the cycle progresses, the average latitude of the spots shifts to lower latitudes, being about latitude 20° at the time of sun-spot maximum, which occurs about three years after the minimum. The latitudes in which most of the spots occur are shown in Figure 37 for the period 1930 to 1950 and because, with the time scale somewhat shorter than in Figure 37, the area looks like the outspread wings of a butterfly, this is called the "butterfly" diagram.

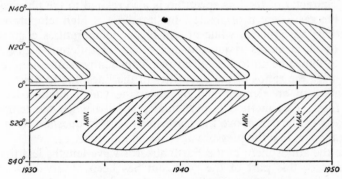

Figure 37.—Distribution of the sunspots from 1930 to 1950.

The Spectrum of the Sun

The spectrum of the Sun includes a continuum, a band of colour spread out from red to violet and beyond, towards both shorter and longer wave-lengths. Throughout its length it is cut by dark lines where narrow divisions of wave-length have been absorbed out of the spectrum by the gases in the Sun's atmosphere. This is called, after an early investigator, the *Fraunhofer* spectrum. The spectrum yields a great deal of information about the physical conditions and composition of the gases in the visible part of the Sun.

If measurements are made of the amount of energy in the continuous spectrum at various wave-lengths, the results may be compared with the curves given by Planck's Law of Radiation for various temperatures. The one that it fits fairly well corresponds to a temperature of 6,000°K. The fit is not perfect, because the Sun is not exactly the same sort of body as the theoretical one to which Planck's Law applies. The presence of so many dark lines in the spectrum is sufficient to illustrate this. Consequently, when the temperature is found in other ways we should not expect to get exactly the same result.

Stefan's Law may be used (see Chapter 3) to make an estimate of the temperature which would give a radiation of energy of 69,000 horsepower per square yard and solve the equation

$$69,000 = 63\left(\frac{T}{1,000}\right)^4$$

for T. This gives a temperature 5,750°K. If the wave-length for which the energy reaches a maximum is estimated, then Wien's Law gives a temperature of 6,050°K. The differences between these figures are sufficient to show that the Sun does not conform exactly to the theoretical pattern on which the formulae are based, but they accord sufficiently well to justify attributing a temperature around 6,000°K to the Sun's surface. This temperature, of course, applies to the level of the Sun from which most of the light is reaching us, that is, the photosphere. Other temperatures have to be allotted to other layers on the Sun.

The character of the line spectrum is also related to the physical conditions in the gas where it originates. In situations of high temperature some of the atoms are ionized, while at still higher temperatures a greater proportion of these atoms is ionized and atoms of different elements more difficult to ionize begin to lose electrons. Thus temperatures may be found by measuring the ratios of the intensities of the lines due to different stages of ionization of an element and by observing which atoms occur in the ionized form. This method is particularly applied when the temperatures of the parts of the sun above the photosphere are in question. It is complicated by the fact that the pressure also has an influence.

Since the atmosphere of the Earth absorbs wave-lengths less than about 0·29 microns, this part of the spectrum has been observable only since the advent of rockets and satellites which enable spectra to be obtained above the absorbing layers. From these vehicles the Sun's spectrum has been observed as far as wave-lengths shorter than 0·01 micron in the X-ray region. Beyond about 0·16 micron the continuous spectrum disappears, and with it the dark absorption lines of the Fraunhofer spectrum. Thereafter, bright emission lines dominate the spectrum. These lines originate above the photosphere in parts of the Sun's atmosphere which turn out to have a higher temperature. The strongest lines are due to hydrogen and ionized helium, wave-lengths about 0·122 and 0·030 micron respectively. Even before these short wave radiations were directly observed the X-rays had revealed themselves by effects on the ionized layers to which they give rise high in the Earth's atmosphere. These are the layers which reflect radio waves and make possible radio communication around the Earth. The X-radiation varies with solar activity, particularly with flaring activity which occurs near sunspots.

Chemical Composition

By comparing the positions of the Fraunhofer lines with positions of lines observed in the laboratory from sources containing known atoms the chemical composition of the outer part of the Sun may be investigated. When this is done, it is found that about two-thirds of the atoms around us on the Earth may be identified on the Sun. One element, helium, was revealed by the lines it shows in the Sun's spectrum in 1868—27 years before it was found in the laboratory.

A quantitative estimate of the amount of an element present may be obtained by measuring the intensity of the lines which belong to it. The amount of light absorbed to form a line in the spectrum depends, for one thing, on the number of atoms in the state from which a change may occur to absorb the energy corresponding to the particular spectrum line; and for another, on the probability of the transition which gives rise to it. The basic information for the calculations is obtained in the laboratory. If the amount of light taken from the Sun's continuous spectrum by the lines of various elements is measured, the information can be made to yield an estimate of the proportion of atoms of the elements in the solar atmosphere.

As an important example of the factors which must be taken into account it may be mentioned that, in the conditions of temperature in the atmosphere of the Sun, only a small proportion of the atoms of hydrogen can be in a state capable of absorbing visible radiation, while a large proportion of calcium atoms are ready to do so. Hence, although the lines of calcium are stronger than those of the hydrogen, the calculation shows that hydrogen is far more abundant. Hydrogen and helium are the predominant components of the Sun in accordance with the following table. It happens that, except for a faint infra-red line, the Fraunhofer spectrum does not show suitable lines of helium. The abundance of the helium must be judged from the spectrum of outer parts of the Sun, where conditions for their excitation exist.

Element	Percentage of atoms by number	Percentage by mass
H	88	62
He	12	36
O, N, C, and all others	about 0·1	about 2

Magnetic Fields

Sunspots possess a magnetic field which can be investigated by examining the lines in the spectrum of the spot. Some of the spectrum lines of a source of light are divided if the source is in a powerful magnetic field. In Figure 38 the hatched area represents a powerful magnet whose north pole is marked *N* and south *S*. *L* is a source of light placed in the field and on the right are shown various aspects of a spectrum line which is single, as at *P*, in the absence of the field. When the spectrum of the light is examined through a hole in one pole in the direction *A*, that of the magnetic field, some of the lines are split into two components as shown at *Q* in the Figure. Examined in a direction across the magnetic field towards *B*, there may be three components as indicated at *R*. The distance between the components so divided is proportional to the strength of the magnetic field, which may accordingly be measured by this process.

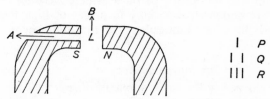

Figure 38 —Effect of a magnetic field on spectrum lines.

The division of the spectrum lines by a magnetic field, of which only the simplest case has been described, is called the *Zeeman effect* after its discoverer. The component lines as at Q and R are polarized and therefore have characteristic modes of vibration associated with them as explained in Chapter 3. This polarization varies with the direction of the magnetic field. Its polarity may, as in Figure 38, be such that the non-perforated pole of the magnet is attracted to the north or, if the polarity is opposite, to the south.

In one case, the vibration of the shorter wave-length component lines Q, as examined at A, may be circular and clockwise in which case the other would have vibration in the opposite direction. If the polarity of the magnet is changed, the direction of the vibration is exchanged between the two components. Thus the direction of the magnetic field can also be found. These methods, developed in the laboratory, may be applied to examine the magnetic fields of enough strength in any source which is bright enough to allow its light to be spread sufficiently to reveal the Zeeman components.

The fields of sunspots are very powerful, often several thousand times the magnetic field which controls compass needles at the surface of the Earth. It is found that at the centres of many sunspots the field is nearly perpendicular to the surface of the Sun so that, if the sunspot appears to be near the centre of the Sun's disc, the lines are divided as at Q in Figure 38. Moreover, the leading components of pairs of sunspots in the same hemisphere of the Sun have the same polarity, which is opposite to that of the following components. That is, if the leading spots in the one hemisphere are, say, north seeking poles, the following ones are south. In the other hemisphere of the Sun these polarities are interchanged, the leading component having the same polarity as the following component in the other hemisphere. Remarkably, too, when a new sunspot cycle begins, these polarities are interchanged and so a cycle of twenty-two years, rather than eleven, governs the magnetic changes.

The magnetic fields of the sunspots were the first ones detected away from the Earth. The fields away from the spots have been explored with the detection of a remarkably intricate and varying magnetic activity, not as strong as in the spots. There are fields associated with other features on the Sun and the field of a sunspot may persist for a time after the spot itself has disappeared. The predominance of opposite polarities near the poles of the Sun's rotation is taken as evidence of a weak magnetic field. The magnetic fields on the Sun, and elsewhere in space, are important because of their influence on the motion of particles which carry an electric charge. Such particles are common, especially in places of high temperature like the surface and the outer atmosphere of the Sun where the gases are highly ionized.

The Appearance of the Sun during an Eclipse

The Moon has nearly the same apparent diameter as the Sun. When it comes between the observer and the Sun, it can just cover the bright disc of the Sun, thus giving opportunity for the observation of the faint outer parts of the Sun's atmosphere which ordinarily cannot be seen because of the overwhelming brilliance of the body of the Sun. In such circumstances the lower part of the Sun's atmosphere shows around the dark Moon as a rosy ring which led to its being called the *chromosphere*. The chromosphere extends a few thousand miles above the photosphere. Often visible are enormous flame-like extensions, called *prominences*, around the Sun's limb; and, extending more than the diameter of the Sun outwards, the delicate pearly white solar *corona* (see Plate 28). Close around the Sun, also, are small spiked extensions of the solar atmosphere called *spicules*, which are related to structures in the chromosphere.

The total light coming from the whole of the outer parts of the Sun varies from eclipse to eclipse but, on an occasion when it is fairly bright, may be about as much as from the full Moon. The light of the corona is spread along streamers which are no doubt conditioned by magnetic lines of force. At times of sunspot minimum these extend greatly in the plane of the Sun's equator while at maximum the corona takes a more nearly circular shape. Since it is so very much fainter than the main body of the Sun, the light scattered in the Earth's atmosphere ordinarily overwhelms this faint source and special methods have to be sought to observe it away from the time of an eclipse.

Although instruments have been devised for observing the outer parts of the Sun at other times, the eclipses still offer the best opportunity for certain studies. The faint distant parts of the corona can be photographed only during an eclipse and the general spectrum of the chromosphere is best studied at such times when the advancing limb of the Moon covers, or uncovers, the successive layers of the Sun. The spectrum of the Sun's chromosphere, arising as it does from hot gas, is one of bright lines. The red colour is due to a strong emission of hydrogen. Owing to different physical conditions the intensities of the lines have different relations from those that occur in the ordinary Fraunhofer spectrum. It is found that lines arising from atoms which have electrons knocked from their outer shells are, in the chromosphere, more intense relative to the lines of the neutral elements. This is owing to higher temperature and lower pressure. At the lower density the atoms remain ionized longer because there are fewer electrons for them to recapture. The higher temperatures are sufficient to excite lines of helium which do not occur in the ordinary dark-line spectrum. There is a quick rise of the temperature at higher levels in the chromosphere. At a height of 600 miles above the photosphere the temperature has reached 10,000°K and goes on increasing though it varies greatly from one chromospheric structure to another. The coldest layer of the Sun, and the region of minimum ionization, is not far from the level of the photosphere.

Monochromatic Observations of the Sun

Ways have been found to observe, away from eclipse time, solar features which formerly were too faint to see except during an eclipse or which were invisible in the general white light coming from the surface of the Sun. The first example of this was the examination by means of the spectroscope of prominences beyond the limb of the Sun (see Plate 27). The slit of the spectroscope is placed tangentially to the image of limb of the Sun and widened a little. Images of a prominence form in places in the spectrum corresponding to bright emission lines from the prominence. The continuous radiation arising from the light scattered by the atmosphere is diluted by spreading it out along the spectrum. Thus the image of the prominence in a bright line is favoured. In this way it became possible to examine the prominences around the Sun at any time. This has been done intensely for many years, while techniques have so improved that motion pictures have been taken. The pictures have shown dramatically the dynamic character of the Sun's atmosphere. The prominences are seen in a wide range of latitudes, but those within the spot zone of the Sun are more numerous and larger, and vary in latitude and frequency with the spots. They commonly appear as quiescent loops where material appears to condense at heights some tens of thousands of miles above the photosphere of the Sun and rain down on its surface. The quiescent prominences which may last for long periods have little motion. Occasionally there are great *surge prominences* in which the material jets outward from the Sun at 60 to 120 miles per second and even, in extreme cases, at 600 miles per second. In the motion pictures the material in the outgoing jet sometimes appears to fall back into the Sun over much the same path, as though it were shot out and then withdrawn. These extremely active prominences are associated with sunspots.

The spectroscope has been applied also to examination in one colour of the whole surface of the Sun. A second slit is placed along a line in the image of the spectrum so that light of only this one colour is allowed to reach a photographic plate. Then, by moving the Sun's image across the ordinary spectroscope slit and simultaneously traversing the photographic plate across the second one an image of the Sun, in one colour (a monochromatic image), is built up. The colours usually chosen are within either the red hydrogen line called Hα, or the line called K, originating from ionized calcium in the Sun's spectrum. Although these lines appear dark in the continuous spectrum of the Sun, there is nevertheless in them the light emitted in the chromosphere by hydrogen or calcium atoms.

This modification of the spectroscope, the spectroheliograph, gives a picture of the Sun, which can thus be observed in a way which has provided much new data. (Such a view of the Sun is given in Plate 30.) In recent years elaborate filters have been devised to let through very narrow parts of the Sun's spectrum. These transmitted wave-lengths may be placed within spectrum lines and the filter made to do work similar to that of the spectroheliograph. Pictures taken in this way still show the sunspots, but there is also much greater variety and contrast in parts of the Sun which, on photographs in white light, may be clear of detail. The picture in calcium light has a coarser more mottled structure than appears when the picture has been taken in hydrogen-alpha light. This is because the radiation of calcium is easier to excite and more sensitive to temperature differences, which therefore show up more clearly than in the spectroheliograms in Hα.

These techniques, which make possible continuous observation of the chromosphere, offer the opportunity for examining different layers in the solar atmosphere. If the second slit of the spectroheliograph is so placed or the monochromatic filter so tuned that a wave-length at the centre of the line is used, the light recorded is mainly from a high level in the atmosphere. This is because more of the light is absorbed at the centre of the line, and so the radiation can come through only a small depth of the gases in the Sun's atmosphere. On the other hand, if a wave-length more towards the edge of the line is used, the atmosphere is more transparent and a deeper layer is seen.

The fact that each picture is in light of one colour does not prevent the Doppler effect from being used to indicate motions of the recorded features. If the picture on the short wave-length side of the line centre shows a feature brighter than one a similar distance on the long wave-length side, it must be because the wave-lengths of the radiation from the object are shortened by its motion towards us. A motion away from us, usually downward on the Sun, is similarly revealed by a stronger image on the long wave-length side of the line. By such means investigations are being made of the details of the Sun's atmosphere.

The spicules, previously mentioned as a feature of the chromosphere visible on the Sun's limb during eclipses, are also seen in the monochromatic light within the strongest Fraunhofer absorption lines. They reach heights of several thousand miles above the photosphere. The problem of deciding such an apparently simple question as to whether they originate in the bright or dark mottles of the chromosphere as seen on the disc of the Sun shows the difficulty of solar research, for such observational data must be available for a theory to be placed on a firm basis. Careful techniques seem now to make it clear that the spicules must be associated with the bright mottles.

Plages and Dark Flocculi

In the monochromatic pictures there are bright areas which are often associated with sunspots. Being of longer duration they both precede the spots and remain after the spots have died away. Formerly called flocculi, these regions are now called *plages*. The faculae are plage areas visible in white light, although some authors apply the term faculae even to the bright areas in monochromatic light. The active areas which appear as plages do not always develop spots.

These regions of activity on the Sun reveal themselves in other ways. At radio wave-lengths of about a metre or somewhat less there is a component of radiation which varies slowly with the activity of the region and the rotation of the Sun. The plage areas are also a source of X-ray emission, for the bright patches on X-ray photographs taken by a pinhole camera carried by a rocket above the Earth's atmosphere correlate with the calcium plage areas. As would be expected for a source high in the Sun's atmosphere there is brightening towards the limb where the radiation must be derived from a greater path length towards the observer. The X-ray emission of the plage areas varies almost hourly by amounts of the order of 5 per cent.

In the monochromatic pictures, particularly in the hydrogen line, there are narrow dark markings called *filaments* or *dark flocculi*. They may be more than 150,000 miles long and some 4,000 miles wide. When the rotation of the Sun brings them to the limb, it is revealed that they coincide with the prominences and their dark appearance on the surface of the Sun is due to the absorption of the light from the background by the material of the prominences. The two views of the prominences brought together show that they are narrow blade-like structures. They are no doubt supported by magnetic fields for the great gravitational attraction would otherwise quickly draw them into the Sun's surface.

Flares

Monochromatic examination of the Sun, particularly in Hα light, often reveals, near developing sunspots, a sudden increase in the intensity of the light. These *flares*, which are just occasionally strong enough to be seen in white light without the aid of a filter, are probably due to energy communicated to the ionized gases by the rising magnetic field of the sunspot. They may repeat several times in the same neighbourhood.

Many of the flares are accompanied by great surges of material which are identifiable with the surge prominences mentioned as visible at the limb of the Sun. These flares throw into space a stream of particles with such a range of velocities that some of them reach the Earth only a few minutes after the light, while others take up to 40 hours. The Earth continuously receives from the depths of space a bombardment of highly energetic particles called *cosmic rays*, which have a velocity near that of light. The greater part of these are protons. Since their motion has been twisted by the magnetic fields of space as well as that of the Earth, there is usually no way of deriving their source. The increased count of cosmic rays yielded by a flare on the Sun is the only case in which we can actually observe the generation of cosmic rays. The Sun always emits a "wind" of particles, chiefly of electrons and protons, observed by space probes (for example, the Mariner II Venus probe). This is increased at the time of such solar disturbances.

Often, too, the flare is the source of a great burst of radio waves which for a short time may enhance the radiation of the Sun to more than a million times its emission at a quiet period. These bursts arise from disturbances which travel outward in the Sun's atmosphere at speeds of many hundreds of miles per second. At the beginning of the burst wave-lengths are short, about a metre or two, and the frequency high. However, as the disturbance progresses to less dense parts of the solar atmosphere, the wavelengths become longer to correspond with the natural frequency belonging to an environment of lower density. Depending on the way in which the wave-length and intensity vary the bursts are divided into types. The rapidly varying types which occur at the beginning of the disturbance with blasts of duration measured in seconds may be followed by types of longer duration, which may last some hours when the disturbance reaches out into the corona. The flare may also be accompanied by greatly increased emission of X-rays.

These great disturbances on the Sun may have interesting effects on the Earth. It frequently happens at the time of an intense flare that short wave radio communication is cut in the Earth's sunlit hemisphere. This occurs when the arriving X-rays cause increased ionization of the layers in the upper atmosphere which ordinarily reflect the radio waves back to the Earth's surface. At such times the waves longer than about 10 metres are absorbed. When the stream of particle radiation arrives at the Earth after a day or so, it enters and distorts the Earth's magnetic field enabling some of the particles to penetrate far enough to cause an aurora, one of nature's most beautiful sights. The particles tend to enter the atmosphere in regions surrounding the magnetic poles and so the aurorae are most frequent in zones about 23° from each magnetic pole. They are, in fact, much more frequent than is realized by most people who live in latitudes away from the poles. At the same time the magnetic field on the Earth's surface is disturbed, upsetting the usual pointing of compass needles, as well as the strength of the field. Such magnetic storms can also occur independently of flares but appear to be associated with disturbed solar areas, often sunspot areas.

The practical importance of these phenomena, especially as related to radio communication, as well as their scientific interest, has led to establishment of patrol observations to detect and study the flares.

The Solar Corona

The coronagraph, a special instrument for observing the Sun, was produced by the French astronomer Bernard Lyot in 1930. Special precautions are taken to avoid scattered light in the instrument which is then set up in a place where the atmosphere is outstandingly clear. A disc is placed over the image of the main body of the Sun so as to arrange an artificial eclipse by which the brighter parts of its outer atmosphere may be kept under continuous observation.

The spectrum of the corona, like that of the Sun, has a continuous background which arises from reflection of sunlight by the material of the corona. It includes also bright emission lines which for many years defied identification, at one time even being attributed to an unknown element. When the riddle was solved, it was shown that the lines come from ordinary atoms of iron, calcium, nickel and argon which have had from 9 to 14 electrons knocked out of them. In some cases the lines are forbidden lines which can occur only in conditions where the atoms can travel for relatively long periods between collisions with their neighbours. The high degree of ionization in the corona indicates a very high temperature, of the order of a million degrees. The fact that the corona extends so far is an indication of its high temperature, and the high velocity of its particles.

The continuous background of the coronal spectrum is sunlight, scattered, on the one hand, by the electrons torn from the atoms in the corona surrounding the Sun, and on the other by the interplanetary particles which have also appeared in the zodiacal light. The contributions from these two sources can be separated by careful measurement. The zodiacal contribution shows the Fraunhofer lines of the ordinary solar spectrum, whereas the part due to the coronal electrons does not show the dark lines because they are so widened as to be masked in the continuous spectrum. This broadening of the spectrum lines occurs since, at the high temperature prevailing, the rapid movement of individual electrons in random directions makes the light reflected by some much bluer and by some much redder than normal, so that the whole effect is to widen the line. The greater part of the light of the corona is the sunlight reflected by electrons.

Radio observation makes a valuable contribution to study of the outer parts of the Sun. At very short wave-lengths—about one centimetre—the observed area coincides with the disc observed in the optical wave-lengths. At longer wave-lengths, which are generated at higher levels and not transmitted from lower ones, the observed area is greater and there is an increase of intensity around the limb because there the radiation comes from a longer path in the Sun's atmosphere. This is a prominent effect at 20 to 60 centimetres wave-length. At still longer wave-lengths of some metres the limb brightening disappears. The area from which the radiation is coming resembles the corona and spreads over a much larger area than the visible Sun. Thus the observations over a range of wave-lengths demonstrate a continuous transition from chromosphere to corona. The brightness of the corona in the radio part of the spectrum again displays the temperature of the order of 10^6 degrees K. The corona is not bright at visual wave-lengths, despite the high temperature, because of the extreme tenuity of the matter present.

At heights of several hundred thousand miles there sometimes occur "noise storms" of much enhanced radio emission with wave-lengths of several metres. The noise storms occur over the disturbed areas of the Sun and, although they do not extend over wide areas, they may endure for several days.

The corona shades off into interplanetary space—the material in which may, in a sense, be regarded as an extension of the corona. When the Sun passes over the distant radio source in Taurus the effect of the corona on the source can be traced to more than ten times the solar radius. The solar wind, consisting chiefly of electrons and protons, has been observed by the space probes to increase with solar disturbance. It is believed that at the disturbed period there is enhanced activity of comets, which have been considered as possible indicators of solar particle and ultraviolet radiation.

Although the chief components of the corona are recognised, the physical processes by which it is maintained still wait to be unveiled.

8

THE OTHER STARS

THE SUN is the only star whose surface can be examined in detail. All of the other stars appear only as luminous points, even with the greatest telescopes in the world. The night sky in the country away from the city lights can scarcely fail to impress the observer with its beauty and with its multitude of stars. Yet when actual count is made, the number of stars individually visible to the naked eye is not so very great. Over the whole sky the average eye can discern only about 6,000 stars, and at any one time rather less than 3,000 would be visible. However, the telescope and astronomical camera reveal that there really is a multitude of stars. They form the most obvious component of the universe beyond the solar system.

When we have to investigate anything which exists in large numbers it is usual to begin with measurements of properties of individual members of the group. Then, in order to systematize the results of the observations, classification is introduced. If the classification is meaningful, it must lend order to our ideas and suggest new knowledge. To embark on such a programme for the stars it is natural to consider first the properties that are most clearly derivable from observation.

THE BRIGHTNESS OF THE STARS

Stellar Magnitudes

The most obvious thing that can be measured about a star is the amount of light that it sends us. Measurements of this kind have great importance and form part of the activity of many astronomers.

The scale of brightness is very ancient since it originated with Hipparchus over two thousand years ago. His observation of a bright new star, where none had been visible to him before, led him to make a record of the positions and brightnesses of about a thousand stars. As mentioned in Chapter 1 he classified the brightest stars as first magnitude and the faintest that he could see as sixth magnitude. When, during last century, the need for a quantitative expression of stellar brightness was felt, two principles were used. First, it was found that, if an observer ranks as equal the differences in intensity of a number of sensations, provided they are neither very strong nor very weak, it is the ratio of the energies of the stimuli that are the same. In the case being considered the ratio of the amount of light received from a second magnitude star to that from a third magnitude star is the same as if the stars had been fourth and fifth or, in fact, any two consecutive magnitudes. Second, it was found that a first magnitude star on the scale of Hipparchus gives about a hundred times as much light as one of the sixth magnitude. In the definition it was therefore agreed to accept a difference of five magnitudes as corresponding exactly to a ratio of 100 in the amount of light received. The scale was fixed so that the sixth magnitude in a catalogue of stars compiled at Bonn in Germany was perpetuated.

The use of telescopes and sensitive devices for measuring light makes it necessary to extend the magnitude scale far beyond the original sixth, and the existence of objects brighter than magnitude 0 makes necesssary the use of negative magnitudes. Sirius, the brightest star, has magnitude $-1 \cdot 6$. Acceptance of this ratio means that an increase of brightness of one magnitude corresponds to an increase of the amount of energy received in the ratio of $2 \cdot 512$; so, if you wish to compare approximately the amount of light received from two objects whose magnitude difference is given, multiply by 100 for each whole five magnitudes and then by $2 \cdot 5$ for one additional magnitude, 6 for two, 16 for three and 40 for four. Thus 160,000 times as much light is received from a third magnitude star as from one of sixteenth magnitude. A telescope of aperture $2\frac{1}{2}$ inches reveals stars of magnitude 11, a hundred times fainter than the naked eye can see, and a 25-inch telescope reaches magnitude 16 while photographic plates record still fainter stars.

Measuring the Brightness of Stars

The accurate measurement of magnitudes of celestial bodies is by no means a simple matter. First, the range over which the scale has to be maintained is enormous. The magnitude of the Sun is $-26 \cdot 7$ and that of the faintest stars observed with great telescopes 23, a range of 50 magnitudes and an energy ratio of 10^{20}. Secondly, the measurements are affected by the distribution in wave-length of the light of the star—that is, its colour —and by the passage through the Earth's atmosphere, the telescope and a filter, if one has been used, and by the response of the measuring device at different wave-lengths and at different intensities.

After a stage in which the eye, aided only by the telescope to gather the light, was the measuring device visual photometers were invented to diminish by known amount the light from the star or a comparison source, often itself a star. By this means the two sources could be made to appear equal. This was a fairly satisfactory method as the eye matches equally bright sources with more accuracy than it can estimate a difference between unequal sources. The introduction of photography was an advance because, by careful procedures, the results could be made less dependant on the individuality of the observer and because many stars, to a faint magnitude, could be made available for study on just one photograph. Notice that in this book, in the illustrations which portray stars, the brighter stars produce more prominent images. This is the basis for photographic measurement of brightness.

Later the photo-electric instruments mentioned in Chapter 3 have been introduced. These are sensitive enough to observe very faint stars and have the great advantage that the electric current produced is proportional, over a very wide range of intensity, to the amount of light falling on the sensitive screen. The introduction of these instruments has revolutionized stellar *photometry*, measurement of brightness. The stellar magnitudes now depend on a number of standard stars distributed over the sky. The brightness of these has been measured with great care and accurate measures on other stars depend ultimately on their accepted magnitudes, which therefore virtually constitute the definition of the system of stellar magnitudes. Often in places where the stars are crowded together both photo-electric and photographic methods are used so that the advantages of both methods are exploited. The comparison star magnitudes are set up photo-electrically by referring them to standards and the results extended to many stars by photographs on which the stars in the field may be compared with the stars calibrated photo-electrically.

Colours of the Stars

The methods of photometry permit measures of the colours of the stars. Even with the naked eye stars display different colours. Betelgeuse and Antares have a distinctly reddish hue, while Regulus and Rigel appear blue-white—and there are colours intermediate between these. The introduction of photography for measuring brightness brought this fact into prominence. The early photographic plates were sensitive to the blue end of the spectrum and insensitive to red light and so stars like Betelgeuse and Antares, although bright to the eye, appeared relatively faint on the photographs. A separate scale of magnitudes had therefore to be established for photography. The *photographic magnitudes* were defined so as to equal the visual magnitudes for white stars like Sirius. The difference photographic magnitude minus visual magnitude gives a measure of the colour of the star and is called the *colour index*. The colour indices of the four stars mentioned are Antares 1·7, Betelgeuse 1·7, Regulus –0·2, and Rigel –0·2. The colour indices of red stars are positive and of blue-white stars negative. Photographic plates have now been introduced with good sensitivity in other parts of the spectrum, and combinations of filter and plate giving results similar to those obtained visually provide what are called *photovisual* magnitudes.

Unlike the magnitude the colour of a star is not changed by distance, except by intervening material, and so in measuring colour an observer is finding an intrinsic property of the star. Combinations of filter and photo-electric device now measure the light from narrow parts of stellar spectra and magnitude measurements are made in colours from the ultraviolet to beyond the red end of the spectrum. The difference between magnitudes found for each pair of spectral regions yields another colour index. These indices naturally depend on the distribution of light in the spectrum and correlate particularly with the temperature of the stars. Thus, if a star field is photographed on a blue sensitive plate and then on a yellow sensitive plate, with a filter, to determine photovisual magnitudes, information is available on the temperature of all of the stars recorded. The colour of a star may be changed by its passage through material in interstellar space and so measurement of colour affords valuable information for investigating this material.

THE DISTANCES OF THE STARS

Measurement of Distances

Distance is fundamental in astronomy since interpretation of the character of bodies, and of any system to which they may belong, depends very much on a knowledge of distances at which they lie. So this is the next subject for discussion even though it is founded on measurements of refined character and not at all obvious. The basic methods of determining distances of stars are geometrical, depending on measurements of apparent displacement of their directions arising from known motion of the observer or motions of the stars themselves.

Just as distances within the solar system may be measured by using as a base line the distance between two widely separated places on the Earth, so, for the stars, the widely separated situations into which the orbital motion takes the Earth may be used to provide a base line. In Figure 39 S represents the Sun and E and F positions occupied by the Earth at times about six months apart. X represents the place of a star in space and the

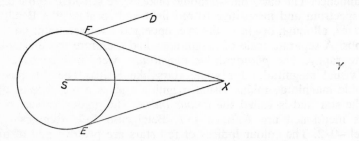

Figure 39.—Trigonometric measurement of the distance of a star.

line EX its direction from the Earth at the first epoch. After six months the original direction of the star is FD, but the movement of the Earth has changed the apparent direction of the star to FX. Because the angles of the triangle EFX are accessible to measurement, the observer who knows the distance from E to F may calculate the remaining sides of the triangle and obtain the distance of the star. The angle EXS which the radius of the Earth's orbit subtends at the star is called the *parallax* of the star. The distances of the stars are very great, and the angle DFX to be measured has been greatly exaggerated in the Figure. No star is known to have a parallax as great as one second of arc, which is the angle subtended by a disc one inch in diameter at a distance of more than three miles. For this reason the measurement of parallax is a delicate operation, and it was not until about 1838, almost three hundred years after the publication of the Copernican system which implies that parallaxes exist, that within a short time the first measurements of the distances of three stars were revealed.

The change of the direction of a star is always measured relative to stars in the distant background. In Figure 39, for example, the star at X must move relative to more remote stars at Y as the Earth passes from E to F. This movement is found by taking photographs at the two epochs, actually several times, and measuring the displacement of the closer star relative to the background stars. Even for the relatively few stars with parallax as large as $0''.1$ the displacement to be measured on photographs taken with a large telescope is only about 1/5000 inch. About six thousand stars have parallaxes measured in this way. For many of these the parallax is not sufficiently greater than the errors of measurement to inspire confidence.

As the distances of stars expressed in units we use on the Earth would lead to cumbersomely large and not easily visualized numbers, new units suitable for expressing stellar distances are introduced. A star whose parallax is one second of arc is said to have a distance of one parsec. So if p is the parallax of a star in seconds of arc, its distance in parsecs is given by

$$d = 1/p$$

This unit, usually used in the technical literature of astronomy, has the merit of direct relation to the way in which the distances are found. Another more graphic unit will be used here, however—the *light-year*, the distance travelled in one year by light, the speed of which is 186,000 miles per second. A light-year is equal to nearly 5·9 million million miles and one parsec equals 3¼ light-years. Now that fundamental distances are measured by radar the light-year, too, has a relation to observation.

Absolute Magnitude

An important characteristic of a star is the amount of light which it radiates. This may be described by stating how bright it would be at a standard distance. The standard distance chosen is such that the corresponding parallax is $0''.1$—that is, the distance is 10 parsecs or 32·6 light-years. The magnitude a star would have at this distance is called its *absolute magnitude*. The necessary calculations rest on the rule that the amount of light reaching a given area, such as the pupil of an eye or the object glass of a telescope, varies inversely as the square of the distance of the star. To illustrate this, Figure 40 shows that at twice the distance the light is spread over four times the area so that a given area receives only a quarter as much light. This rule, together with the relation, given in the section on magnitudes, for the ratio of the amount of light corresponding to a change in magnitude yields an equation of great importance in astronomy. If m is

K

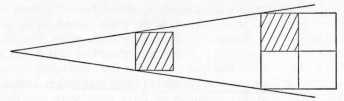

Figure 40.—The inverse-square law for light.

taken as the observed magnitude of a star, d its distance in light-years, and M its absolute magnitude the equation is

$$m - M = 5 \log d - 7 \cdot 57$$

If the distance is known, this enables the absolute magnitude to be found from the measured value of m. For example, the brightest star Sirius has a distance of $8 \cdot 7$ light-years and an observed magnitude $-1 \cdot 6$. The equation gives the absolute magnitude as $1 \cdot 3$. At a distance of 326 light-years this star would have a magnitude $6 \cdot 3$ and be barely visible to the naked eye.

Luminosity Methods

When the distance of a star is 600 light-years or more, the actual parallax that it may have begins to be submerged in the errors of observation. As this turns out to be only a small distance in space there is a constant search for new methods to find distances. These often depend on finding some characteristic of the star which indicates its intrinsic brightness, that is, its absolute magnitude. If this can be done and the apparent brightness measured, the values of m and M can be entered in the above equation which can then be solved for d. Thus it is that the value of m–M is called the *distance modulus*. The equation is represented in Figure 41, from which d may be read if m–M is known, or vice versa. For example, if a star in the Large Magellanic Cloud is shown to have a value of $18 \cdot 6$ for m–M, a distance of 170,000 light-years is indicated.

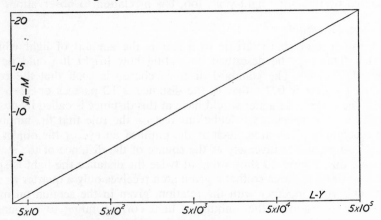

Figure 41.—Relation of distance modulus to distance.

Provided that the necessary characteristic that reveals M can be recognised, a luminosity method can be applied to great distances for objects bright enough to be observed when far away. Even when a suitable characteristic which correlates with absolute magnitude has been recognised, it is still necessary to calibrate it by finding the distances of some of the stars by a geometrical method so that the actual value of M becomes known. The relation to the geometric parallax need not be direct. For example, if the distance of a cluster of stars has been found by using some component stars whose absolute magnitudes are known, the distance of all of the stars in the cluster may be taken as available to calibrate suitable characteristics for the other stars. The question of distance is so very important that it is often necessary to return to it when the discussion reaches a point where a stellar characteristic which correlates with absolute magnitude can be mentioned.

MOTIONS OF STARS

The Copernican picture of the solar system, with the Earth moving around the Sun, leads to the idea that the stars are objects like the Sun scattered at vast distances in space. This being so, not only must the motion of the Earth make the stars appear in different directions at different times, with nearer stars showing more effect, but observations of the stars for long periods should surely reveal changes in the positions of stars in space due to their own motions. The fact that these effects were at the time not observable was one reason why a great observing astronomer like Tycho Brahe, who worked at the end of the sixteenth century, was not able to accept the Copernican system. Eventually the motions of stars were disclosed. The first were revealed by Halley who, in 1718, claimed that three stars, including Arcturus which has a large motion, had moved since ancient times.

Proper Motion and Radial Velocity

To illustrate the observable effect of the motion of a star suppose that in Figure 42 E represents the position of the Earth, the line ES the direction and distance of a star at some time and EP its direction and distance at a later time. Its movement is divided into two parts to correspond to the two ways in which the motion is measured. The angle SEP represents the motion across the sky which may be measured by the observer from measurements of the star's position at the two epochs. Dividing by the number of years intervening gives the yearly angular motion of the star. This motion is called *proper motion*. The proper motion of Arcturus is about $2 \cdot 3$ seconds of arc per year. The largest known motion, for a faint star in the constellation Ophiuchus, is ten seconds per year which would carry the star across an angle equal to the diameter of the Moon in under two hundred years. For most stars the motion is only a small fraction of a second of arc per year.

The other component of motion represented in Figure 42 is the differ-

ence in the distances *ES* and *EP*. The star is moving away from the Earth.
This motion may be determined from measurements of the spectrum of the

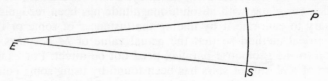

Figure 42.—Proper motion and radial velocity.

star for, as explained in Chapter 3, the spectrum lines of a receding star
are moved towards the long wave-length end of the spectrum, and of an
approaching star towards the short wave-length end, by an amount proportional to the *radial velocity*. The proper motions and radial motions, from
the Doppler shifts, form important data for astronomical research. The
motion of the observing instrument, of the Earth in fact, makes a difference
to both of these motions. The distance of the star from us has no influence
on the radial motion. During the part of the year when the Earth is moving
away from the direction of the star the radial motion is increased, while it is
decreased during the part when the Earth moves towards the star. The
influence of the annual motion of the Earth is always calculated and removed so that quoted radial velocities are taken relative to the Sun. On the
other hand, the distance of the star makes a difference to the effect of the
movement of the Earth on the star's proper motion which appears less for
a star at greater distance.

Part of the motion of each star, peculiar to the star, is random and
taken to depend by chance on which star is examined, but there are influences which are systematic and affect the motion of the star in ways
which depend on its position in space. One of these influences is the average
motion of the stars in any vicinity about the centre of gravity of the system
of stars. This is to be discussed in Chapter 10. Another, the influence of the
motion of the Sun, will be described here.

The Sun's Motion

The situation of the Sun in space among the other stars leads naturally
to the thought that it probably has a motion among them. The terrestrial
observer is carried along with this motion which has, on the apparent
motions of the stars, effects which were looked for and found by William
Herschel in 1783 when only 13 proper motions of stars were available.
Suppose the Sun is moving towards a point of space, called the *apex* of its
motion, and then suppose at first that the stars have no individual motions:
the stars at right angles to this direction will appear to drift backward.
The stars in the direction of the motion will appear to spread outward from
the solar apex just as the trees of a landscape do from the direction towards
which we may drive along a road. In the direction from which the Sun
moves the stars appear to close in. These effects are observed in the proper

motions. The radial motions, measured by observing Doppler shifts of the spectrum lines, are also affected. The stars in the direction of the solar apex will, as a reflection of the motion of the Sun, appear to move towards us and those in the opposite direction appear to move away. The fact that the radial motions are measured directly as velocities and are not influenced by distance is an advantage.

The discussion so far has neglected the individual motions of the stars which complicate interpretation of the observations so that it is not easy to get, from a small number of stars, a reliable result for the motion of the Sun. However, if the individual motions of the stars are taken to be random in direction the analysis leads to a value of the Sun's motion relative to the group of stars considered. The result is that, relative to the stars in our vicinity, the Sun is moving towards a point in the constellation Hercules, right ascension 18 hours, declination $+30°$, at a speed of 12 miles per second.

Distances Derived from Motions

If a group of stars is numerous, their velocities relative to the standard of rest on which the solar motion described in the last section is based may be supposed to be random in character. Hence a mean may be taken which will leave the effect due to the motion of the Sun. When trigonometric parallaxes are determined, the displacement depends on a base line provided by the diameter of the Earth's orbit. The solar motion in one year is twice this and, unlike the Earth's orbital motion, continues in the same direction, so increasing the base line as time goes on. Thus a geometrical procedure is available for determining the average distance of the group of stars. Parallaxes found in this way are called *secular parallaxes*.

The average distance of the group of stars is given significance by the selection of stars to be included. If, for example, the stars are chosen because there is evidence that they have a characteristic that indicates the same, but unknown, absolute magnitude, the secular parallax reveals what this absolute magnitude is. This may then be used for later distance determinations of groups of stars which include some with this characteristic. The method is particularly useful if no example of the type of star is near enough for ordinary trigonometric distance determination.

There are other ways of combining the proper motions and radial velocities of stars to determine distances. These have contributed a great deal of fundamental data about the stars. The distances found trigonometrically and from the stellar motions, used to calibrate absolute magnitudes of stars of characteristics to be discussed in following sections, serve as the foundation for determination of distances far beyond what is observable by any geometrical effect.

THE SPECTRA OF STARS

After being gathered by the telescope the light from a star may be passed through a spectrograph and the spectrum recorded for subsequent examination. By the study of the spectrum of a star a great deal may be learned about the layer in which the light originates and the atmosphere through which it passes before it leaves the star. Both the continuous spectrum and the line spectrum yield information.

The Temperatures of Stars

The continuous spectrum of a star may be matched against the curve derived from Planck's law of radiation to derive a temperature for the star. The matching may be done by comparing the intensity of the radiation at two wave-lengths in the spectrum. The theoretical curve and its corresponding temperature which fits this ratio are then found. This process, carried out on the stellar spectrum, is comparable to measuring the magnitude of the star in two regions of the spectrum and determining a colour index. Thus it is that there is a close correspondence between the colour indices and surface temperatures.

For a cool star the ordinary colour index, found by subtracting the visual magnitude from the photographic magnitude, is about $1 \cdot 4$ and the temperature about $3,500°K$. Such a star would appear reddish to the eye. As we pass to hotter stars, the maximum of the energy moves in accordance with Wien's Law, from beyond the red at one end of the spectrum to shorter than the blue wave-lengths at the other. For a very hot star which appears blue the temperature might be about $25,000°K$ and the colour index near $-0 \cdot 3$.

The Spectrum Lines—Spectral Classes

The line spectrum of a star is also affected by its surface temperature. In a gas the energies, and velocities, of the particles are related to the temperature—the higher the temperature the greater the velocities. The lighter particles, such as atoms of hydrogen and helium, have higher velocities while the heavier ones move more slowly. Of course, all of the particles, even of the same kind, do not have the same velocity. There is a range of speed with a few having much more than average energy. The representative speed of the hydrogen molecules, which consist of two atoms, at a temperature of $273°K$—that of melting ice—is about 4,000 yards per second. The velocities increase in proportion to the square root of the temperature. They are five times as great for a temperature of $6,800°K$. Hence, as the temperature becomes higher, the collisions between the particles in a gas become more violent, while there is an increase in the proportion of the radiation in the more energetic short wave-length end of the spectrum.

The great diversity in the appearance of the line spectra of different stars is chiefly a function of the temperature although changes in pressure and differences in composition have effects of interest. The various aspects of the spectra form the basis of the classification of stellar spectra. To illustrate this: suppose the state of a gaseous mixture which, like that on the Sun, contains hydrogen, helium and small amounts of most of the other elements is considered in a series of stellar atmospheres of increasing temperature. This is justifiable because analysis of the stars by the method described for the Sun accords with a similar chemical constitution for many of the stars. At a temperature of 3,500°K the maximum of the radiation is in the red end of the spectrum and the energy of the particles and the radiation is not enough to break apart many combinations of atoms. So the spectrum is distinguished by absorption bands of molecules and the lines of metals for which not much energy is needed. In its lowest energy state the lines produced by hydrogen are in a region of the spectrum not observable through the atmosphere and at this temperature not enough hydrogen has been brought to a higher level for the accessible lines to be prominent, despite the abundance of this substance. Stars with these characteristics are called, depending on their peculiarities, class M or N. In class M, the more common, the bands of titanium oxide are strong, while in class N there is a predominance of those of carbon and cyanogen, a compound of carbon and nitrogen.

The temperature becomes higher in class K and higher still in class G. With the rising temperature and more energetic collisions owing to the greater speeds of the particles in the atmosphere, most of the molecules are broken apart and become less prominent in the spectrum. The lines of the metals become prominent, and in class G many of the atoms have electrons removed by the hurly-burly of the surroundings. Such an atom has a new set of energy states, the changes of which give rise to absorption of a set of lines different from those of the neutral atom. So it is that in the Sun, which is of class G, at a temperature of about 6,000°K the lines of ionized calcium appear strongly in the violet part of the spectrum.

Passing to the higher temperatures of classes F and A the lines due to the ionized atoms become important and the lines of hydrogen become the dominant feature of the line spectrum. At the temperatures, from 6,000°K to 11,000°K, reached in these classes a much greater proportion of the hydrogen atoms have acquired energy from a collision or by absorbing a quantum of light to bring them to a state from which they can produce the observable lines. So many of the atoms of the metals are ionized that the lines of neutral atoms are less prominent than those of the ionized atoms.

For higher temperatures, in class B, the removal of more electrons from the metallic atoms puts many of their lines in the ultraviolet, hydrogen is almost completely ionized and therefore unable to enter into energy changes that produce absorption lines, and the energy is sufficient to bring helium to a state where it can produce lines. Class O includes very hot stars in which even the very durable helium atoms have an electron knocked off, so that the lines of the ionized atom appear. Lines of other atoms which have lost several of their electrons are also present.

The transition along these classes in descending order of temperature O, B, A, F, G, K, M is continuous, and each spectral class is further divided. For example, the hottest members of the class A are called A0 and then in order A1 to A9. The letters were allotted before their present arrangement in a more natural physical order. When more description of the spectrum is needed, further letters may be added; for example, the letter "e" is added to a classification to indicate the presence of bright emission lines. The classes of stellar spectra are illustrated in Plate 31.

The temperature of a star may be estimated by considering, in relation to the spectrum lines, the extent of ionization of the various atoms and the energy needed to excite them to the states which are revealed. This may differ somewhat from the temperature obtained by matching its continuous spectrum to a Planck curve, for the atmosphere of a star is highly complex. The estimates found in different ways usually agree fairly well because the range of levels of the star in which the spectrum is produced is not very large. In Table 6 are given representative surface temperatures and colour indices for the various spectral classes.

TABLE 6

Spectral Class	Temperature	Colour Index
O5	70,000°K	−0·4
B5	23,000	−0·2
A5	11,000	+0·2
F5	7,600	+0·4
G5	6,000	+0·7
K5	4,500	+1·1
M5	3,000	+1·6

Distances from Spectra

There are some properties of stellar spectra which correlate with their absolute magnitudes and provide for determination of distances. Parallaxes found in this way are *spectroscopic parallaxes*. Stars of the same temperature and spectral class radiate nearly the same amount of energy per unit area. The brightness is proportional, therefore, to the area of the star. As is mentioned in the section on binary stars, the masses of the stars do not have the great range that exists for their energy output and size. Accordingly, large stars have a lower average density and a lower surface gravity, and the portion of the atmosphere of a giant, highly luminous star from which the light comes to us may be expected to be very tenuous. Hence spectrum lines which are sensitive to differences in density of the atmospheres in which they arise are useful as indicators of brightness, dividing the stars into luminosity classes. Lines of ionized calcium and strontium have been used in this way. When the density is low, and the star is a large bright one, there are fewer electrons present for recombination with ionized atoms such as produce the lines of calcium and strontium, which are therefore stronger than in the spectra of dwarf stars.

This characteristic may be exploited by comparing the strength of these lines with that of the lines of other atoms, such as iron, less affected by the tenuous environment. Effective ways have been found to obtain a good result by measuring directly the width in the spectrum of the ionized lines of calcium. When the absolute magnitude is known and the apparent magnitude measured, the distance is calculated from the equation given in the section on absolute magnitude. The result may be affected, as with all luminosity methods, by absorption of some of the light by material scattered in space between us and the star. This influences the measured magnitude, *m*. The interstellar matter is discussed in Chapter 10.

The Size of Stars

If the distance of a star is known, it is possible to calculate from the energy received at the telescope the total amount of radiation emitted by the star. Then, if the temperature has been found from observation, the radiation from unit area of the star's surface can be calculated by Stefan's Law (given in Chapter 3). Hence the area necessary to produce the total radiation is found and from that the star's radius.

If a bright star is red, and consequently radiates but little per unit area, it must be of great size and conversely if a star is faint and hot, it must be very small. These latter are called *white dwarfs*.

By the use of an instrument which collects the light from a star from points more widely separated than the diameter of any telescope, angular diameters of stars too small to be resolved by the telescope itself may be directly measured. The diameters of only a few stars have been measured in this way. Antares has a diameter more than 200 times that of the Sun, but the radius of the white dwarfs, far too small for any chance of measurement, can be only of the order of ten thousand miles, comparable with planetary dimensions. A modification of this instrument, near Narrabri in New South Wales, which is able to collect light from two places as far apart as 600 feet is being applied to measurement of stellar diameters. Apart from that of the Sun some other diameters are found from the study of eclipsing binary stars, discussed later in this chapter. When the radius of a star is actually measured the computation may be carried out in the reverse direction to find the *effective temperature* from Stefan's Law. The diameters so far measured conform as well as could be expected with those derived from distances and temperatures found from the spectra. The comparisons are of interest because they make trial of the extent to which the radiation from the stars conforms to that of the ideal body from which the radiation laws are derived.

VARIABLE STARS

Reasonably careful observation by only the naked eye of the brightness of the stars reveals that some of them vary in magnitude. The nova of Hipparchus has already been mentioned and Omicron Ceti (called Mira) was noticed to be variable in 1596. As a result of careful observation and deliberate searches nearly 15,000 variable stars are listed in the General Catalogue of Variable Stars and a good many thousands more are known or suspected. The naming of variable stars began before it was realised that so many would be found. If the star has no already existing designation the first variable found in a constellation is named R followed by the constellation name. The letters are used in order and when Z is reached two letter combinations are used after which the letter V followed by a number is adopted. Examples of this are T Tauri and RR Lyrae, which are important ones because they are type stars for two classes of variables. The nearest star, Proxima Centauri, being variable is called V645 Centauri.

Observing Variable Stars

When a star has been found to be variable it is desirable to keep it under observation at least for a period to see how its light varies. There are so many variables and so much work to do in this field that much is done by amateur astronomers for whom the work, some of which does not require expensive equipment, is well suited. A chart is prepared for the area of the sky around the variable, and stars, ranging in brightness between the faintest and brightest limits reached by the variable, are selected and their magnitudes accurately determined so that they can be used as standards. All that need be done then to determine the magnitude of the variable is to make a careful comparison with the calibrated stars. There are of course many variables for which the highest precision of photo-electric photometry is needed. By plotting the observed magnitudes on a graph called the *light curve* the character of the variation can be clearly visualised.

Classification of Variable Stars

By means of their light curves the variables are divided into classes so that when the curve of a particular star is known it can be listed among its fellows. The study of variable stars is of great importance, because the whole, or a large part, of the light from a star may be concentrated at one place on the sensitive material (either photographic or photo-electric), so that faint stars may be observed—fainter, for example, than with the spectrograph. The recognition of the type of a variable and its magnitude can, as we shall see, be made to yield information about the environment where it occurs, and close study of variables has helped towards the understanding of the structure of stars. The classification of variable stars depends firstly on whether the variations follow a regular pattern or are irregular, secondly on whether the cycle of variation has a short period, such as a day or so, or a long period such as several hundred days, and thirdly on well defined characteristics of the light curve itself. A brief account of some of those which play an important part in our story will be given, dealing first with the periodic variables. Stars whose light varies on account of eclipse by a companion star are better left until double stars are discussed.

Regular Variables

Cepheid variables are so named from Delta Cephei, the light curve of which is shown in Figure 43A. Its behaviour is typical of variables of this class. The period is about 5·4 days and the light varies through a range of 0·7 magnitude. These are representative of the most frequently occurring Cepheids although the periods range from a day to as much as fifty days.

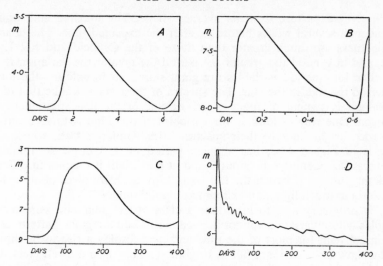

Figure 43.—Light curves of variable stars. A: δ Cephei; B: RR Lyrae; C: o Ceti, beginning about mid-1957; D: Nova Aquilae, 1918.

Usually the rise from minimum brightness to maximum is quicker than the fall although a small proportion of these stars have the two parts more nearly equal. The cycle of variation is almost invariably very regular and repeats year after year with very little change. The Cepheids are stars of great brightness and, as they can be recognised by their characteristic variation, they serve as landmarks at great distances in space.

W Virginis stars, or type II Cepheids, form a group of variables which in recent years have been separated from the "classical Cepheids". They occur typically in globular clusters where the stars have had a different history from those within many parts of the Milky Way. The stars in the globular clusters have different average characteristics and are said to belong to Population II. The W Virginis stars can be distinguished from ordinary Cepheids by the differences in the light curves and spectra, including the presence of emission lines.

The star RR Lyrae gives the name to another type of regular variables which was first found in globular clusters of stars and which until recently were called cluster-type variables, but now that many have been found outside clusters it is proper to change the name. Their periods range about half a day. RR Lyrae, whose light curve is shown in Figure 43B, has itself a period of 0·6 day and a range of variation of about 0·8 magnitude. The light curves of these variables are not so constant in shape as those of the classical Cepheids.

Long Period and Irregular Variables

The long period variables form a numerous class of stars most of which have periods between 150 and 500 days. The light curve of such a variable is subject to departure from its average shape. The maxima and minima may happen several weeks before or after the expected time. The changes in brightness are much greater than those of the Cepheid and RR Lyrae types, and in general the greater the period the greater the variation in the light. The long period variables are giant stars, red in colour—the longer the period the redder the star. The spectra of these stars, unlike that of the Sun which is typical of many stars, exhibit bright lines particularly of hydrogen. One way of looking for variables of this kind is to seek out red stars with bright lines in their spectra. Mira, Omicron Ceti, whose light curve is in Figure 43C, has a mean period of 330 days. At minimum brightness its magnitude is about 9 and at maximum it reaches in different cycles magnitudes between the third and fifth. So Mira gives about a hundred times as much light at maximum as at minimum.

It is necessary also to introduce a class of irregular and semi-regular variables whose variation cannot be made to fit into a regular pattern. Some remain constant for most of the time and then display a rise in brightness. Others show an occasional fall in brightness. They also are red stars. One example of this class is the bright red star Betelgeuse which varies by about a magnitude in brightness.

The space between stars is not empty of material, and there are places where gas and dust are much more prevalent. Such a patch is called a *nebula* and may be dark or, if there are very luminous stars near or within it, bright. Within nebulae occur variables of a class called T Tauri stars from its type star. The variations in brightness of these stars are very irregular with a range not so large as for other irregular variables. The nebulosity in which the star is involved may also be observed to vary in brightness, as does the nebula, known as NGC 1555, in which T Tauri itself is situated. This is a faint nebula, not easy to observe. The Great Nebula in Orion contains several T Tauri stars. The T Tauri stars often show emission lines in their spectra—they may well be stars recently formed from the material of the nebulae in which they occur and not yet settled down to a stable state.

The Nature of Stellar Variation

The regular, long-period and semi-regular variables and many of the irregular variables are shown by measures of their spectra to be pulsating in size. In the case of the regular variables there is a movement, by Doppler shift, of the spectrum lines, which change in a regular period exactly the same as that for the variation of the light. As the star expands with a movement of approach by the surface, the lines are shortened in wave-length and later, as the stellar atmosphere falls, the wave-lengths again become longer. The pulsation in the size of a Cepheid variable may amount to about 7 or 8 per cent. At the same time the temperature varies, being greatest at maximum light.

The pulsation with fixed period parallels the vibration of a weight held by a spring. If the star is expanding, it overshoots the equilibrium position and then is pulled back towards it until the expansion stops and the return movement starts. It then overshoots in the other direction, and so the oscillation goes on.

The long period variables, like Mira, are cool stars of spectral class M and temperature sometimes less than 3,000°K. The oscillation in the radius is somewhat more than for the Cepheids and in the temperature is several hundred degrees. Apart from the change of size and total radiation in accordance with Stefan's Law there is a shift of the maximum of the energy from the infra-red towards the visible when the temperature rises and this increases the observed variation of the light. Mira itself is one of the stars whose diameter has been measured. It is a giant with diameter more than 400 times that of the Sun.

Exploding Stars

The most spectacular variable stars are the *novae*. Occasionally a bright "new star" appears where none was prominent before. In a fair proportion of cases it is possible to find the faint pre-outburst star on some photographic record, and the change of brightness may be estimated. The rise is sudden and may be through ten to fifteen magnitudes corresponding to an increase in brightness of 10,000 times or more and sometimes much more as in the case of Nova Puppis 1942. The light then diminishes rapidly at first, and then more slowly so that the star fades back to obscurity. The light curve of Nova Aquilae 1918 is shown in Figure 43D. This star rose from magnitude 10·5 on June 5 to magnitude —1·1 on June 9. There are many novae found photographically which do not reach conspicuous naked-eye prominence.

The spectrum of a nova is complex, but consistent with the star having exploded and thrown off shelis of gas. There are dark absorption lines whose displacements towards the short wave-lengths indicate that the material in which they arise is moving towards us. As the expansion continues and some of the light comes directly from the shell of gas which has greatly expanded rather than from the original star, the bright line spectrum of the gas accompanies the absorption spectrum. The gas from which the bright lines are coming is expanding in all directions so that the lines are greatly broadened by the Doppler shifts from differing velocities. An absorption line arises only in the gas lying directly between us and the star, and so appears as a narrow line on the short wave side of the corresponding emission line. The displacement of the lines indicates high velocities of expansion, sometimes more than a thousand miles per second, and several times, after an interval, the actual expanding envelope has been observed photographically.

Some of the novae greatly exceed the usual type in brightness and, to judge by their spectra, in magnitude of the explosion. Their increase in brightness is several hundred times that of a normal nova although the shape of the light curve is similar. These are called *super-novae*. The novae observed by Tycho Brahe in 1572 and the one by Kepler in 1604 were super-novae.

The Crab Nebula is the expanding remnant of a super-nova observed in

China in 1054. The motions observed in points of this nebula are consistent with its origin from a star at that time. It has been recognised as a source of radio noise—the first to be so identified. Since its identification, several other expanding masses of gas have been found which may have begun their careers in this way. The most intense of all radio sources, Cassiopeia A, is a nebula in which different parts have relative velocities of several thousand miles per second. Analysis of the velocities indicates that the nebula originated in a super-nova explosion about 250 years ago.

Super-novae are not common and possibly only one outburst occurs in several hundred years in a whole system of stars. Nevertheless quite a few have been found by keeping watch on a number of systems of stars. The super-novae occur in at least two types with different light curves and different spectra. If the distance is known—as, for example, it is in the case of a super-nova which occurs in a star system of known distance—the actual brightness can be calculated. Type II super-novae give 2×10^8 times as much light as the Sun and type I ten times as much again with absolute magnitude about —20. The type I super-novae, the brightest of which might radiate in one day as much energy as the Sun does in ten million years, are among nature's truly awe-inspiring phenomena.

The super-novae, like the ordinary novae, eject material. This is known from their spectra which include emission lines from the shell of gas thrown out from the star. The type II super-novae have spectra similar to those of ordinary novae but displaying greater energy. The Doppler shifts of the spectrum lines indicate ejection velocities of more than 3,000 miles per second. The spectra of the super-novae of type I are not yet satisfactorily explained.

Distances Determined from Variable Stars

Since the light curve of a variable star affords a signature by which it can be classified wherever it may be observed, it is natural that such stars should have come to be used as indicators of distance—especially as some of them are very bright, making them accessible to observation even when they are far away.

A fundamentally important step in the development of luminosity methods of finding distance occurred early in this century when Henrietta Leavitt found, in investigating a number of Cepheid variables in the Small Magellanic Cloud, that those of like period have the same apparent magnitude. As these belong to the same structure, their distances must differ but little and their absolute magnitudes also must be the same. There is a relationship between the brightness and the period of the variation. The stars of longer period are brighter. The conclusion is that wherever such a star is found, once the distances of some of the stars are known so as to provide a calibration of the curve connecting period with luminosity, its distance can be derived.

The RR Lyrae variables which are often present in globular clusters of stars also have a similar property. When a number of them occur in a cluster, they have the same magnitude and it is concluded that they have nearly the same luminosity wherever they occur.

No Cepheids or RR Lyrae stars are near enough for distances to be found by direct triangulation, and so distances, for calibration purposes, must be found by study of their proper motions and radial velocities. The determination is made difficult by uncertainty in the absorption of light by the material in interstellar space. The relation between period and luminosity turns out not to be so simple as was suspected before it was realised that more than one class of star, and consequently more than one period-luminosity curve, is present. The classical Cepheids are about 1·5 magnitude brighter than the W Virginis stars of the same period. The classical Cepheids range in absolute magnitude from about —2·5 for periods around three days to —5 for a 40-day period. Such bright stars are observable even when they are very remote. The foundations for the measurement of great distances depend on observations of the Cepheids. The RR Lyrae variables have absolute magnitude about 0·5 and so are a good deal fainter than the Cepheids. They are nevertheless very valuable indicators of distance for they are among the more common types of variable stars and are widely distributed.

BINARY STARS

The telescope reveals that many stars which appear single to the naked eye really consist of two components. Some of the bright stars—among them Sirius, Castor and α Centauri—have two components, and surveys carried out for the purpose have revealed about 64,000 such *double stars*. Large telescopes are able to resolve closer pairs. Of the stars brighter than ninth magnitude about one star in eighteen can be resolved and of the naked-eye stars about one in nine. Of course, if the stars were scattered at random in space, two would occasionally lie in nearly the same direction and form a double star only because they are situated so near the same line of sight. The fact that there are far more double stars than could be explained in this way shows that most pairs must be physically associated. This is further confirmed because the great majority of pairs have common proper motion across the sky, and because the proportion of doubles increases as the observable distance between them is diminished by the use of larger telescopes. The doubles are therefore usually true *binary stars* which are close together in space. Multiple stars also are not uncommon. As a rule, a triple star consists of a close pair with a more distant companion, or a quadruple star of two widely separated close pairs.

The study of binary stars yields valuable information about the properties of stars. Since the components revolve about one another under their mutual gravitational attraction, they have orbits, which may sometimes be determined from observation and analysed to determine stellar masses and, in some cases, distances and dimensions. There are methods other than direct telescopic examination that enable binary stars to be revealed and studied. They can be discussed according to the observational method, which provides the data from which, in turn, the orbits and characteristics of the stars may be found.

Visual Binaries

The binary stars which are observed as double in the telescope are called *visual binaries*. An observation of a visual binary star consists in measuring the angular distance between the components and the direction of the companion, the fainter star, relative to the primary, the brighter, taken from a fixed direction through the star towards the North Celestial Pole. This direction is easily distinguished because the star drifts towards the west if the drive of the telescope is stopped and the northerly direction is 90° away. Such measures may be made and plotted for widely different times.

To interpret the motion allowance must be made for the fact that usually we do not look straight down on the plane of the orbit, and the shape of the plotted curve is the projection of the true orbit perpendicular to the line of sight. The revolution of the components about their common centre of gravity is controlled by the same law of gravity which governs the motions of the planets about the Sun. So the movement of the companion about the primary is in an ellipse in which Kepler's laws are obeyed, and, if the motion is sufficient, continued observation makes it possible to solve the problem of finding a satisfactory true orbit in accordance with Kepler. The orbital motion is in most cases so slow that it is not revealed by the observations made in the few decades that may have passed since the discovery of the binary. However, about one eighth of the visual binaries show measurable motion about one another, and in about 300 cases a sufficient arc has been observed to enable a determination of an orbit to represent the relative motion. Of the visual binary stars whose orbits are calculated only about two hundred are allotted periods under 200 years, and a fair proportion even of these must be classed as poorly determined. Figure 44 shows the apparent orbit of the companion of Sirius about the bright primary.

If the distance of the star is not known, the size of the orbit—that is, the length of the long axis of the ellipse—must remain in the units of angle in which it is measured. If the distance is known to be d light-years and half the length of the ellipse appears as a seconds of arc, then its length in terms of the distance of the Earth from the Sun is $l = a\,d/3 \cdot 26$ and the law of gravitation enables the mass of the double star to be calculated in the same way as explained in Chapter 5 for the masses of the planets with satellites. The work on binary stars has importance because of this. If m and M are the masses of the two components in terms of the Sun's mass as unit and P the period of revolution in years, the sum of the masses is given by $(m + M)P^2 = l^3$. If the separate motions of the components of a double star can be observed against the background of the stars so that the distance of the centre of gravity of the system from each star is known, then the masses can be determined separately. The masses generally are of the same order as that of the Sun, being rarely less than a tenth of, or more than twenty times, that of the Sun.

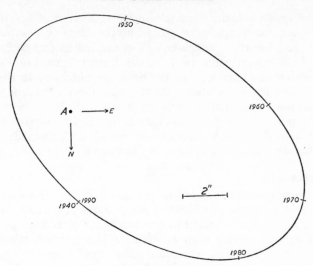

Figure 44.—The orbit of Sirius.

Spectroscopic Binaries

Binary stars may also be observed spectroscopically because, as the radial velocity of each component varies during the orbital motion, unless the plane of the motion is at right angles to the line of sight, the Doppler shift of the spectral lines permits the velocity at different parts of the orbit to be measured. This renders possible the discovery and observation of binary stars which are so close together that there is no chance of their being seen visually as double. These *spectroscopic binary* stars are not uncommon. About a fifth of the stars show variable velocity, mostly due to origin of the light in a binary system and the proportion is higher for hot blue stars. For such binaries the lines of the spectrum of each component—although most commonly only one spectrum may be observable—oscillate backwards and forwards with the period of the revolution. Usually the stars are much closer together than is the case with the visual binaries since with bodies close together the velocities, and their changes, are greater and occur more quickly and so their detection and observation are easier. As a consequence periods of the order of a few days are common and some stars complete a revolution in less than a day.

If the velocity is determined on a number of occasions spread over the period most of the characteristics of the orbit can be calculated giving, by the use of the laws of motion, information about the masses. Since it is not possible by analysing the radial velocities alone to distinguish between a change in the size of the orbit and a change in its inclination to the line of sight the information is not complete, but it is useful for statistical analysis. The revealed range of mass of stars is increased by these observations but only the most massive stars appear to have masses more than 50 times that of the Sun.

L

Since the radial velocities are measured in kilometres per second, the solution of the spectroscopic orbit problem gives the distances moved in the line of sight in kilometres, which can be converted to any desired unit. If spectra of both components of a visual binary have been sufficiently observed the actual dimensions of the orbit are obtained. In the equation $l = a\,d/3\cdot26$ of the last section l comes from the spectroscopic observations, a from the visual, and the only unknown is the distance d; and since the variable part of the two velocities is inversely proportional to the masses, the individual masses can also be found. Unfortunately such complete information is available in only very few cases.

Eclipsing Binaries

Binary stars may be revealed in yet another way. If we in the solar system are near the plane in which the components of a binary are moving, it is possible for each component to come between us and the other, giving rise to two eclipses during each revolution. The eclipses, which may be partial, annular or total, cause unequal reductions in the magnitude unless the two stars have the same surface brightness. The first discovered of these *eclipsing binaries* was the variable star Beta Persei (Algol). Such stars, of which many are now known, are studied by forming light curves in the same way as is done for other variables. Analysis of the light curve yields information about the orbit and about the component stars. The duration of the eclipses in relation to the whole period depends on the relation of the respective sizes of the stars to the dimensions of the orbit. The relative sizes may be determined even though the problem is complicated by the necessity of finding some other information about the orbit, such as its inclination to the line of sight, by which the analysis is affected. If spectroscopic observations of the velocities are available, the dimensions in terms of those of the orbit may be transformed into kilometres, as in the similar application to the dimensions of visual binaries. Then, too, the distribution of light over the surface of the stars can be investigated since during the progress of an eclipse different parts of the area of the eclipsed star are covered providing for a kind of sampling over the surface. This is unique information, for no star other than the Sun presents an extended surface to us.

The kind of information found from the light curve of an eclipsing binary may be illustrated by considering that of Algol (Figure 45). The period is $2\cdot9$ days. One component is brighter than the other by about $1\cdot5$ magnitude and its eclipse produces a deeper drop in the brightness. The fact that the brightness is not constant away from the time of eclipse shows that the stars are elongated by the tidal force that each exerts on the other. As the side of the fainter component facing towards the more luminous one is hotter and brighter than the rest of the star, the maximum brightness occurs just away from the lesser eclipse when this bright patch is facing us. The radius of the brighter component is $0\cdot22$ that of the relative orbit while that of the fainter—and larger and cooler—component is $0\cdot24$. Spectroscopic observation shows the radius of the relative orbit to be $15\cdot7$

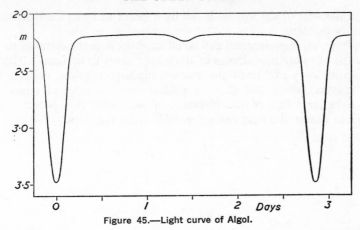

Figure 45.—Light curve of Algol.

times the radius of the Sun, and so the radii of the component stars are respectively $3 \cdot 6$ and $3 \cdot 8$ times that of the Sun. The mass of the brighter component is five times, and of the fainter one equal to, that of the Sun. It is interesting that so much can be discovered—and, of course, there is yet more known—about a system that can always be seen only as a point of light. There are, for example, changes in the period and corresponding complexities of the orbital motion, which are probably due to perturbations from at least one additional companion.

Information Derived from Binary Stars

The information on the dimensions, masses and distances of stars and on the surface distribution of their light is of great value. We depend entirely on double star data for our knowledge of stellar masses. When the masses of stars are plotted against their absolute magnitudes, most of the points lie on a smooth curve which defines the *mass-luminosity relation*. This relation accords with the theories of structure of most of the stars which are built on the same model as the Sun. There are stars which are not on this model, an example being the dwarf companion of Sirius which is discussed in Chapter 12, and the points for these do not lie on the curve. The luminosities of the stars have a much wider range than their masses, and an increase in mass in going from one star to another is accompanied by a much greater increase in brightness. A star ten times as massive as the Sun would give more than six hundred times as much light.

The distance obtained for a binary from a combination of the visual and spectroscopic data is usually better than could otherwise be obtained. By combining the equations given in the section on visual binaries with the mass-luminosity relation *dynamical parallaxes* are derived. First an estimate of the sum of the masses is placed in the equation $(m + M)P^2 = l^3$ from which l is obtained and placed in the relation $l = a \, d/3 \cdot 26$ to find d. This distance is likely to be a fair approximation because the range of mass is not so very wide and because the distance depends on taking a cube root;

so that if the sum of the masses is out by a factor of three the distance is in error by 44 per cent.

However, an improvement can be effected because the distance so found enables the absolute magnitudes of the components to be found. The absolute magnitudes yield, from the mass-luminosity relation, revised values of the masses, which can then be placed into the original equations to obtain a better value of the distance. If necessary this process can be repeated to obtain the best value derivable from the data.

9

POPULATIONS OF STARS

IN the previous chapter, dealing with the ways of collecting information about the stars, the observations that can be made and the interpretation of these observations, the stars were thought of as individuals. Now it is time to consider the characteristics of "populations" of stars—that is, stars when regarded in great numbers—to find what range they have in the properties of mass, brightness, size and temperature, to inquire about the nature of correlations between the properties, and to examine how the stars are distributed in space. Additional information is derived from our observations and combined with what is known of the structure of stars and the way in which they derive their energy to unfold the life story of the stars.

The Nearest Stars

If a population which has many members is to be examined, it is usual to take a sample from which the properties of the whole population may be inferred. Samples of stars will usually appear different if selected in different ways. If, for example, all stars to a limit of apparent brightness are taken, it would be natural to expect the collection to contain more than a fair share of intrinsically very bright stars. Because the extremely bright stars still appear bright enough for inclusion even from great distances, the sample would include them over a much larger volume of space and reject all except the close ones among the intrinsically faint stars.

A first sample, representative of the stellar population, may be given by the stars within 16 light-years of the Sun. The collection within this volume is more nearly complete than for any other volume in space and the information on the individual stars more satisfactory. There are about 50 stars on this sample, uncertainty in the distance making it impossible in some cases to say whether the star is just inside or just outside the boundary. Among the stars there are two triples and eight doubles each component of which has been counted separately in the fifty; so the sample contains a fair quota of multiple stars. Only six of these nearby stars are visible to the naked eye and only two, Sirius and Procyon, are intrinsically much brighter than the Sun. So is Altair which appears to be just outside the sixteen light-year distance. The brighter component of the double star Alpha Centauri gives off about the same amount of light as the Sun.

Most of the stars in the volume are red stars of spectral class M and intrinsically much fainter than the Sun. About a quarter show emission lines in their spectra. The faintest one is Wolf 359 which has an absolute magnitude $+16 \cdot 6$ and gives less than 1/40,000 as much light as the Sun, the absolute magnitude of which is $+4 \cdot 7$. There are several known stars which are even fainter than this.

As would be expected these close stars invariably have an appreciable proper motion across the sky, and often their distance has been measured only after their motion has drawn attention to them. Barnard's Star, 6 light-years away, has the greatest known proper motion. Two of the stars, Wolf 359 and Proxima Centauri, are flare stars whose brightness occasionally increases suddenly for only a few minutes. About a quarter of the stars have a velocity several times that of the Sun's motion mentioned in a previous section. This is what might be expected. Stars mingling for long ages among their fellows in space, with occasional gravitational interaction, would tend to have more or less equal energies. So the less massive ones, like most of those in the sample, would tend to have higher velocities.

Unseen companions of a star which is not too distant can be looked for by careful measurements of the proper motion. The gravitational attraction of the unseen companion, acting in different directions at different parts of the orbit, causes the visible star to trace a slightly wavy path across the sky rather than a straight one. Observations of this kind have revealed invisible companions of several stars in the volume of space under consideration. None of these companions is small enough to rate certainly as a planet, and indeed the test is too insensitive to reveal anything of Jupiter's size even for such close stars.

TABLE 7

Stars Nearer than Ten Light-Years

Name	R.A.		Dec.	m	d	M	Sp	Mass
	h	m	o					
Sun				$-26 \cdot 9$		$4 \cdot 7$	G0	$1 \cdot 0$
Proxima Cen.	14	27	$-62 \cdot 5$	$11 \cdot 3$	$4 \cdot 3$	$15 \cdot 7$	Me	
Alpha Cen. A	14	36	$-60 \cdot 6$	$0 \cdot 3$	$4 \cdot 3$	$4 \cdot 7$	G0	$1 \cdot 1$
B	,,	,,	,,	$1 \cdot 7$	,,	$6 \cdot 1$	K5	$0 \cdot 9$
Barnard's Star	17	55	$+ 4 \cdot 5$	$9 \cdot 5$	$6 \cdot 0$	$13 \cdot 2$	M5	
Wolf 359	10	54	$+ 7 \cdot 3$	$13 \cdot 5$	$7 \cdot 7$	$16 \cdot 6$	M6e	
Luyten 726—8A	1	36	$-18 \cdot 2$	$12 \cdot 5$	$7 \cdot 9$	$15 \cdot 6$	M6e	
B	,,	,,	,,	$13 \cdot 0$	,,	$16 \cdot 1$	M6e	
Lalande 21185	11	0	$+36 \cdot 3$	$7 \cdot 5$	$8 \cdot 2$	$10 \cdot 5$	M2	
Sirius A	6	43	$-16 \cdot 6$	$-1 \cdot 6$	$8 \cdot 7$	$1 \cdot 3$	A0	$2 \cdot 3$
B	,,	,,	,,	$7 \cdot 1$	,,	$10 \cdot 0$		$1 \cdot 0$
Ross 154	18	48	$-23 \cdot 9$	$10 \cdot 6$	$9 \cdot 3$	$13 \cdot 3$	M5e	

The columns of the Table give the right ascension, declination, visual magnitude, distance in light-years, absolute magnitude, spectrum and mass with the Sun's mass as unit.

This sample of stars is too small for us to imagine that it tells a great deal about the multitudinous population of the stars about us, but surely any property of the stars which can be mentioned twice—as with the flaring of faint stars—in so small a number must be common in the universe. Surely, too, the sample gives a truer picture of the predominant number of intrinsically faint objects than would appear in any other way.

Table 7 is a short list which shows information for the stars within ten light-years.

The Luminosity Function

Figure 46 is designed to show the number of stars of various absolute magnitudes in a million cubic light-years in our neighbourhood of space. Thus, the average number of stars having absolute magnitudes between 7·5 and 8·5 in this volume is 130—the height of the step in the graph

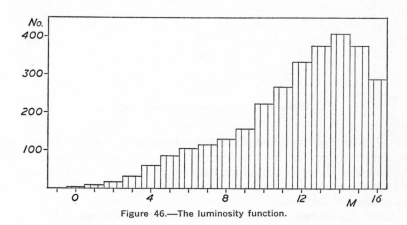

Figure 46.—The luminosity function.

over the 8. The figure relies, for faint stars, on more extensive compilation depending on direct measurement of distance; but for the bright stars, which must be estimated from a great volume of space, the information must depend on data from the whole battery of distance-measuring methods. This display of the distribution of the stellar population, whether in a graph like this or in a table, is called the *luminosity function*. For stars of the very faintest absolute magnitudes which are difficult to find, the figures may be unreliable. It does show that space holds relatively few stars more than a hundred times as bright as the Sun and many a thousand times fainter. There is no star with negative absolute magnitude among the 50 nearest stars, for the closest one is Arcturus, 36 light-years distant, with $M = -0 \cdot 2$. Even so, working from information of this sort, it is found that most of the light of the universe comes from the stars which are giants in brightness. On the other hand, much of the mass resides in the faint dwarf stars.

The Hertzsprung-Russell Diagram

A great deal may be learned about stars by plotting their spectral classes and absolute magnitudes on a diagram like Figure 47 which was formed from lists of the nearest stars and the brightest stars. In this Figure the

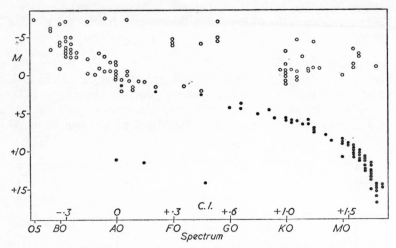

Figure 47.—The Hertzsprung-Russell diagram.

vertical scale represents the absolute magnitudes and the horizontal scale the spectral type. The information for the nearer stars is represented by black dots and for the brighter naked-eye stars by small circles. The diagram is called, after the two astronomers who originated it, the *Hertzsprung-Russell diagram*.

Since the colours of the stars, as already shown, are related to the spectra and may be more easily available they are used often on the horizontal scale instead of spectral types. In this case the plot may be called a *colour-magnitude diagram*. For stars of known distance the colours which represent the spectral classes and temperatures and the absolute magnitudes are the most directly accessible intrinsic properties of the stars. However, the diagram can still be plotted for stars which lie in a restricted volume of space even if the distance is not known. For example, in a cluster of the kind discussed in the next section, the stars may be taken to lie at a common distance, so that if the apparent magnitudes are used on the vertical scale the diagram will have just the same form, except for graduation of this scale, as if absolute magnitudes had been used. In preparing Figure 47 the magnitudes were visual and the colour indices were given by blue minus visual magnitudes.

The points which represent the stars on the Hertzsprung-Russell diagram do not lie at random but form a pattern whose shape depends on the history of the stellar population to which they belong. Hence diagrams of this kind, exhibiting the relation between the temperature and brightness of a star, constitute a powerful device for research. They give useful information on the classification of samples of stars and provide basic data for the study of the evolution of stars and determination of stellar distances.

A feature of the Hertzsprung-Russell diagram in Figure 47—which is fairly representative of the stellar population near the Sun—is that the points representing the stars lie most frequently along a line running downward from left to right on the page, from very bright hot stars to cool faint ones. This is called the *main sequence*. Convenient classifying names are given to stars according to the location of their representative points on the H-R diagram. Stars of absolute magnitude about 0 are called *giants* and those of absolute magnitude —5 or brighter are *super-giants*. Above the main sequence are the red giants which correspond in spectrum with stars of low brightness on the main sequence but are still giants in magnitude. Below the main sequence are the *sub-dwarfs*—which are white dwarfs if they are hot and lie to the left in the diagram.

CLUSTERS OF STARS

The stars are by no means uniformly distributed in space and there are places where they are crowded together. Some of these *clusters*, positions of which are given in Chapter 12, are easily visible to the naked eye. The Pleiades form one in which some of the brightest stars may be seen individually with the naked eye, and Praesepe is resolved in binoculars. Along the Milky Way there are many hazy patches of light which are resolved into stars when examined telescopically.

Types of Clusters

There are two different types of clusters. The *globular clusters*, so called because of their shape, are very densely packed clusters which contain enormous numbers of stars. The *galactic clusters*, so called because of their occurrence along the Milky Way, are less closely packed aggregates of stars, often hard to distinguish among the hosts of stars which may merely lie in the same direction. They are also called loose or open clusters. A globular cluster is illustrated in Plate 29 and an open cluster in Plate 32.

More than a hundred globular clusters are known, not counting those identified in distant star systems, and their number does not tend to increase much as time passes as they have been fairly easy to distinguish against the background of the stars, if they can be seen at all. About 600 galactic clusters are known. The study of star clusters has played an important part in the progress of knowledge about stars and their evolution.

The number of stars in a cluster may be obtained by counting the stars in areas, possibly bounded by concentric circles, in the region of the cluster. The area of the cluster is taken to lie in those parts where the average number for the surrounding area is exceeded, and the excess of stars above the average is taken as the number of stars in the cluster. This process does not indicate which stars are actually members of the cluster, but merely reveals its extent and the number of stars it contains.

An attempt may be made to distinguish the stars which belong to the cluster in two ways. The proper motion of the stars in the vicinity may be found by accurate measurements of photographic plates taken at widely separated times. It may happen that a group of stars centred on the cluster has moved, in the interval between the two photographs, in a way sufficiently different from the motion of the background stars to form a distinguishing mark. Stars whose motions correspond to this are taken to be cluster members. Of course the proper motions measured are relative to neighbouring non-cluster stars and the method may still be applied even if the cluster is very distant. In such a case it is more natural to regard the motions as belonging to the field stars which would mostly be nearer than the cluster. The other method of sorting consists in plotting the colour-magnitude diagram for the stars in the area. It will be found that the stars of the cluster lie near well-defined lines of the diagram, and this distinguishes them from background stars which do not conform. Even so mistakes may be made in particular cases because a non-cluster member may imitate the proper motion or a colour-magnitude position normal for the cluster.

The same techniques distinguish aggregates of stars which do not appear as clusters. If O- and B-type stars or T Tauri variable stars are plotted over large areas of the sky, they are found to show regions of concentration called *associations*. These stars are interspersed among the other stars. They are not sufficient in number to make much difference to the total numbers within various volumes and would not be found without the preliminary selection of type. Several groups of scattered stars are shown by measures of their proper motions and radial velocities to have remarkably similar motions through space. The famous examples are in Ursa Major, the Hyades in Taurus and a group distributed through the constellations Scorpius and Centaurus. These are the *moving clusters*.

The galactic clusters commonly contain just a few hundred stars, but the number may be as low as a score or as much as many hundreds. The globular clusters, however, commonly contain tens of thousands of stars, and the richest ones several hundred thousands. So rich in stars are the globular clusters that this is one barrier to investigating them since any photographic exposure long enough to show faint stars is so over-exposed at the centre of the cluster that the stars cannot be seen as individuals. Accordingly many studies refer to the outer parts.

Distances of Clusters

The moving clusters provide another geometrical method of finding distances of stars. The parallel paths converge towards the point of the sky which lies in the direction towards which the stars are moving, or diverge if the motion is towards us. This is the same perspective effect that was mentioned in the case of meteor showers. The convergent point is determined by measuring the proper motions of the stars and finding the point of the sky towards which they are converging.

The basis of the distance measurement is explained by the aid of

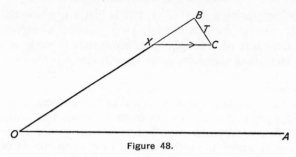

Figure 48.

Figure 48 in which O is the place of the observer, OA the direction of the convergent point and OX the direction of the star. XB represents the radial velocity of the star and XC, parallel to OA, its motion in space. Then the geometry of the triangle XBC gives the transverse velocity T, which may be expressed in kilometres per year. If μ is the proper motion in seconds of arc per year, d the distance in light-years, f a factor for changing light-years to kilometres and F a factor for converting radians to seconds of arc, the following relation holds,

$$\mu = \frac{TF}{df}$$

in which the only unknown is the distance d.

Most clusters are too far away for parallax measurement by a geometrical method and so the distances are found by examination of their stars. Stars of known absolute magnitude M are sought. RR Lyrae stars are often present in globular clusters, and sometimes a galactic cluster contains type I Cepheids. An observation of the apparent magnitude m then gives a value of $m–M$ and hence of the distance. If the colour-magnitude array of the cluster is observed with apparent magnitude on the vertical scale it can be seen how much this scale must be altered to make the values correspond to absolute magnitudes of a standard colour-magnitude diagram, and this value of $m–M$ in the formula given in the section on measuring distance discloses how far away the cluster lies. The result may be affected by absorption of the light by material in interstellar space. This would make the stars of the cluster appear fainter and give a falsely large estimate of the distance. When several different ways of finding the distance of a cluster are available a valuable opportunity occurs for making a comparison of the methods.

When the distance and the angular size of a star cluster have been found by the methods outlined, an easy multiplication gives the actual size of the cluster in any unit as in the case of the planets. The galactic clusters commonly range in size from 10 to 60 light-years across, while the globular clusters range from 80 to 300 light-years. Once the dimensions and the number of stars have been found, the number of stars in each unit of volume or the average distance between the stars can be estimated. In a galactic cluster the mean distance between stars may be of the order of four light-years. This figure varies a great deal, but is given to show the amount of crowding that goes to make a cluster. In a globular cluster the distances would be of the order of one light-year. Even here there is so much space between the stars that collisions must be extremely rare.

Stability of Clusters

An interesting question arises in regard to star clusters. Are they stable? Do they endure for very long periods even with the time scales that apply to astronomy, or are they but brief features of the stellar scene? Each star of a cluster moves under the influence not only of members of the cluster but also of other bodies outside it. It is obvious that these outside forces may tend to pull a cluster apart. The clusters are situated in a vast system of stars. The stars in the part of the cluster nearer the centre of the system are more attracted than the outer ones, and so there are forces, somewhat parallel to those which raise tides on the Earth, which tend to disrupt the clusters. Within the cluster itself close encounters between stars could occasionally give one of them enough velocity to enable it to escape from the cluster. Non-cluster members must pass through the cluster and while the distances between stars, even in a cluster, are large enough for this usually to happen without much result, it must occasionally happen that the intruder gives enough energy to a member of the cluster to separate it from its fellows.

Against these forces the mass of the cluster itself is working to hold it together. Which will prevail? Obviously a very dense cluster with large total mass is in a better condition to survive and the globular clusters are thought to be so stable that they must lose only a small proportion of their member stars even in thousands of millions of years. At the other end of the scale the stellar associations have no claim to stability. A galactic cluster like the Pleiades would be fairly stable, while a loose cluster like the Hyades—which includes most of the stars in the A-shaped group in Taurus—is much less so, as it is spread over such a volume that it must contain more than a score of non-cluster stars.

Stellar Population Types

The important idea of types of stellar populations can be introduced through the star clusters although it arose in a different connection from the study of galaxies by Walter Baade. When the Hertzsprung-Russell (or colour-magnitude) diagram of the member stars of a globular cluster is drawn, the lines along which the points for the stars lie have taken a shape different from that for the stars in the vicinity of the Sun. In Figure 49 are shown the shapes of the lines for the two kinds of population. The region filled in by dots corresponds to the pattern given by the stars in the neighbourhood of the Sun. Such a population is called *population I*. The hatched region shows the type of the colour-magnitude diagram on which lie the points for the stars of a globular cluster such as the cluster M3 in Canes Venatici. Groups which give this pattern are said to be of *population II*.

Although the division of space into regions of population I and of

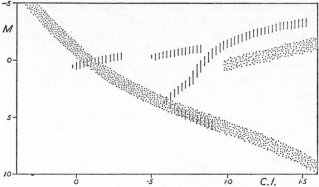

Figure 49.—Colour-magnitude diagrams for population-types I and II.

population II cannot be made as simply as may at first have been hoped, the conception has proved very suggestive of ideas on the structure of star systems and on the evolution of stars. There are fundamental differences between the characteristics of apparently similar stars in the two types of region. For example, the type I Cepheid variables appear to be more than a magnitude brighter than those in population type II, as was mentioned in the section on star distances. Population I is characterised by the presence of very luminous hot stars and of interstellar matter. The type II stellar population is characterised by the absence of hot super-giant stars.

THE INTERNAL CONSTITUTION OF STARS

The inside of a star, being completely inaccessible to observation, can be investigated only by applying such knowledge as we have of the physical laws which govern the behaviour of matter in the state it must have in the deep interior of a star. The model constructed by using the theory must be one which on the outside conforms to the observational data on masses, surface temperatures and luminosities. It is not possible to explain in short space how the structure of a star is derived, but the factors which need to be taken into account can be outlined to show that it is a problem which is amenable to treatment.

The stars are usually stable. They do not rapidly contract or expand. (Stars which vary or collapse or explode require special discussion, not given here.) So the forces in the interior of a star must be regarded as being in equilibrium, the portions having no tendency to move upward or downward. Part of a layer of the material within a star is shown diagrammatically in Figure 50. The first force to consider is gravitation which is the force which holds the star together and causes it to contract if the balancing forces are not sufficient. This, for each unit of mass in the layer, is proportional to the mass, that is, the average density and volume, of the material closer to the centre of the star and inversely proportional to the square of the radius of the layer.

The next force is the difference between the upward pressure of the material below the layer and the downward pressure from above. The law which enables the force to be calculated from the density and temperature of the material depends on the state of the material. It is simpler if the material is gaseous, and, at the great temperatures which prevail inside a star, the material behaves as a gas despite the great pressures and densities that occur.

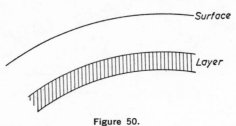

Figure 50.

The gas equation which may be used for calculating the pressure p, of a gas of density d, and temperature T in degrees Kelvin is $p = RdT/m$, where R is a constant of nature for all gases and m is the average mass of the gas particles present. It would seem that the chemical composition of the stars, through the value of m, should therefore make a difference to their structure. This does not produce the difficulties in the theory that might appear, since at the high temperatures which prevail the electrons around each atomic nucleus are torn off and distributed in the gas. For many of the common atoms this yields about the same average weight for the particles, nearly twice that of a hydrogen atom. For example, calcium, whose atom has a weight forty times that of hydrogen and has 20 electrons around its nucleus, breaks into 21 particles. The exceptions are hydrogen for which $m = 0 \cdot 5$ and helium of atomic weight four which breaks to three particles, this giving $m = 1 \cdot 3$. Thus, given the ratio of hydrogen to helium and the proportion, which turns out to be small, of the other elements the pressure can be calculated from the gas equation. Obviously for the layer of the star to be supported the pressure must increase inward and this implies, according to the gas equation, that the density or the temperature must increase towards the centre of the star. Actually the computations show that both do so. Another force which has an effect in some very bright stars is the pressure of the amount of radiation present. This too tends to hold the layer upward.

The transport of energy which, in accordance with the second law of thermodynamics, is in the direction of decreasing temperature—that is, outward through the layers of the star—is another factor that has to be taken into account. If the star is to be stable, the energy which enters the bottom of any layer plus what is produced in the layer must equal what leaves the top of the layer; and finally, at the surface, this must equal the total radiation of the star. If this were not so, the layer would heat up or cool down and a change of state of the star would ensue.

The energy may be transferred in either, or both, of two ways. It may be carried by the radiation which, at temperatures within a star, is present with a very high intensity. In this case however the energy does not flow through the star at a velocity near that of light, as it does, for example, in the Earth's atmosphere, but is absorbed and re-emitted or deflected many times per second by the material through which it has to flow. One part of the calculation for each level in the star is to find from the temperature and density of the gas and from its chemical composition how opaque the material is to the radiation present. The other way for the energy to be transferred is by convection, the actual inter-mixing of material of different layers to transfer the energy outward into the cooler layers of the star. This, for the greater part of a star, is usually less important. The way in which the energy is generated affects the problem too.

It is naturally a formidable problem to set up and solve the equations to satisfy all of these conditions and to give a structure which conforms to the observed conditions on the outside of the star. The boundary condition that the pressure is zero at the surface of the star must be satisfied, and the mass, luminosity and radius must agree with the observations. The mass-luminosity relation mentioned in the previous chapter is in general accord with the theory, with some dependence also on chemical composition. The theory of stellar interiors has been the work of a line of astrophysicists, the great pioneer being Eddington. In recent years electronic calculating machines have played a part in making the necessary calculations.

Of the mass of a star like the Sun only about two per cent consists of elements other than hydrogen and helium, and of the remainder three-quarters is hydrogen and a quarter helium. The temperature at the centre of the Sun works out to be about $14,000,000K°$ and the density about a hundred times that of water, seventy times the mean density for the whole Sun, and the pressure of the order of 10^{11} times that of the Earth's atmosphere. These may be regarded as representative of the conditions at the centres of stars. The very hot B stars of the main sequence would be hotter at the centre, while the M stars would be cooler. A star which contained less hydrogen, and hence had a higher mean molecular weight, would also have a higher temperature near the centre.

The Source of Stellar Energy

The source of the energy of stars was for long a mystery. The great outpouring of the Sun has already been emphasized and it has been shown that many stars radiate far more. The energy which could be provided by chemical change, as in the burning of fuels like coal or oil, was known to be quite inadequate. It could not possibly provide the energy to keep the Sun shining, as geological evidence indicates, through ages comparable with the age of the Earth; and in any case the temperatures are too high for the necessary chemical changes to occur. The gravitational energy, derived from the contraction of a star by its own gravitational pull with consequent increases in pressure and temperature, was suggested as a possible source. Neither would this provide enough energy, although it does seem that at some stages in its development each star derives its energy from such contraction.

As a consequence of the theory of relativity, Einstein showed that energy and matter should be related by the formula $E = mc^2$ where E is the energy equivalent to the mass m and c is the velocity of light. This shows that enormous amounts of energy are made available by the conversion to energy of comparatively small amounts of matter. The destruction of matter at the rate of one ounce per second would liberate energy at the rate of more than three-million-million horsepower, which is many times the power production of the whole world. Atomic explosions are based on this rapid destruction of comparatively small amounts of mass. It was soon agreed that the energy of the Sun and the other stars must come from some process by which mass is annihilated in their intensely hot interiors, but knowledge of processes by which this might occur had to await the development of an understanding of the structure of atoms.

At the speeds associated with ordinary temperatures, the electric charges on the nuclei of atoms are sufficient to repel one another to prevent their union. This effect is greater for the heavier atoms which have greater charges on their nuclei. At stellar centres, where the temperatures run to millions of degrees, the velocities become vigorous enough for the repulsion to be overcome for some atoms of lighter elements and, at the extreme temperatures reached at some stages of the history of a star, even for the heavier ones. The most important reactions are those which involve the union of successive atoms of hydrogen to form an atom of helium. Since, on the scale of atomic weights, a hydrogen atom weighs $1 \cdot 008$ and a helium atom $4 \cdot 004$, there is a loss of mass of $0 \cdot 028$ units which is converted to energy.

One set of these reactions is called the proton-proton chain, the steps of which begin with the union of one proton nucleus of hydrogen with another proton to form a hydrogen atom of mass 2. The reactions, with the approximate masses of the atoms in brackets, are given below. The radiation in these equations may be in the form of particles or electromagnetic waves of short wave-lengths:

proton (1) + proton (1) = hydrogen (2) + radiation
hydrogen (2) + proton (1) = helium (3) + radiation
helium (3) + helium (3) = helium (4) + 2 hydrogen (1)

Another series of reactions is called the carbon cycle because in it a carbon atom of mass 12 has protons successively added until it is built to a nitrogen atom of mass 15—which on the addition of another proton ends the chain with the reaction nitrogen (15) + proton (1) = carbon (12) + helium (4). The net result is that the carbon atom remains to take part in the same chain of reactions again and four hydrogen atoms have gone to make the one of helium. The mass lost on the way has been given off as radiation or as particles which mostly have only a short independent career before they are destroyed to yield energy.

In the main sequence stars like the Sun the proton-proton chain is the chief agent, while the carbon cycle, which speeds up more at higher temperatures, contributes more for the hotter stars.

The rate of production of nuclear energy as a function of temperature can be found from the theory and experimental data of nuclear physics. The temperature near the centre of a star, as derived from the theory of stellar interiors, thus combines with the knowledge of atomic physics to give the rate of energy production in the star—which must balance the amount it radiates. At the place where it is produced the radiation is highly energetic and of very short wave-length, but as it passes out through the stellar layers it alters, by frequent collision and interchange of form, to the character appropriate to its surroundings. Subsequently, when it finally radiates, the spectral distribution is that appropriate to the surface temperature.

While it is clear that there exists a good basis for understanding the structure and processes of stellar interiors, it is well to remember that, considering the number of variables in the theory, the observational tests are few and not secure. The faults of theories explaining the activity of the solar atmosphere are pointed up by observation in such detail, and if we had a similar mass of data relevant to stellar interiors the difficulties might well be multiplied.

THE LIFE STORY OF A STAR

From the fact that each star is using up its store of energy, usually by dissipating its own mass, it follows that the stars must be subject to change and not able indefinitely to continue radiating. Indeed some stars radiate at such a prodigious rate that a simple calculation shows that they would use enough of their mass to change them greatly in only a few million years, a time short compared with, say, that of the age of the solar system. So it is natural to seek the way in which stars evolve.

The evolution of a star cannot be directly observed since even the stars that use up their energy most quickly have lives many times as long as the history of astronomy. It is only occasionally that a star is observed in a quick-moving phase, as in a super-nova explosion, and even this must be interpreted as part of an evolutionary pattern. The problem may be attacked in two ways. First, by using the knowledge of the internal constitution of stars and of the physical processes that occur to generate their energy it is possible to calculate how a star is developing at any stage, how the energy is flowing in it and how its chemical composition is being changed by the atomic reactions. Second, by regarding the stellar population as providing a sample from which, by proper selection, we can observe stars of all ages the life stories of the stars may be derived—as some imaginary observer might construct a picture of human life if he could observe the population of a city for half an hour or so. There are situations in space where there exist material from which stars may even now be forming and where the stars show signs of extreme youth. On the other

M

hand, there are places—for example, in the globular clusters—where the stars have been isolated for long ages and where they may be expected to be old. In general the star clusters provide valuable observational evidence, since each of them exhibits a stage in the life of the component stars which must have comparable origin and environment during their lives. Although good progress has been made towards understanding the life history of a star, there are still stages where the story is obscure and where changes in present ideas are likely.

The first thing to decide is how the story of a star is to be told, what is to be the form in which the various stages of its life may be described. The way is already available in the Hertzsprung-Russell diagram, for the essential external qualities of a star correspond to the position that its representative point occupies on the diagram. These qualities are its absolute magnitude, its temperature and colour, its size and, at least on some parts of the diagram, its mass. So the development of a star can be displayed by following the path that its representative point traces on the H-R diagram.

Something can be learned from the diagrams already shown. It is generally taken that the material from which a star is to form begins as an extensive, diffuse, cool aggregate in interstellar space. Since, despite much searching, we know of no adequate way in which stars can replenish their matter and energy, they must eventually, even if the time is enormous by any standard, end by being cool. They are therefore evolving in some way and there must be times when the development is rapid and others when they remain stable for ages of time. Those parts of the H-R diagram where stability is implied must contain the representative points of many stars, while those parts of the diagram which correspond to instability must have fewer stars.

The conclusion, therefore, is that the main sequence of the H-R diagram is occupied by the stars which are in a stable stage of their lives. The dwarf stars which lie below the main sequence must also be in an enduring state since, to judge by the nearest stars, there are many of them. This is scarcely surprising since their small radiation is using their resources so sparingly.

The next obvious conclusion is that the enormously hot blue luminous stars represented in the top left-hand corner of the diagram cannot remain there long. A star which radiates ten- or twenty-thousand times as much energy as the Sun cannot have been doing so for more than a few million years, which is a short time compared with the life of the Earth and the Sun. Even atomic processes will not provide enough energy for a long life at this rate; hence these stars must be young, and cannot remain so long in their positions on the main sequence as their less massive fellows lower down in the sequence.

The significance of the types of stellar populations now becomes apparent. The population I occurs in those regions of space where stars can form from the interstellar material and new bright giants can be born to replace those which fade to comparative obscurity. Where the material is not available to form new stars, as in the globular clusters, there can be no young stars spending their energy at a prodigal rate. As the giants of a cluster of stars exhaust the sources of the energy which keeps them shining as stars of the main sequence, they leave it and the point of departure moves down the main sequence line of the H-R diagram of the group to a point depending on the age of the cluster. These departures, observed in the diagrams of star clusters, combine with the theoretically derived history of the stars to permit the ages of the clusters to be estimated.

To derive the story of a star the changes in the physical variables which describe its interior and energy generation have to be followed during its history. The great computing machines make such voluminous computation accessible. In the regions favourable to star formation exist concentrations of interstellar material which consist mainly of hydrogen. These may be gathered together under the influence of gravitational attraction, and of the forces exerted by radiation from neighbouring stars and by magnetic fields of the region. Magnetic fields exercise a strong control over the motion of any of the particles which have an electric charge. At some stage the mass becomes an entity destined to develop as a star. It is then comparatively large. It is cool, not luminous, and away to the bottom right of the H-R diagram. Its gravitational field then takes command and it is compressed. When the gas becomes opaque, the heat derived from the potential energy released as the gases move inwards towards the centre of gravity is trapped within it. The mass becomes hotter and brighter, and its point on the H-R diagram moves upwards and to the left, to reach a position on the main sequence which depends on its mass. The final movement to this stage is slightly downward. If the star has about the mass of the Sun it becomes, like the Sun, a yellow G-type star with absolute magnitude about $4 \cdot 5$. A very massive aggregate would become a blue star giving perhaps 20,000 times as much light as the Sun. This contracting stage for massive stars is believed to take only a few million years, a very short span in the life of the star systems, but very much longer for less massive stars.

When the star reaches the main sequence, its internal temperature has become high enough to stimulate the atomic processes described in the last section. The great source of energy so tapped enables the star, unless it is a very bright, prodigal one, to remain in a steady condition as a main sequence star for astronomical ages. Eventually the hydrogen begins to be exhausted and reactions involving heavier atoms, at first helium, are pressed into service.

The star then leaves the main sequence in another more quickly developing stage and moves to the right, and, for the lower stars, upward. Many star clusters contain stars in this red giant stage. Thereafter, the star moves to the left to cross the main sequence line, and then, probably after shedding some of its mass, is translated to the sub-dwarf class below the main sequence—where, by energy expenditure which is niggardly compared with its prodigal prime, it can eke out a long old age. The initial stages of star formation and the course of the changes from red giant to white dwarf are not well understood.

The interior of the white dwarf stars is still gaseous in the sense that the particles move at high speeds, but the ordinary gas laws do not apply, for the electrons, torn from the atomic nuclei, are packed to the limit allowed by the quantum theory. The energy radiated by the white dwarfs is taken from the kinetic energy of the atomic nuclei and eventually the dwarf must reach a cool stage. The radiation is so small and the life so long that possibly no star in the system has become dark. Such a star could be detected only because of its gravitational effect on a neighbour.

The life history of a star, as outlined, finds its counterpart in the H-R diagrams of the star clusters. Figure 51 shows the positions of the points corresponding to the stars at three stages in the history of star clusters. The detached horizontal branches which occur about zero absolute magnitude in the main population types in the diagram shown in Figure 49 have been omitted for simplicity. The stars in these parts of the diagram are observed for most clusters because they are so luminous, but their number is small compared with that of the main sequence stars. These three stages, and intermediate ones, have been observed.

The curve *DCA* represents a cluster at the early age of a few tens of millions of years. The early-type stars are beginning to break away from the

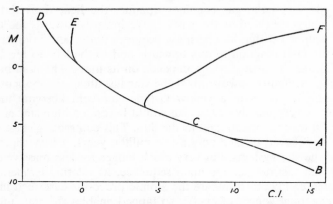

Figure 51.—Colour-magnitude diagrams for populations of different ages.

main sequence while the less massive ones have not yet reached the main sequence. It is even suspected that in environments like this stars have been observed to begin their luminous careers. The two estimates of the age of such a cluster, from the two points of departure of the population from the main sequence, have several times shown satisfactory agreement. The curve *ECB* represents a later stage, for the age of which only the upper turn-off point is available. Such a cluster is Praesepe, reckoned to have an age of the order of 500 million years. The curve *FCB*, the type exhibited by globular clusters, corresponds to an age running to several thousands of millions of years.

In the constellations Orion and Carina there are regions of high density of interstellar material, like the Orion Nebula, and associations of giant young stars and of T Tauri variables. Here are regions active in forming stars. The T Tauri stars lie near the horizontal low luminosity branch of the young cluster diagrams.

Element Building

Much attention has been given in recent years to the study of relative abundances of the elements. This is important because the structure and evolution of the stars depends on their chemical constitution and because the distribution of the elements yields information on their origin—and, from that, on the origin of the universe.

The quantitative determination from spectroscopic observation of composition was outlined in the discussion on the Sun. Hydrogen is always found to be the most abundant element with helium second. However, the proportion of the heavier elements may vary a good deal for stars in different environments. A theory has been worked out which attributes the present abundance distribution to atomic reactions which occurred, during a very short time, near the "origin" of the universe. Now, however, it is thought likely that the heavier elements originated in the reactions which occur deep within the stars at some stages of their evolution.

When the hydrogen near the centre of a star becomes depleted and the helium produced from it accumulates, the temperature rises and the star leaves the main sequence. The star expands in size and the surface temperature falls so that its radiation calculated by Stefan's Law balances its energy output. It has become a red giant. The calculation indicates that the central temperature continues to rise, owing to contraction, until it becomes high enough to induce reactions between helium atoms of mass 4. This builds up elements the masses of whose nuclei are multiples of four on the atomic mass scale. At a later stage the star may be able to produce a supply of neutrons to add to the already formed elements to build heavier ones.

As the elements whose nuclei contain more protons and neutrons are built up, mass is being lost. The difference in mass between the number of protons and neutrons of a nucleus and the mass of the nucleus is called the *mass defect*. The mass defect is greatest for iron, and so when the central temperature reachest the stage where iron is entering into the reactions —several times 10^9 degrees K—the process absorbs energy. This is an unstable situation and the core of the star collapses, the nuclear reactions spread with great rapidity among the lighter atoms of the outer parts of the star, which explodes. This may be the explanation of the super-novae. At any rate, shedding of matter into space from stars has been observed many times. If a new generation of stars is then formed from this material, a greater proportion of the heavier elements should be expected, and some of the observed abundances conform to this explanation.

The globular clusters in our star system are very deficient in the heavy elements. They have a much lower iron-to-hydrogen ratio than appears in the population I stars which have formed in the space in the vicinity of the Sun. This seems to indicate that the globular clusters consist of first generation stars, whereas many of the galactic clusters contain later stars formed from the debris of a former generation in which heavier elements have formed. Some of the smaller star systems have old metal-poor stars, indicating a single generation of stars.

REVIEW

Nearly the whole of the information available about the stars has been gained during this century. In the previous chapter we surveyed the observational methods and results which, now established by tradition, form the basis of our knowledge of the stars and provide the means of extending the boundaries of that knowledge. The additional information gained by considering the population characteristics of the stars was introduced in the present chapter. A great deal of firmly based knowledge of the stars is available. In the last sections of this chapter we reviewed current opinions in some fields where more complete knowledge is needed. Here it is well to remember that science advances with many false steps—which must be retraced—and modifications to the story of the stars may later be necessary.

10

THE MILKY WAY

THE Milky Way, or Galaxy, which extends as a luminous band around the whole sky, is a glorious sight when viewed high in the sky in clear country air away from the lights of a city. It is composed of numerous stars too faint to be seen individually by the unaided eye, as was shown by Galileo who first examined it with a telescope. The way in which the Milky Way extends around us suggests that our Sun is placed within a great disc-shaped star system with a denser population and greater extent in the plane of the Milky Way. Our situation within this great star system has made it hard to untangle its structure, the details of which still prove elusive. However, we now have satisfying answers to broad questions about its composition, size and shape, about our situation in it and about its character as a dynamical entity.

Much of the wonderful beauty of the Milky Way can be revealed with the aid of ordinary binoculars or a small telescope. The maps of Chapter 2 show when the best views may be seen. In July evenings the beautiful constellations Scorpius and Sagittarius are high in the sky. For the northern observer the Milky Way extends thence into Cygnus and Cassiopeia while in the Southern Hemisphere it extends into the brilliant groups in Centaurus, Crux and Carina going down to the south-west. The opposite side of the Galaxy may be seen in the January evenings. Orion, near the equator, is visible in both hemispheres and in this month and February the brightest stars of the heavens are presented to us. In the Southern Hemisphere Crux is now in the south-east and the Milky Way stretches from there, across the sky through Orion and Taurus to Auriga, Perseus and Andromeda, where it may be scanned by the northern observer.

THE CONTENTS OF THE MILKY WAY

Stars

The great multitude of stars make the most important contribution to both the mass and light of the Milky Way (see Plate 34). The remaining contents of the Milky Way, to be discussed after the stars, usually become visible only because of the latter. As telescopic power increases, the number which can be observed increases rapidly from the 6,000 seen by the naked eye to more than a million with a four-inch telescope. Table 8 shows how the numbers of stars per square degree to various limiting magnitudes varies in different parts of the sky. The magnitudes are photographic because the classical work on this subject was done photographically. The parts of the sky are selected according to angular distance from the Milky Way, called *galactic latitude*. For example, the average number of stars per square degree brighter than magnitude 14·0 at 30° from the Milky Way is 132. For visual magnitudes the numbers would be about twice as great. The final column gives totals for the whole sky.

TABLE 8

Gal. Lat.	0°	30°	60°	90°	Total for Whole Sky
Limit of m	N	N	N	N	
6·0	0·15	0·06	0·04	0·04	2,950
10·0	9·3	4·6	2·5	1·9	166,000
14·0	525	132	62	51	6,500,000
18·0	15,800	2,200	740	520	144,000,000

This table gives N, the number of stars per square degree, at various angular distances from the Milky Way, brighter than the photographic magnitudes of the first column. The final column gives the number brighter than these limits for the whole sky.

With the aid of a little arithmetic this Table can be used to reveal several important characteristics of the distribution of the stars. For each magnitude limit there is a concentration of stars towards the Milky Way, a concentration which is more pronounced for the fainter limits. The ratio of the numbers in the 0° column to those in the 90° column increases from under four at magnitude 6·0 to about thirty at magnitude 18·0. This is just what would be expected if a disc-shaped collection of stars were being viewed from the inside, for the selection to fainter limits would naturally include more distant stars, the direction of which must be lower towards the plane of the disc.

The Table yields also some information on the apparent distribution of the stars with distance from us. Suppose first that all of the stars are, intrinsically, equally bright. A step of four magnitudes, as in Table 8, would correspond to a ratio of 40 in brightness; and hence, by the inverse square law for light received, to an increase to 6·3 times the distance at which a star would be included—that is, an increase of 250 times in the volume. Of course the stars are not all of the same brightness but the same argument should apply for each absolute brightness—and so, equally, for all stars. Hence on the assumption of uniform distribution the entries in each row of Table 8 would be 250 times those on the previous row. This is not in accord with the observations represented in the Table. In the plane of the Milky Way, galactic latitude 0°, the ratio of number to limiting magnitude

14·0 is 56 times that to limit 10·0, and the ratio for limiting magnitudes 18·0 and 14·0 is 30. This is far short of the ratio expected for uniform distribution. The deficiency is greater for fainter stars and increasing distance. Evidently, then, the Sun is situated in a part of space where there is some concentration of stars; or there is some veil of material in interstellar space which decreases the brightness of the more distant stars and gives rise to the observed deficiency of their numbers. Actually, as the evidence of the structure of the Milky Way is brought together, it will be found that both of these circumstances apply. Any attempt to estimate the total number of the stars in the Milky Way by a continuation of the last column of Table 8 is completely frustrated by the influence of the interstellar material.

The ratio of the numbers in successive rows in Table 8 becomes smaller for higher galactic latitudes until, at right angles to the Milky Way, the ratio of the number of stars brighter than magnitude 18·0 to those brighter than magnitude 14·0 is about ten. This shows, as might be expected, that the stellar population thins out more rapidly in this direction than in directions within the Milky Way plane.

Star Clusters

The star clusters are among the most beautiful components of the Milky Way when viewed through the telescope. A low power which concentrates the stars in the field is often of advantage for the galactic clusters while a high power may be needed to resolve the globular clusters. The clusters have already been referred to because of their importance for study of the stars which they contain. In this chapter we are concerned with their relations with the star system in which they occur. Because their distances can be found—as referred to in Chapter 9—by recognition of their stars, the clusters can be made to serve as beacons to map the extent of the Milky Way or to delineate features in the system. This will be taken up in later sections.

It was in a study of the galactic clusters that R. J. Trumpler was led to the discovery of the general absorption of light by the dust that lies between the stars. The diameter of a cluster is found in the same way as that of any celestial object, by multiplying the angular diameter by the distance. At first it seemed that the average size of the clusters increases with increasing distance from the Sun, and so the conclusion was reached that the derived distances must be at fault because the influence of the absorption of light by interstellar material had been neglected. The reduction of the light makes the stars appear fainter and consequently further away. With allowance for loss of light in this way the anomaly is resolved. The absorption reduces the light of stars 5,000 light-years away by an amount corresponding to a magnitude.

Bright Diffuse Nebulae

Besides the evidence from absorption of light there are other more evident and longer known indications of matter lying between the stars.

There are hazy patches of light in the Milky Way which appear with small optical aid and cannot all be resolved into stars by the most powerful telescopes. They are of such a faint filmy character that it is usually better to use a low telescopic power to observe them so that the light is not too spread out. Often a fair amount of detail of a rather disordered kind may be seen in these beautiful objects.

Even with the naked eye it can be seen that θ Orionis (near η on Map III and on Plate 24) has a hazy appearance. *Nebulae* like this one, known as the Orion Nebula, are associated with hot stars and have spectra of bright lines which show them to be gaseous. The very short wave-length radiation in the ultraviolet from the very hot stars situated in the nebula has energy enough to remove electrons from the atoms. Then as the electrons recombine and the atoms return to the lower energy states, the lines characteristic of the gases present are radiated.

The lines of hydrogen, helium, oxygen and nitrogen and some other gases are observed. The lines of oxygen and nitrogen are from ionized atoms and the strongest of these are the so called "forbidden" lines—mentioned in the section on interpretation of spectra in Chapter 3—which occur only in extremely tenuous gases. The lines of hydrogen which can be observed after the light has come through our atmosphere are those for which the lower energy state is the second lowest state of the atom. If the change of state of hydrogen is to the lowest state, the line is in the ultraviolet and cannot come through our atmosphere and so can be observed only from rockets or satellites. Much of the radiation must be in this form. Careful consideration of the spectroscopic observations shows that most of the matter in the interstellar material is hydrogen. For each ten atoms of hydrogen there is one of helium which much exceeds in abundance all of the other elements. One of the nebular spectrum lines is the line of hydrogen in the red called Hα, associated with the second lowest energy state of hydrogen. By taking photographs of the sky using a filter which passes light only near this colour the parts of space radiating in this colour are emphasized. Near hot stars the time a hydrogen atom can spend in its neutral state without being ionized by radiation is much shorter than the period before the released electron meets and combines with another proton. So most of the hydrogen atoms are ionized. The regions found by photography in Hα are called HII regions since the hydrogen which has lost its electron is called HII.

The gaseous nebulae sometimes appear in the telescope as small circular or ring-shaped discs, and because the appearance in some cases reminded observers of the pale discs of outer planets, they have been called planetary nebulae. These nebulae are in the form of a shell of gas which has been thrown from a star, perhaps some tens of thousands of years ago. They often appear as a ring because at the edge we look at a greater thickness of gas than in the centre where the light path is straight through the shell.

The energy by which they shine comes from a hot star at the centre of the nebula. The atoms after being ionized by the ultraviolet radiation of the star recapture an electron, and then radiate the energy at their own characteristic wave-lengths as the atom falls into lower energy states. Calculation shows that to provide enough ultraviolet radiation to account for the light of a planetary nebula the central star must be very hot, in some cases with a surface temperature near 100,000°K. Because they are intrinsically bright and can be observed at great distances, they have been used in researches to find the extent and structure of the Milky Way. There are over six hundred known, many as the result of deliberate search. The Ring Nebula in Lyra is a well-known example which is visible in fairly small telescopes.

The Crab Nebula in Taurus, shown on Plate 22, is another case of a nebula of gas thrown from a star for it originates from the explosion of a super-nova. This star was seen by Chinese astronomers in A.D. 1054 when for a short time it became bright enough to be visible in full daylight. Careful measurements on photographs taken at widely separated times show that the nebula is expanding at a rate consistent with its origin in the eleventh century.

Much of the light of this nebula originates from high energy electrons, still flying about in the magnetic field as a result of the explosion. Hence it is radiation of the kind called synchrotron radiation. The characteristics of the radiation of the Crab Nebula—its polarization for example—are consistent with its origin in this way, which is also effective in producing radio waves. The Crab Nebula is one of the strongest sources of radio astronomy. On the assumption that the motion measured across the line of sight results from the same velocity as that in the line of sight indicated by Doppler shift of the spectrum lines at the centre of the nebula the distance is found to be about 4,000 light-years. Its diameter is about three light-years. Other radio sources also originated in the remnants of super-novae, one example being the intense source Cassiopeia A.

The Veil Nebula in Cygnus is a vast shell of gas ejected some tens of thousands of years ago by an exploding super-nova. The shell is still expanding at a speed of 75 miles per second so that its atoms are colliding with those of the gas of interstellar space. The energy of the motions is transferred by the collisions to the atoms which then give out their characteristic radiations.

The proportion of dust indicated by absorption as being present in interstellar space sometimes gives rise to a reflection nebula in which the light is derived from illumination of a nearby star. In this case the light is reflected with the continuous spectrum and colour of the star, or stars, imbedded in the dust. The best known example is the nebula in which the Pleiades are involved. The nebula around the red star Antares shows up more clearly in red light.

As always in astronomy, distance is a fundamental part of the information sought about the gaseous nebulae. The diffuse luminous nebulae with bright line spectra are associated with bright stars of population I, often with open clusters, and the reflection nebulae are connected with bright stars. The distance may then be determined by finding that of the associated stars. The Orion Nebula is 1500 light-years away from us and its diameter is 25 light-years; while for the Lagoon Nebula (M8) the corresponding figures are 2,500 light-years and 30 light-years. The case of the planetary nebulae is more difficult because their central stars have no known characteristics from which their absolute magnitudes can be derived. However, observations of the motions of the planetary nebulae have been used to find distances in a way similar to that described for stars in Chapter 8.

Dark Nebulae

The interstellar matter may be evident even in places where it is not illuminated by stars for it can produce a dark patch by absorbing the light of stars or nebulae which lie beyond it. An example is shown on Plate 36. To be noticeable such an obscuring cloud must be relatively close—otherwise the foreground stars would destroy the contrast upon which it depends for detection. The dark area known as the Coal Sack near the southern constellation Crux is one example; another is the dark lane which divides the brightest part of the Milky Way from Centaurus to Cygnus (see Map V). These features are plainly visible to the naked eye and make it surprising that astronomers doubted for a long time the great influence that the interstellar matter has on the apparent distribution of the stars. In many places along the Milky Way the bright and dark nebulae form an intricate pattern with details of all sizes. The very small dark globules seen against the bright background of some nebulae may represent places where there is an accumulating body of material which will eventually shine as a star. T Tauri variable stars, often thought to be stars in an early stage of evolution, occur near some of the best-known dark nebulae.

The interstellar material not only absorbs the light from distant stars but, as the dust of the atmosphere does for the light of the setting Sun, lets through more of the red end of the spectrum. The existence of stars whose line spectra indicate that they are of B class but which are nevertheless red was something of a puzzle until the influence of the dust of interstellar space was taken into account. The way in which the colour is altered in passing through space depends on the size of the particles with which it is populated. If the particles were an inch in diameter, they would make no difference to the colour of the star light, and there would in any case need to be an enormous amount of material to produce an appreciable absorption. For particles with diameter of the order of the wave-length of light a given amount of material is more effective in producing absorption and in reddening the starlight.

The change of colour of a star is measured by the difference between the colour index of the star as observed and the colour index belonging to its spectral class. This is called the *colour excess*. The spectral distribution of the energy as it left the star is found by recognising the spectral class of the star, and then, by observing the distribution as it reaches the observer, the influence of the interstellar matter can be estimated. The way in which this varies along the spectrum indicates the size of the interstellar particles and the total amount of the absorption. It seems that the particles are of the order of 1/100,000 inch or somewhat less in diameter. The total absorption in magnitudes for photographic light is about four times the colour excess of the star, and amounts, even in fairly clear parts of space, to half a magnitude in 3,000 light-years.

Allowance for an interstellar absorption of A magnitudes, estimated from the measured colour excess, must be made in the formula given in the previous chapter for finding the distance of a star. Suppose the absolute magnitude M can be derived from observed characteristics of the star. Then because the star would appear brighter if the absorbing material were absent the distance d corresponding to an observed magnitude m is given by the formula $(m-A)-M = \log d - 7\cdot57$. Lack of knowledge of the amount of the absorption which hides great sections of the Milky Way leads to uncertainty in great distances and has made more difficult the problems of elucidating the structure of the system. Despite the effect of the dust on the appearance of the Milky Way estimates of its amount from the absorption show that it must be much less in mass than the gaseous component of interstellar space, possibly only about two per cent of it.

The distance of a dark nebula may be found from a count of stars in the area of the nebula, somewhat of the kind outlined at the beginning of this chapter. As the count extends to fainter stars and greater distances, their number in the absence of absorbing material of the dark nebula increases regularly. When the stars beyond the dark nebula should begin to enter the count, their absence due to the absorption and consequent deficiency in the count is noted, and the corresponding distance derived. This process is necessarily complicated by the range of brightness of the stars and, even more, by the general absorption of light in parts of space other than that occupied by the nebula. Results having some consistency are nevertheless obtained. The Coal Sack, one of the largest, has a distance of 500 light-years, a diameter of 30 light-years and absorbs about $1\cdot8$ magnitudes of the light from the background stars.

Interstellar Material Observed in Other Ways

The presence of gases between the star and the observer of its spectrum is sometimes revealed by the occurrence in the spectrum of dark lines which evidently do not belong to the star but arise from absorption in the path of the light. These lines are clear in the spectra of hot early-type stars which have fewer lines to obscure the interstellar lines. The latter are marked by having different Doppler shifts from those of the star. In fact the lines were first detected because they did not display the same velocity changes as were observed in the lines of spectroscopic binaries. The multiplicity of the interstellar lines, with components corresponding to different Doppler shifts and velocities, often shows that the light from a star has passed through several clouds of interstellar material.

Also, the neutral hydrogen atom has energy states close together which, by a change from the higher to the lower, give radiation at a wave-length of 21cm observable by radio telescopes. By these means the most common atom of interstellar space may now be observed and its distribution mapped. As will be seen later this has become a powerful aid to investigating the structure of the Galaxy. In an interval as long even as a year only a small proportion of the hydrogen atoms make the change which gives rise to the 21-cm radiation, but the presence of so much hydrogen within the Milky Way makes it observable. The intensity of the radiation permits an estimate of the amount of hydrogen lying in the direction being observed and hence of how much there is in the whole Milky Way system. A characteristic feature of the distribution of hydrogen is the thinness and flatness of the layer in which it lies. This is particularly so in the direction of Sagittarius— which, it will be seen, is towards the centre of the system—where, for a very large area, the thickness of the layer is less than 1,000 light-years. Another detected hydrogen line has wave-length 6cms.

At the end of 1963 four spectral lines of the molecule OH were detected at wave-lengths near 18cms in the radio spectrum. A feature of apparent distribution of the OH is concentration in a direction towards the centre of the galaxy in Sagittarius. Study of these lines appears to be presenting some interesting problems. The ratio of OH to H varies enormously in different gas clouds. The OH lines have been observed in both absorption and emission and the radiation intensity of the lines varies from place to place and even from time to time. The lines may be strongly polarized. During 1966 lines arising from helium were observed.

Review

Most of the material of which the Milky Way is constructed lies in the stars. The widely distributed gas has a composition in which hydrogen is predominant. The remaining constituents of the gas have about the same proportions as in the stars, and contribute only a small proportion of the mass. Even where the gas is most dense, it is millions of times less dense than the best vacuum that can be produced in the laboratory. So it is that the atoms can go for long periods without collisions and the forbidden lines of their spectra have an opportunity to occur. A much smaller proportion again consists of particles of dust which, nevertheless, by their capacity to absorb light, make a considerable difference to the appearance of the sky and to observation by optical means. Observation by radio waves, which have much greater penetrating power, opens new avenues.

Instruments are now being carried in rockets and satellites. These can detect radiations which cannot penetrate the atmosphere. Sources of X-rays, including the Crab Nebula, have been discovered and the lines corresponding to transitions to the lowest energy state of hydrogen have been observed. Orbiting observatories with fairly large telescopes open many interesting possibilities, including that of observing molecular hydrogen for the first time. But limitations still exist, because space will lose its transparency at short wave-lengths through absorption by the atomic hydrogen.

THE SIZE OF THE MILKY WAY

Our situation within the Milky Way has made its structure, and our own position in it, hard to disentangle. The first questions to answer are:

How large is the system? In which direction does the centre lie and how far away is it? For a long time it was thought that we must be nearly centrally placed, for the differences in brightness along the Milky Way are not sufficient to indicate definitely a preference for a particular direction as that of the centre. The star counts of the kind outlined in the first section of this chapter seemed to indicate, before the role of the interstellar matter was appreciated, that the star population diminishes with distance in all directions. Clearly other methods are needed and those used fall into two classes. First, a search is made for objects which appear to be coextensive with the Milky Way and which are very bright, and can therefore be observed to great distances. They act as beacons to delineate it. Second, there has been intensive research for areas near the Milky Way which appear to be free of interstellar absorbing material, in order that observation may reach far out into space.

Globular Clusters as Markers

The globular clusters were first used by Shapley in 1917 to show the limits of the Milky Way. Neglect of the interstellar absorption at first distorted the picture somewhat, but, with this taken into account, a description was derived for the system which has remained in accord with the subsequently accumulating evidence.

When the distance and direction of a cluster is known, the point which it occupies in space is fixed. For clusters containing RR Lyrae variables the distances of the clusters were found by measurements of their apparent magnitudes. These estimates were used to calibrate other methods. The assumption that the globular clusters do not differ greatly in actual size or total brightness gives another criterion of distance which may be applied after size and brightness have been calibrated by using those clusters whose distances have been found by employing the variable stars. Then when a new cluster is being discussed, the relation between the agreed size and its angular diameter in the sky gives the distance; the smaller it appears the more distant it is. Another method depended on the assumption that in clusters with so many stars the brightest fraction of the stellar content would be much the same from cluster to cluster. Statistical variations, and the danger of influence of the result by inclusion of foreground stars not in the cluster, were dealt with by taking the mean of the 25 brightest stars or the brightness of the thirtieth star to have the same absolute magnitude in any globular cluster. The absolute magnitudes of these being determined from the clusters containing variables, it then became a matter of measuring the apparent magnitudes to obtain the distance modulus $m-M$ and hence the distance by using the usual equation.

When the distances and directions of the globular clusters are assigned, their actual positions in space can be plotted. They outline a region of space which appears to surround the Galaxy. Similar arrangements of globular clusters have since been found around other star systems. The majority of the clusters are situated in one half of the sky and the centre of their system lies in a direction towards a point within the Milky Way in

Sagittarius close to the corner where it joins with the constellations Scorpius and Ophiuchus. The diameter of the system of globular clusters is about 100,000 light-years and our distance from the centre about 30,000 light-years. The main body of the Milky Way is a flat disc which lies in a more or less spherical space defined by the distribution of the globular clusters.

High Luminosity Objects

This picture is confirmed by other high luminosity objects which are observable at great distances. The novae are concentrated towards the Milky Way and are most frequent in the direction of the centre of the Galaxy. In this direction lie the densest star clouds, and the Milky Way itself is wider, indicating a central bulge to the system.

Since the red Hα light penetrates fairly well the interstellar dust, photographic surveys which record at this wave-length have disclosed planetary nebulae at considerable distances in obscured regions. When their positions are plotted on a chart of the sky, they also appear as a flattened system loosely concentrated about the plane of the Milky Way, again with a high concentration in the direction of the central bulge in Sagittarius.

Evidence from RR Lyrae Variables

In some fields not too far from the central plane of the Milky Way there are indications that the interstellar absorption is low enough to permit examination of the space right through the system. These places of good transparency are revealed by the presence of galaxies which are star systems beyond the reaches of the Milky Way. If these appear in numbers comparable with those in fields well away from the Milky Way, an area of low absorption is indicated. There is one such region in the constellation Telescopium about 20° from the central plane. In such areas RR Lyrae variables may be found, their magnitudes measured and distances derived. On the assumption that their distribution is symmetrical about the centre of the Galaxy the distance of the centre may be found. This leads to a distance of 27,000 light-years to the centre of the Milky Way.

The RR Lyrae variables are so valuable for determining distances, and hence for plotting actual positions in space, that they have been sought also in transparent areas of the Milky Way in the direction nearly opposite to the centre and perpendicular to the plane of the system. So estimates may be made of its extent in these directions. The surveys indicate that the population falls off with distance, and are in agreement with a diameter of 100,000 light-years for the system. They are also consistent with the existence of a more or less spherical halo of stars about the main concentration of stars and interstellar matter in the disc of the Milky Way and of about the same diameter. The central bulge of the main body of the Milky Way has a diameter of about 20,000 light-years in its plane and a thickness of 7,000 light-years, which tapers to 1,000 light-years at the distance of the Sun. The system of the globular clusters proves to be coextensive with the galactic halo and the more distant clusters would be contained in a space of diameter rather more than 100,000 light-years in the plane of the main disc and about 80,000 light-years in thickness. The stars of the halo which are of population II to which the RR Lyrae variables belong contribute only a very small proportion of the mass of the Galaxy. As all of the boundaries are indefinite in a system with contents which taper off into outer space, the figures quoted must be regarded as giving only an approximate representation.

Radio Observations

Synchrotron radiation of the kind mentioned in connection with the Crab Nebula is also generated throughout the Galaxy. Although both the magnetic fields and the density of electrons with the necessary very high energies are small, the volume of the system from which the energy comes is so great that it may be measured and its variation over the sky plotted for wave-lengths of a few metres. The power of the radio waves to pass through the interstellar dust means that significant information is available for great distances. Maps of the intensity of the radiation with wave-length of the order of a metre show that the major part of the radio waves is received from along the plane of the visible Milky Way and that there is a great peak in this radiation from the direction of the galactic centre. There is also a weaker component of radiation from the whole sky which indicates that there is a distribution corresponding to a more or less spherical halo around the Galaxy. The peak of the radiation is reached in the intense multiple radio source known as Sagittarius A, whose position—right ascension 17 hours 43 minutes declination —29°—is assumed to coincide with the centre of the Milky Way. The halo is approximately coextensive with the system of globular clusters and with a volume mapped by observing the cluster-type variable stars found away from the plane of the Milky Way. This distribution is supported by radio observations of other star systems which also have concentrations of emission towards the centre and surrounding halos.

THE ROTATION OF THE GALAXY

The contents of the Milky Way having been described and some account given of the way in which its size is estimated, it remains to specify as far as possible how the contents move and how they are distributed in the system. Although other systems of stars exert some gravitational force on the Milky Way, its orderly form makes it clearly proper to study the Galaxy as a single dynamical entity. The stars must have some orbital motion—otherwise the gravitational field of the system would just pull them inwards—and, since the Galaxy is flat, the orbits must lie in one plane. It is natural to think that most of the motions are likely to be in one sense around the centre as is the case in the solar system.

Galactic Rotation from the Stellar Motions

The pattern of the motions of the stars in our vicinity depends on the dynamical structure of the Galaxy and in particular on the distribution of

N

its mass. The structure may therefore be examined through analysis of motions of comparatively close stars as seen from our observing station on the Earth. Figure 52 is drawn to represent circumstances in the plane of the Milky Way with *C* as the galactic centre about which the stars are moving. At some epoch *S* is the position of the centre of a representative group of stars near the Sun and *BDEF* represents a volume which is centred

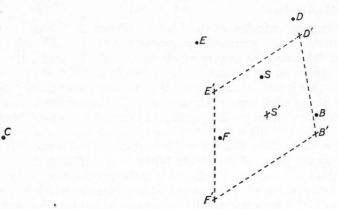

Figure 52.—The effect of galactic rotation.

on the Sun, square in the plane of the Galaxy and thin perpendicular to it. Suppose that attention is confined to the average motion of the stars in this space and consideration given to the shape of the volume which is occupied by these stars after a lapse of time. Since the mean motions perpendicular to the plane of the Milky Way may be neglected, it is only the shape in plan that has to be considered. The volume which, neglecting deviations from the mean motions at any place, still contains the original stars will change shape unless the stars have no motion relative to those near the Sun and the parts of the Galaxy behave as do points of a solid body.

Then consider the case of circular motion in which groups of stars situated further from the galactic centre have slower orbital speed. This is the actual case revealed in the Galaxy. Stars which lie along the side *DB* of the square will in the interval imagined move through a shorter distance than the Sun while those along *EF* move through a longer arc. So, while the Sun moves to *S'*, the original block of stars moves to occupy a volume represented by *B'D'E'F'*. Obviously in this case groups of stars have a motion relative to the Sun and the actual observed motions need to be measured to find how they conform to the model and to see whether a new pattern of motions needs to be tried. Comparison with observation will put the theory on a quantitative basis. The observed data consists of radial velocities measured from Doppler shifts of the spectral lines in the stars and proper motions found by measurement of positions of the stars at widely separated epochs. It is convenient to confine attention to radial motions which have, in any case, been more fruitful.

The stars, which at the first epoch represented in Figure 52 were at F, are at F' at the later epoch. As $S'F'$ represents a greater distance than SF this group of stars must have a radial motion away from the Sun. Similarly stars at D have an outward motion and, as illustrated by $S'E'$ and $S'B'$, being respectively shorter than SE and SB, those at E and B have a component of motion towards the Sun. A curve on which is plotted the radial velocities of stars in different directions around the Galaxy thus has two maxima. At a point midway between E and F towards the centre of the Galaxy from the Sun the radial motion is small. Also, since in the Figure the change SF to $S'F'$ is greater for a larger square, the radial velocities are greater at greater distances in the plane of the Milky Way. Thus is rendered credible the formula derived theoretically for radial velocity arising from the rotation of the Galaxy. The angle between the direction of the galactic centre and the star is taken as l. Thus, for F, l is $45°$. Then take r as the distance of the star and A a constant, depending on the way in which the orbital velocities of the stars varies at the Sun with distance from the centre of the Galaxy. The formula for the radial velocity is then $Ar\sin 2l$. A is called Oort's constant, after the astronomer responsible for analysis of this kind.

The formula is compared with the radial velocities of stars whose distances can be estimated. In the first place a direction for C from which l is measured may be sought to make the formula match the observations with no constant to be added to l. The direction of the centre of the Galaxy found in this way accords well with the direction indicated by methods of the last sections, a valuable and quite independent check. In the second place, if the distribution of mass in the Milky Way were known, it would be possible to calculate the orbital velocity corresponding to circular motion at any distance from the centre and hence the way that the velocity varies with distance. For example, if the great bulk of the mass were concentrated near the centre, the motions would vary in the way those of the planets do in the solar system, the velocities decreasing outward varying inversely as the square root of the distance. On the other hand, if the mass were distributed uniformly throughout the volume, the velocities would increase with increasing distance from the centre. That is, from the mass distribution could be calculated the values of A and another Oort constant B which is needed to describe the proper motions, and hence any acceptable distribution of mass must give values of A and B which conform to those derived from observation.

The way of finding distance of the Sun from the galactic centre has already been indicated and the average velocity of the stars near the Sun about the centre may be deduced from the apparent radial motions of objects which do not share in the rotation of the Galaxy. The globular clusters are suitable for this because their system, being more or less spherical in distribution, cannot be sharing the rotation of the flattened Milky Way disc. So their radial velocities can be analysed to find the velocity of the Sun about the centre of the Galaxy. The velocity of some nearby systems of stars may also be used.

Thus there is a good deal of observational evidence to which the characteristics of the Galaxy must conform. The distance of the Sun from the galactic centre is about 30,000 light-years and the orbital velocity for the Sun's neighbourhood is in the direction of the constellation Cygnus, 90° from the direction of the centre at 150 miles per second. This corresponds to a period of 200,000,000 years needed to make a complete revolution around the centre. The total mass of the Galaxy is about twice 10^{11} times that of the Sun and of this mass about three-quarters lies in the central bulge.

Distances from Radial Motions

Another valuable feature of the analysis that led to the fundamentally important information of the last paragraph is that it gives a method of finding distances. If the radial velocity V of a star has been measured and Oort's constant is known, the only unknown in the equation $V = Ar\sin 2l$ is r. This method is useful when others fail. The object must be far enough away for the velocity arising from the galactic rotation to be larger than the individual motion of the body. Distances of novae have been estimated in this way and methods allied to it become important in discussing the observations of radial velocities of interstellar hydrogen in a later section.

High Velocity Stars and Star Streaming

This rotational motion of the Galaxy, with the Sun moving in the direction towards the constellation Cygnus, gives an explanation of several phenomena previously observed in the motions of the stars. Most of the stars near the Sun conform nearly with the orbital motion of the Sun around the centre of the Milky Way, and have velocities less than 20 miles per second relative to the Sun. However, there do occur stars with much higher velocities which tend to be directed towards the part of the sky away from the direction of the orbital motion of the Sun. These are the stars which belong to the group not closely confined to the fundamental plane of the Galaxy. They are generally stars—like M-type stars or RR Lyrae stars—which belong to population II, by which the halo of the system is inhabited. As their orbits are highly inclined to the galactic plane, they do not share in the rotational velocity of the Sun as do most other stars of our vicinity, and so the motion relative to the Sun has a large component in the direction from which the Sun is moving.

If the motions of the stars in the neighbourhood of the Sun are analysed after removal of the effect of the motion of the Sun among them, it appears that there is a preferred line along which the stars tend to move. This line lies in the Milky Way and runs from a point in the constellation Sagittarius, about 11° from the galactic centre, to a point 180° away. That is, the motions relative to the mean in our neighbourhood tend to lie in either direction along this line. The line approaches more nearly to the galactic centre when fainter stars are considered. This streaming of the stars arises from the departure from purely circular motion about the centre of the Milky Way. In their motion the stars pass, either inward or outward, across the direction of the Sun's orbital motion, and the differences from the average velocity of the stars near the Sun lie across the direction in which the Sun moves around the centre of the Galaxy.

THE ARMS OF THE GALAXY

Recognition of the Milky Way as an individual star system and of other galaxies, to be discussed later, as similar systems naturally led to the search for a spiral structure similar to that observed in other galaxies. For star systems viewed from the outside the larger features of structure became obvious once the necessary optical means for observing them was developed.

However, with the Milky Way the situation is different. We view it from the inside and the characteristics we observe are much conditioned by the absorbing material which conceals the true distribution of the stars. To develop a line of attack on the problem it was necessary to select for intensive study some objects whose distribution could be expected to be related to the spiral arms, the structures being sought.

Spiral Arms from Bright Population I Stars

An examination of the nearer star systems indicated that the spiral arms are inhabited by hot, highly luminous stars of types O and B, by star clusters containing hot stars and by concentrations of the interstellar gas and dust.

By measuring the magnitudes and colours of O- and B-type stars and hence finding their distances by methods of a previous chapter their actual distribution in space was mapped by W. W. Morgan. This revealed that the Sun lies within an arm which extends from the direction of Cygnus through our location and towards the direction of Carina with, according to B. J. Bok, a great branch towards Orion. It contains the Great Nebula in Orion and most of the nebulosity in these constellations. Other more or less parallel arms lie one in the direction of the constellation Perseus, about 8,000 light-years further than the Sun from the centre of the Galaxy, and the other about 6,000 light-years closer to the centre of the Galaxy. These are called respectively the Perseus arm and the Sagittarius arm. Open clusters containing hot O and B stars of population type I occur in these arms where they were formed, while clusters which contain only older stars are distributed more uniformly, having presumably had time to drift away from their birthplace. The interstellar dust, by its absorption, has prevented the charting of the spiral arms by the methods of optical astronomy for distances greater than about 10,000 light-years from the Sun.

Radio Observations

The 21-cm wave-length radiation of the interstellar hydrogen has two properties which make it useful for tracing spiral arms to great distances. First, it passes through the cosmic dust and so can be observed from the furthest reaches of the Galaxy, and second, measurement of shift of its wave-length, by Doppler effect, yields radial velocities of the source from which it came in the same way as for lines in the optical part of the spectrum. The radial velocities in conjunction with a model of the velocity distribution within the Galaxy give information on the distance of the hydrogen from which the radiation is coming, while the intensity tells how much hydrogen is involved. The distances are found by supposing that the average motion of the gas at each place in the Milky Way is circular motion with a velocity which corresponds to distance from the centre. In Figure 53, *S* represents the position of the Sun and *C* the centre of the Galaxy. For places not close to the centre, the orbital velocity decreases at further distances, and for any line of sight, such as *SA*, the highest radial velocity belongs to gas, as at the point *P*, where the line is nearest to the centre. Using this notion and making allowance for the known orbital movement of the Sun the velocity corresponding to the distance *CP* is found from the highest velocity measured in the chosen direction. For parts of the Galaxy further than the Sun from the centre this method cannot be used, and values must be calculated from distribution of the mass of the system.

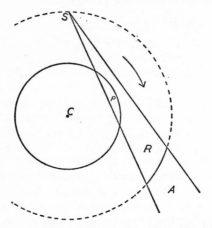

Figure 53.—The variation of radial velocity with position in the Galaxy.

By these means a model may be derived to represent the velocity of the orbital movement throughout the Galaxy, at various distances. The model may then be used to map the hydrogen observed. Suppose, as an example, the radio telescope to be directed along the line *SA*. Then concentrations of hydrogen beyond the distance of the Sun, as in the area marked *A*, have approaching velocities because the Sun is moving more quickly and overtaking them, but inside this distance, in the space marked *R*, where the gases are moving with higher velocity than the Sun, they are receding from us. The way in which the intensity of the radiation from one direction varies with velocity or wave-length, given in miles per second, is shown in Figure 54. Distances for the maximum concentrations of gas, corresponding to the maxima in intensity, may be found by matching the corresponding

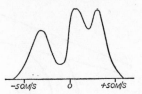

Figure 54.—The intensity of the hydrogen line corresponding to different velocities relative to the Sun near galactic longitude 50°. There is evidence of concentrations of hydrogen at least three distances along the line of observation.

observed velocities with those expected from the model of the Galaxy already determined. If there are two distances corresponding to a given velocity, some judgement is required in the choice. By this means the concentrations of gas in various directions around the Sun may be mapped, and it is found that they lie on lines which curve, after the manner of arms, around the centre of the Galaxy. There is, in most directions, a portion of the gas with low velocity relative to the Sun, corresponding to the arm in which we are situated.

The Perseus and Sagittarius arms and others are also represented and may be traced—as in Figure 55—for a long distance around the Galaxy. The interpretation of the observations is adversely affected by velocities departing, as is known to occur, from those predicted by the model, and by distribution of the material departing from the spiral pattern. A neat spiral

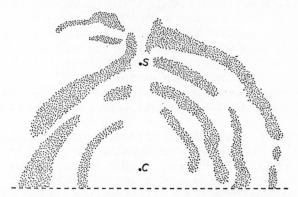

Figure 55.—Concentrations of neutral hydrogen in the Galaxy.

form as shown by some other galaxies does not so far appear and, indeed, may not exist. However, these steps towards elucidation of some of the detailed structure of the Milky Way, are much advanced on what might have been expected in, say, 1950.

Evidence of spiral structure is found in the continuous radio spectrum in a manner illustrated in Figure 56 in which *SL* represents a direction of observation tangential to a spiral arm. One would expect that this arm would contribute to the radiation for lines of sight nearer to the centre

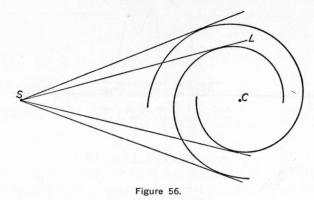

Figure 56.

than *SL*, and that the amount of radiation would step downward to lower values outside such a line. B. Y. Mills has observed steps of this kind in the radiation and based an outline spiral structure on his data.

Stability of Spiral Arms

The existence of spiral shape for the Milky Way and for other galaxies has still to be explained. We do not know how the spiral arms were formed nor how, once they have been moulded, they are maintained through the ages of cosmic time. The awareness of the problem has led to much work on it, but so far it has resisted solution. The calculations seem to indicate that the rotation, which is quicker in some parts of the system than others— for example, in our location the velocity increases toward the centre— should wind the arms tighter than they are and make it easy for random motions of the stars to wash out the distinctive form. At the Sun's distance from the centre the period of revolution is about 200,000,000 years. We know of no process that can maintain a spiral arm for more than two galactic revolutions. Yet the system and its stars must have an age over 20 times as long.

Some influence must be at work to preserve or renew the spiral pattern. Until the 1950s gravitational forces were the only ones seriously considered. Although the possibilities of gravitational action may not be exhausted, the effect of the large-scale magnetic fields which have been detected in the Milky Way is being taken into account and may lead to a solution of the problem. Magnetic forces would not control the motion of a star but the distribution of interstellar matter might well be influenced and, through it, the places where new stars are formed.

Magnetic Fields in the Milky Way

The dust of interstellar space which dims the light from distant stars may also cause the light to be polarized. A number of stars near the plane of the Milky Way exhibit polarization. This is attributed to the influence of passage through the dust rather than to a property of the stars, because those stars which are much polarized also show strongly the reddening caused by interstellar absorption. This is explained if the dust particles of space are elongated and contain some iron which enables a magnetic field in space to condition their orientation. The grains in such a case would spin about an axis in the direction of the magnetic field. The direction of the polarization observed in the stars indicates that the magnetic fields lie in the galactic plane. The fields are very widespread and about 10^{-5} of the intensity common on the Earth's surface. Such fields are of about the strength which might be needed to maintain the spiral arms.

The results of radio astronomy confirm the existence of the cosmic magnetic fields. The synchrotron radiation of super-nova remnants, mentioned in connection with the Crab Nebula, requires a magnetic field. Often the energy of the radio waves received from other sources in space does not decrease with wave-length—as it should if it were derived from the heat of the gas—but corresponds to the distribution for synchrotron radiation. The strength of the magnetic field indicated by such observation is of the same order as that derived from polarization. The radiation originating in this way is polarized, with the electric vibration perpendicular to the line of force of the magnetic field in which it arises.

Now, most of the observed polarization in the Galaxy comes from a zone around the sky which lies perpendicular to the plane of the Milky Way and cuts it at point 160° and 340° away from the direction of the centre in Sagittarius. Thus the direction of the magnetic field 90° away from these points runs from 70° to 250° which coincides with the orientation of the spiral arm in which the Sun lies and is in good general agreement with results from stellar polarization.

A polarized wave passing through an ionized gas (such as exists in interstellar space) in the direction of a magnetic field of force has the plane of polarization rotated. The angle of the rotation is proportional to the distance travelled, to the square of the wave-length, and to a value which depends on the state of the gas and the strength of the field. The rotation is in opposite directions according to the direction in which it passes along the field. This rotation is named *Faraday rotation* after the great pioneer of electrical science.

There are many sources of radio waves outside the Milky Way. These are often star systems like the Milky Way, and since the radiation is often polarized synchrotron radiation, we have an indication that magnetic fields are a characteristic feature of stellar systems. At different wave-lengths the polarization has different orientations corresponding to Faraday rotation occurring along the path from the source to us, with the indication that it happens in the Galaxy. The direction of the rotation changes as we pass from one side to the other of the zone of maximum polarization of the galactic radiation. This again is just what would be expected with the line of the magnetic field perpendicular to this zone and along the spiral arm.

Cosmic Rays

Before the beginning of this century it was known that the air about us has a small electrical conductivity which permits an electric charge to leak away no matter what precautions are taken to insulate it. It was gradually realized that this was due to a radiation that ruptures the atoms of the air to provide ions which carry the electric current. When experiments were carried out higher in the atmosphere, it was found that the ionization is greater. This led to the conclusion that the radiation comes from outer space. On the other hand, the measured ionization decreases—but slowly— if the apparatus is sunk deep beneath the surface of a lake. Hence, we may deduce that the radiation—which constituted one of the most intriguing developments of physical science—is so penetrating as to be capable of passing through thousands of feet of water.

These *cosmic rays*, referred to in Chapter 7, have now been the subject of wide study, including measurements beyond the atmosphere in space probes. Most of the rays and ionization observed in the lower part of the atmosphere are secondary, arising from the rupture of atoms of the gases of the atmosphere to produce several particles which may collide with yet other atoms to produce still more. The original *primary* cosmic rays are mostly nuclei of hydrogen with a smaller number of helium nuclei and a few nuclei of other atoms. Many of them travel at speeds very close to that of light and have energies millions of times more than would be made available if the mass of the same particle at rest were converted to energy and millions of times more than is attainable from the great laboratory particle accelerators. The total energy reaching the Earth in the cosmic rays is comparable to that of the starlight. The particles arrive from all directions which do not indicate their original source because the motions are so much modified by the magnetic field of the Earth and, no doubt, of interstellar space.

The physicist is more concerned to observe the collisions of these extremely fast particles with atomic nuclei in order to examine the mechanism and products of the collisions. From such observation he gains an insight into the structure of the nuclei and into the fundamental particles of physics. The astronomer is interested to discover the source of the cosmic rays which form the most concentrated packets of energy in the universe and to find the kind of environment in which they could arise.

Fermi originated a theory which may explain the acceleration of the ionized particles by the magnetic fields of the Galaxy. When a particle strikes a discontinuity in a magnetic field which may be bound to and carried along by a cloud of ionized interstellar gas, its energy is increased if the magnetic field is moving towards the particle. As this kind of encounter is more likely than the case where the magnetic field is moving away, the long term effect of such meetings is to build up the velocity of the particles. Magnetic fields which might do this have already been shown to exist in the Galaxy. The process cannot begin with a stationary or slow-moving particle but requires the injection of sufficiently fast particles—as with the accelerating machines of the laboratory. As it is believed that the cosmic rays are largely confined to the Galaxy by the magnetic fields which affect their motion, it is a matter of finding sources which can inject a supply of particles sufficient to make good slow losses into space beyond the Galaxy. If this is not true and there is a distribution of cosmic rays comparable with that in our neighbourhood in space between the star systems, it will necessitate some great changes in our ideas of the universe and its energy content.

The Sun has been mentioned as a source of cosmic rays which are in the low energy range but which might be regarded as suitable for acceleration. However, even though there are many stars like the Sun their number is not nearly enough to account for the supply of cosmic rays.

There are much more energetic stars which may make an appreciable contribution. The super-novae certainly throw out a great many particles. The Crab Nebula, the super-nova remnant mentioned as a source of synchrotron radiation, must contain high energy particles as well as a magnetic field. Then, too, many components of binary stars are known to be active, in some cases eruptive, in emitting gases, and these particle streams and accompanying magnetic fields may provide a source of particles for injection into the galactic space, where they could later be accelerated.

This is a new field in which science is still struggling for understanding. We should remember that the picture may soon be modified or even completely changed.

11

OTHER GALAXIES AND THE UNIVERSE

It is now time to examine the knowledge so far gained about the majestic organizations into which the stars of the universe are gathered. Ideas derived from information we have about other star systems were already found useful during the discussion of the Milky Way. So, just as the study of the Sun led to consideration of other stars, an examination of the properties of our own star system has involved the study of other star systems.

HISTORICAL

There are in the sky many other objects apart from the gaseous nebulae in the Milky Way which could not be resolved into stars with the telescopic powers available before this century. These also were given the name nebulae. They have since turned out to be great star systems which we now call *galaxies* by generalising the term "Galaxy" as used for the Milky Way.

Much time and effort were spent before this fundamental fact was fully accepted. Of the 103 objects in Messier's eighteenth-century catalogue 32 were galaxies, which are still known by their M numbers—for example, the Great Nebula, now Galaxy, in Andromeda is M31. Further, more extensive catalogues of this kind were made between 1890 and 1910, and over 13,000 objects the majority of which are galaxies were listed in the New General Catalogue and the Index Catalogues of Dreyer. Names for the objects come from these catalogues. For example, the Great Galaxy in Andromeda also has the name NGC 224.

Even in the eighteenth century there was speculation that these nebulae might be star systems, somewhat like the one in which we find ourselves, and the great astronomer W. Herschel early in his career believed that this might be so. However, his pioneering work on the scale of the Galaxy led him to believe that it was unlikely. In 1864 W. Huggins applied the spectroscope to the nebulae, and while the bright line spectrum exhibited by the nebulae in the Milky Way revealed that the light must be coming from a gaseous source, the nebulae outside the Milky Way showed a spectrum of a kind which would be given if it were made up of many stars. Although this was fairly good evidence, there was not sufficient other data to support it and the time was not ripe for recognition of the nature of this type of nebula.

In 1885 what appeared to be a new star was observed in the Andromeda Nebula, and in later years several more were discovered. The 1885 object was a super-nova, then unrecognised, but assuming that the later ones were novae similar to those which occur in the Milky Way a distance of the order of a million light-years was indicated for this nebula. Then the 100-inch telescope on Mount Wilson was commissioned in 1918, and in the early 1920s its use resolved the Andromeda Galaxy into stars, some of which could be identified as belonging to types which occur in the Milky Way, and which could serve as an index of distance. Among these were Cepheid variables. This work immediately settled the question and opened the way for an enormous enlargement of our notion of the universe.

THE LOCAL GROUP OF GALAXIES

Study of the nearer galaxies outside the Milky Way led to realization that our system is one of a group of galaxies—at present 17 are known —which form a cluster in our vicinity of the universe. This cluster is about 3,000,000 light-years in diameter and includes, besides the Milky Way, the Andromeda Galaxy and the Magellanic Clouds which lie in the Southern Hemisphere. There is another large galaxy, M33 in Triangulum, and a few fainter ones including some inconspicuous objects discovered only in recent years. These nearby galaxies are of great importance since their proximity allows some detailed study of their contents for comparison with the Milky Way and for obtaining an indication of the character of the galaxies throughout the universe.

The contents of the nearer galaxies, in particular of the Magellanic Clouds and the Andromeda Galaxy (M31), run very much parallel to those of the Milky Way. There are great gaseous nebulae, loose star clusters of the kind which occur along the Milky Way and globular clusters whose distribution is coextensive with each system. The opportunity to study these star systems as a whole from outside is of vital importance to the understanding of galaxies for in this way is avoided the handicap of the obscuring clouds which, in the Milky Way, hinder so much of the examination of the system.

The Magellanic Clouds

These are easy to see in a dark sky. They have the appearance of detached portions of the Milky Way. The shape of each is characterized by a bar, into which stars are concentrated, surrounded by an irregular distribution of luminosity. The Large Cloud shown on the South Polar map of Chapter 2 at the boundary of the constellations Dorado and Mensa is about 6° across and the Small Cloud, in Tucana, about 3°. On photographs of long exposure and especially when outlying globular clusters are included, the diameters are much larger. Examination of the clouds in the 21-cm radio emission of hydrogen shows the size to be larger still.

The clouds had previously been resolved into stars and marked by some astronomers as independent star systems, but before the general recognition of the character of the galaxies the important strategic position that they occupy in astrophysics and cosmology could not be appreciated. They contain the full range of astrophysical objects, which can be regarded as at effectively the same distance and intercompared in a way impossible within the Milky Way. The need for detailed observation of the Magellanic Clouds as examples of galaxies and as sources of objects of all kinds is an overwhelming reason for the establishment of large telescopes in the Southern Hemisphere.

The distances, which depend fundamentally on luminosity methods applied to the identified stars, are both about 160,000 light-years. From this the overall diameter of the Large Cloud is about 60,000 light-years and of the Small about 40,000 light-years. The observed apparent brightnesses combined with the distance show that the Small Cloud radiates about as much light as 100,000,000 Suns and the Large Cloud 6 times more.

As the nearest of the galaxies, the Magellanic Clouds may be explored by methods already in use. Broadly their contents parallel those of the Milky Way. With a small telescope may be seen individual stars, the most distant ones the amateur observer can expect to recognise. The study of the brightest stars in these systems reveals several hundreds brighter than $M = -7$ and two of them, H.D. 33579 and the famous variable S Doradus, with apparent visual magnitude about 9·2 have absolute magnitude about −10, radiating about a million times the light of the Sun. There are some very bright red stars whose status in the pattern of stellar evolution provides a problem of intense interest. Many variable stars are known, among them Cepheid variables. The period-luminosity relation was revealed by the study of the Cepheids in the Clouds early this century and now provides an important tool for the observational cosmologist.

Hundreds of star clusters (Plate 37) and gaseous nebulae have been known for many years and many of them have N.G.C. numbers. When the Clouds are mapped in the 21-cm radiation of neutral hydrogen, there is in many cases a correlation with the HII regions found optically. Some of the masses of gas appear on a gigantic scale. The Large Cloud contains one of the largest known gaseous nebulae, larger than any recognised in the Milky Way. It is 30 Doradus (Plate 38) which is visible to the naked eye and contains a great cluster of giant blue stars. This is doubtless a locality in which new stars are being formed. From the point of view of study of such localities it is of interest to realize that at the distance of the Clouds the brightest, and youngest, stars must be within a few minutes of arc of their birthplace for they would not have had a long enough life to have travelled far. The interstellar material of the Clouds can also be recognised by its effect in absorption, as it was in the Milky Way.

Dozens of star clusters in the Magellanic Clouds have been studied by preparing colour-magnitude diagrams in the same way as is done for those of the Galaxy although of course not to the same degree of faintness in absolute magnitude. Some of the clusters have diagrams similar to those in the Milky Way but others have interesting differences. Some of the globular clusters contain blue stars. They may well be young clusters but if so they have a colour magnitude diagram which differs from the young galactic clusters. Other globular clusters are red, like the ones in the Galaxy, and contain cluster type variables.

The Great Galaxies M31 and M33

The two great galaxies of the local group apart from the Milky Way, the Great Galaxy in Andromeda M31 (Plate 25) and M33 in the neighbouring constellation Triangulum, have been extensively studied. They too serve as stepping stones to knowledge of the great assemblage of galaxies that inhabit the universe. Both show on photographs a beautiful spiral structure. A list of the contents of M31—gaseous nebulae, dust clouds, open star clusters, globular clusters, Cepheid variables, and novae—reads much like one for the Milky Way; although, of course, much fainter stars are observable in our own system.

M31, like the Galaxy, is surrounded by a system of globular clusters over 200 of which have been recorded. About 26 novae per year occur in M31. The boundary of the system is indefinite. On good photographs the extent is about 3° x 1° but careful photographic techniques extend this greatly and a radio halo, such as was found surrounding the Galaxy, occupies a still larger volume. The total radio emission is about the same as that of the Milky Way. Its distance, revealed by identifying the types of the resolved stars, is estimated at two million light years. As its apparent total magnitude is 4·3, it is visible to the naked eye as a small hazy patch. It is awe-inspiring to think that we see this great star system by light which has travelled towards us for far longer than the existence of mankind on the Earth. The apparent angular size and the distance combine to yield a diameter of more than 100,000 light-years for M31.

M33 lies at about the same distance as the Andromeda Galaxy. It has a diameter of about 60,000 light-years and ranks third in size in the local group. The contents are similar to those of the Milky Way and M31. The spiral arms of M33 are much more loosely wound than those of M31. In each case the spiral arms have population I characteristics. Indeed, it was the recognition of the prevalence of giant blue stars in the spiral arms of such neighbouring galaxies that led to their use to delineate the arms of our own Galaxy. Not long ago those who wished to say what the Milky Way would look like from outside used to draw a parallel with the Andromeda Galaxy. Those who make a study of galaxies urge caution nowadays. However, until something better is known, we are probably as well to continue to use M31 as showing how the Galaxy would look from a distance of about 2,000,000 light-years.

M31 has two much smaller companion galaxies M32 (=NGC 221)

and NGC 205. These are smaller and fainter and are elliptical in shape
without spiral arms. Their stellar population is of type II and devoid of
super-giant stars. As a consequence although they are at the same distance
as M31, they resisted resolution into stars until 1943, when Baade detected
individual stars in photographs sensitive to the red end of the spectrum. At
the same time the Andromeda Galaxy's central portion, which is also of
population II, was resolved.

DISTANCES OF GALAXIES

In the study of the nearer galaxies characteristics are sought to form
the basis for determining the distances of galaxies in space beyond. It is only
in galaxies of the Local Group that many stars can be recognised and even
the brightest stars can be made to yield distances of only a few galaxies
beyond this group. Research in the near galaxies gives estimates of the
luminosities of the brightest stars, of globular clusters, of star clouds or
large patches of gaseous nebulae. The recognition of these in slightly more
distant galaxies enables further distance estimates to be made.

The process depends on calibrating the absolute magnitudes so that a
measure of the apparent magnitude yields a value of $m–M$ and hence
the distance. The methods can be intercompared and improved in the nearer
galaxies. The globular clusters give estimates to distances of a few tens of millions of light-years. Some confidence may be felt in these distances, but the
super-novae, great star clouds and gaseous nebulae have such a large range
in brightness that from them only rough distances are derivable. So, by these
methods, which are tied—perhaps not as strongly as we would wish—to the
methods in use within the Galaxy, it is possible to explore the nearer regions
of outer space and to form an idea of the character of the galaxies in our
vicinity. Even among these the distance may make it difficult to distinguish
surely on the photographs between images of single bright stars and of
groups of stars.

The domain in which recognisable contents of galaxies can be used for
determination of distance proves to be very tiny in the vast region in which
they are observed. So it is necessary to use the diameter or the total brightness which are the only characteristics measurable at very large distances.
By comparing the apparent observed values with the intrinsic diameters
and absolute magnitudes calibrated for the nearby galaxies the distances
of the further ones can be estimated. The very large range that exists in
these measurable quantities makes the distances found in this way subject
to a good deal of error. In the Local Group the total absolute magnitudes
range from about —21 for the Andromeda Galaxy and the Milky Way system down to about —10 or —11 for the smallest members. The same
galaxies vary in diameter from over 100,000 light-years to about 5,000 light-
years. Since the 200-inch telescope on Mount Palomar can observe to
magnitude 23, the Andromeda Galaxy could still be recorded if its distance
were several thousand million light-years. Although the range in absolute
magnitude that some galaxies might have can be reduced by recognising

some of their properties, it must be acknowledged that distances found in this way for individual galaxies may be in doubt by a large factor.

MASSES OF GALAXIES

Just as the measurements of orbital velocities in the Milky Way were used to explore its mass, so the distribution of mass within galaxies, and the total mass, is found by measuring the characteristic velocities of the components at various distances from their centres. This may be done by measuring the Doppler shifts in either the optical spectrum or the 21-cm hydrogen radio line. If the distribution of mass in a galaxy were known, the velocities for circular motion at various distances from the centre could be calculated by using the law of gravity and the law of motion. If a set of observed values of velocity in various parts of a galaxy is available, the inverse process, using the same laws of nature, may be used to find a distribution of mass which accords with the velocities. As a simple case the orbital speeds in the outer parts of a galaxy beyond the bulk of the mass become slower approximately in accord with Kepler's Law. The motion of a star in such a position then enables the mass of the galaxy to be calculated in much the same way as the motion of a satellite yields the mass of a planet.

The velocities in the Magellanic Clouds have been investigated by measurements on some stars and by surveys in the 21-cm hydrogen line. The mean velocities of recession of 170 miles per second for the Large Cloud and 105 miles per second for the Small Cloud are mainly reflections of the Sun's motion about the centre of the Galaxy. There is a smooth variation of velocity across the Large Cloud with a decrease beyond $3°$ from the centre, as if the system were flattened and subject to a differential rotation like the Galaxy. The mass is somewhat uncertain, because of doubt as to the inclination which is needed to convert radial velocities to orbital velocities, and because an inaccuracy in the distance would lead to uncertainty in the scale of the system. A mass about a tenth of that of the Milky Way seems likely for the Large Cloud and an appreciably smaller one for the Small Cloud. The proportion of interstellar hydrogen in the Clouds, estimated from the total amount of 21-cm radiation, is greater than in the Milky Way.

The velocities in M31 around its centre are approximately proportional to distance from the centre as far as $1°$—equivalent to about 30,000 light-years. The density of stars falls off after this distance and the orbital velocities decrease. The mass indicated is about 2×10^{11} solar masses, perhaps somewhat more than that of the Galaxy. A rapidly rotating small volume near the centre of M31 indicates a core of higher density. The remaining members of the Local Group are lower in mass. One estimate for M33 gives $3 \cdot 4 \times 10^{10}$ solar masses and several of the smaller systems may be only a few million solar masses.

Galaxies often occur in pairs which, since there are too many to be explained as chance alignments, must be moving under their mutual gravi-

o

tational attraction, as was the case with the binary stars. The relative radial velocities of a pair can be measured from Doppler shifts in their spectra, but since the orbital periods must be many millions of years there is no chance of finding an orbit from which the masses could be derived. However, by making the radial velocity measures for many pairs and assuming that their orbits are oriented at random it is possible to find average masses. The results of such analyses show that, contrary to what might have been expected from the sample in the Local Group, the most massive galaxies are usually not spirals but elliptical galaxies without arms. The masses obtained for spirals from pairs agree more or less with those obtained from internal motions at about 2×10^{10} solar masses, but the pairs of ellipticals may give masses fifty times as great.

TYPES OF GALAXIES

The discussion so far has indicated the great variety in size, brightness, and shape of the galaxies. They have been classified according to shape, largely following the great pioneer E. P. Hubble. The forms are *spiral, barred spiral, elliptical* or *irregular*. A selection is shown on Plates 25, 33, 39, 40, 41, 42, and 43.

Galaxies which show spiral arms are represented in the Local Group by the Great Galaxy in Andromeda and M33. The arms are typically of population I, with a proportion of highly luminous stars and clouds of gas and dust in which the young stars are born. The Galaxy and M31 are large examples of the type, which has a spread in size down to about 1/5 of these in diameter, and to about 1/100 in brightness. These galaxies have a nucleus which has characteristics of population II, free of bright blue stars and nebulosity, and therefore not easily resolved. The spiral type is subdivided according to the character of the arms and their relation to the nucleus. One type, S*a*, has a large nucleus and closely wound spiral arms which do not form a great proportion of the system; the S*c* type (Plates 33 and 41) consists mostly of spiral arms loosely wound about a small nucleus; S*b* lies between the two.

About a quarter of the spiral galaxies are of barred spiral type. This consists of a bar across the centre, from the ends of which the spiral arms emerge more or less at right angles. The barred spirals are also divided into classes SB*a*, SB*b* and SB*c* in increasing order of looseness of structure. A barred spiral is shown in Plate 42. Radial velocity measurements in the bars show that the velocity of revolution increases outward more or less as would be the case for a solid wheel spoke. This is what might be expected if the bar is to endure, but it is not easy to explain the mechanics. A type S0 is introduced to include galaxies which are flattened like the spiral galaxies but contain no spiral structure.

Then there is a large class of galaxies like NGC 205, which is a companion galaxy to M31. These elliptical galaxies are divided into classes from E0 to E7 in order of increasing ellipticity. They contain no trace of spiral arms. Some are shown on Plate 39. The change in outline is sometimes due to the orientation in which the galaxy happens to be placed and which could make even a much-flattened system appear circular as we view it; but there are too many almost circular ones to be accounted for in this way. There must be many whose true shape is almost spherical. The elliptical galaxies are of population II, typically lacking in highly luminous blue stars, dust and conspicuous emission nebulae. Globular clusters may be present. They shade off into intergalactic space so that it is not easy to define where the boundary lies. However, it is clear that they range enormously in size from the dwarf galaxies of the Local Group which are only a few thousand light-years across to the giants indicated in the previous section which are the most massive, most luminous and largest among the galaxies.

The irregular galaxies are represented by the Magellanic Clouds. The galaxies of this class do not have a nucleus nor the symmetry displayed in the other classes. It seems that the Large Magellanic Cloud is a large example of this type, some members of which give only a hundredth as much light. There are also irregular galaxies which do not contain population I objects.

Among the brightest galaxies the spirals are most common. This is because they have a high average luminosity, so that they are still relatively prominent from a greater distance than the dwarf galaxies, which may give less than a hundredth as much light. However, the distribution in the near parts of space is quite different. Of the Local Group ten galaxies are elliptical, three spiral and four irregular, and it must be believed that the dwarf galaxies are similarly more numerous throughout space but not detected because of their faintness.

The Evolution of Galaxies

The age of galaxies is a subject in which there is growing interest. Its importance lies partly in the relation that the origin and evolution of galaxies must have to the kind of universe in which they arise. That galaxies do evolve is evident because of the irreversible processes that take place in them. Their stars are subject to change so that their stellar populations are being modified. They are continually shedding energy—some of them in vast quantities—in the form of light, radio waves, X-rays and cosmic rays. There are dynamical forces at work which must reduce differences of motion and lead to change in each galaxy.

It must be assumed that each galaxy forms from a large turbulent mass of gas which becomes detached from the surrounding universe. This cloud becomes an entity. Consequently theories should be rejected if they suggest a massive galaxy as a product of the evolution of a less massive one. The young galaxies must be those in which the stars are young and constantly being renewed. Most irregular galaxies and the Sc and SBc systems have great supplies of gas and dust from which are being formed young, luminous blue stars in which they abound. These are likely to be the youngest galaxies and as their inter-stellar material is used up so that new stars become less common and the first formed ones grow older, their character must change. The S*b* and S*a* galaxies have progressively less interstellar material, fewer supergiant stars and a redder colour index to correspond with their ageing population of stars. The same applies to the SB*b* and SB*a* galaxies. The S0 and E-type galaxies are almost entirely of population II. They usually have little interstellar matter and are reddish in colour, characteristic of the stellar content. This, then, may be the direction of evolution of the galaxies.

The varying circumstances in which a galaxy may originate and develop may well be responsible for their many forms. The one constant accepted is that its matter is subject to the same law of gravity that we know in the solar system. The mass of the cloud which gathers to make the eventual galaxy may vary greatly as may also its energy content and rotational momentum. The value of the magnetic fields may vary and the direction of the field may have different relation to the axis of rotation. For the formation of spiral arms the gas is compressed by magnetic forces into a tube.

A history of the Galaxy has been proposed by J. H. Oort. The stars formed in the early stages were distributed throughout the mass of gas which detached itself from the surrounding universe. These, by attraction to the centre of the system, would acquire elongated orbits not concentrated on any plane. Thus the halo of stars about the Galaxy is of ancient origin and of population II. The non-condensed gas would suffer collisions which tend to eliminate non-circular or inclined motions leading to encounters. At the same time the angular momentum would be maintained and so a disc formed having a concentration toward the centre and more or less circular motions. Star formation would go on during the whole period, the stars formed during the last few hundred million years constituting the present population I of the disc of the Milky Way.

NUMBER AND DISTRIBUTION

The number of galaxies which can be observed by great telescopes is enormous. There are about 1,000,000 to the eighteenth magnitude according to Harvard Observatory surveys. Several hundreds of millions must be observable with the 200-inch telescope on Mount Palomar—which in some fields of the sky can record more galaxies than stars of the Galaxy. Since the smaller ones, which examination of our neighbourhood shows to be most common, cannot be seen to the greatest depths, the total number in space must be many times as great. Their distribution covers the sky except for a wide zone of avoidance where the distant galaxies are hidden by the absorption in the Milky Way.

Clusters of Galaxies

Surveys of galaxies reveal their strong tendency towards clustering. The clusters may contain from just a few to several thousand galaxies. In the constellations Coma Berenices (Plate 44) and Virgo, for example, there are clusters of galaxies with many hundreds of members. The brightest stars— not the Cepheids—can be recognised in the Virgo cluster, the nearest one to us, which lies at a distance of 40,000,000 light-years. The brightest galaxies of the cluster are brighter than apparent magnitude 10 and so can be seen in a small telescope. Sixteen of them have Messier numbers. It has moreover been shown by de Vaucouleurs that on an even larger scale the nearer galaxies are not distributed at random but tend to occupy a flattened space which lies more or less perpendicular to the plane of the Milky Way. Some observers believe that there is indication of general tendency for the galaxies to be organized on a larger scale than the clusters and the local super-cluster may be an example of this.

The examination of photographs taken with the 48-inch Schmidt camera on Mt. Palomar has revealed more than 2,700 clusters of galaxies. The surveys show that there are more galaxies in the northern half of the sky than the southern.

Studies of clusters of galaxies are important in two ways. First, they represent an opportunity to study populations of galaxies because they provide a sample of galaxies which lie at nearly the same distance—so that diversity in appearance which arises merely from difference of distance is eliminated. It seems that study of clusters of galaxies may advance knowledge of their evolution, as the study of star clusters assisted in unfolding the life story of the stars.

Secondly, because they provide a sample of many galaxies at the one distance, the averaging of properties may be used to eliminate the uncertainty which arises from the great variation in brightness and size that renders unreliable the estimate of the distance of a single galaxy. Thus the clusters of galaxies are the most distant objects for which reasonably trustworthy distances are obtainable by using as the criterion of distance the difference between the measured apparent magnitude and the absolute magnitude found from experience with nearby galaxies. The brightest members of a cluster may have an absolute magnitude near —22. The great cluster of galaxies in Coma Berenices is distant 220,000,000 light-years. There are several clusters in Ursa Major—one distant cluster being listed as 2,200-million light-years.

There are several interesting trends in the population of the galaxies. Spirals are more common among single galaxies than in clusters which, however, tend to contain members of particular type. A cluster in Ursa Major contains spirals, but dense clusters like the Coma Berenices cluster contain a great proportion of elliptical and S0 galaxies, population II objects lacking gas and dust. This could be accounted for by collisions among cluster members. In a collision between two galaxies the stars are so far separated that the stellar content of each galaxy would pass through the other with little perturbation and leave the encounter intact. The interstellar gas clouds, however, would suffer real interference and most probably be removed from the galaxies, which would thus lose their capacity to form spiral arms although retaining their disc shape. Most of the galaxies in a densely populated cluster may have taken part in collisions during their lifetimes.

The observation of Doppler shifts in the spectra of the member galaxies yields estimations of masses for whole clusters. From the shifts may be obtained the velocities of the galaxies, or at least the part of velocities in the line of sight, relative to the centre of the cluster in which they occur. Then, by assuming that the cluster is stable and that galaxies are not escaping from it, the gravitational field and hence the total mass needed to retain galaxies having the observed velocities may be calculated. The cluster masses derived in this way are many times greater than the masses of galaxies obtained by observation of internal motions of galaxies and of double galaxies. If the light and mass of the Sun are taken as units, the ratio of the mass to the light of the brighter members of the Local Cluster is about 10, and for the elliptical galaxies of our vicinity it ranges up to about 100. But for clusters of galaxies the ratio is about ten times greater.

This leaves us with a dilemma: Is there really a great deal of non-luminous matter within the clusters in the form of inter-galactic matter? Or are the clusters unstable, having about the mass indicated by their light and a lifetime but a fraction of the smallest age we can admit for the universe? Certainly the prevalence of the clusters has in the past appeared to justify confidence in their permanence. Is it possible that the resolution of these questions will contribute towards understanding of the evolution of galaxies or of the universe? Or will some misinterpretation be found in the basic data, as happened in 1952 when recognition of the complexity of the period-luminosity law for the variable stars led to revision of distance estimates?

Counts of Galaxies

By making counts of galaxies to various limits of magnitude the attempt may be made to explore their distribution in depth in the same way as was described for the stars. If the galaxies are distributed uniformly through space, their number will grow by a well-defined rule as the limit of faintness is increased. If $N(m)$ is the number brighter than apparent magnitude m, the rule is $\log N(m) = 0 \cdot 6m +$ a constant. Since $\log 3 \cdot 98 = 0 \cdot 6$ this is, in slightly different form, the same rule as was considered at the beginning of Chapter 8 in connection with counts of stars in the absence of interstellar absorption. Counts to magnitude 18 do conform to this formula. Departure from it at fainter magnitudes may arise through error in the scale of faint magnitudes, through the existence of a tenuous veil of absorbing intergalactic material or through a real characteristic of the structure and evolution of the universe. It is, of course, the aim of the observational astronomer to reduce the first and to discover and allow for the second so as to make possible the disclosure of the third.

THE RED SHIFTS

By photography of their spectra the shift of the spectral lines of the galaxies can be measured and made to yield observations of the speeds with which they are moving in the line of sight from the observer to the galaxy. Nothing very special is noticed in the case of the galaxies of the

Local Group, whose velocities are largely a reflection of the speed of the Sun in its orbit around the centre of the Galaxy, but when the same measurement is applied to distant galaxies it is found that the spectrum lines are always shifted towards the red. The velocity is invariably away from us and moreover is, on an average, greater in proportion to the faintness of the galaxy—that is, in proportion to its distance.

The relation can be investigated most reliably in galaxy clusters. The investigator thus avoids the deviations from the average which are likely to be possessed by an individual galaxy to the detriment of the estimate of its distance. From strict consideration of what is observed the relation is one between magnitude and red shift. Careful statements sometimes emphasize this, for the velocity-distance relation relies on confidence in the distance scale and in the interpretation of the red shifts as velocities. Accepting this interpretation, it has been estimated that the velocity increases by about 20 miles per second for every million light-years of additional distance. The value is known as the *Hubble constant* after the investigator who announced the law of the red shifts in 1929. (The figure is liable to revision.) The relation between red-shift and distance is shown on Plate 45.

Taken at face value this result means that the universe is expanding at a rapid rate, but it does not mean that we occupy a privileged position from which the expansion is taking place. The nature of the expansion would appear the same to an observer wherever he were situated. The circumstance is similar to what occurs when a rubber balloon bearing spots is blown up. As it expands every spot recedes from every other one—and so no spot may be taken to have a favoured position from which the others stretch.

The velocity-distance relation seems so firmly established that the radial velocities of very distant objects are now commonly used to give estimates of their distances. Indeed there are objects discovered through radio astronomy—and shortly to be discussed—for which no other way is available. The law of the red shifts which applies over such an enormous volume of space must surely represent a characteristic to be accounted for in any theory of the structure of the universe. If the law is directly interpreted, taking the velocities proportional to distances, the galaxies were packed, at a past time corresponding to the period taken to travel 1,000,000 light-years at 20 miles per second, into a space small compared with that which they now occupy. This was about 10,000-million years ago. Of course, such calculations must be regarded with caution because either the relation may not be one of proportionality but may depend in some way on the properties of the universe, or the value of the constant may not always have been the same.

RADIO OBSERVATION OF GALAXIES

Radio astronomy is making increasingly important contributions to the study of galaxies and their distribution in space. Many discrete sources of radio energy were found to be distributed over the whole sky in a way not related to the Milky Way. This indicates that most of them are situated at distances beyond the Galaxy; and the identifications that have been made accord with this.

The radio observation of normal galaxies has already been discussed. The Milky Way has been mapped by radio, and observations of great value have been made in the Magellanic Clouds and the Great Galaxy in Andromeda. The 21-cm line of neutral hydrogen as well as the radio continuum has been observed in these and in M33 and M101. This opens the way to radial velocity measurements from Doppler shifts. The velocities obtained agree with those found from the optical observations. This agreement is a confirmation that the shifts are due to velocity rather than to some unknown physical cause. A curve giving the variation of the orbital velocities at different distances from the centre in M31 agrees satisfactorily with that obtained in the optical spectrum.

There were, however, strong sources of radio energy in places where no bright optical object could be seen, and it was obvious that the ratio of radio to optical energy in these must be unusually large. In 1951 the radio source known as Cygnus A, one of the strongest in the sky, was identified with a faint double galaxy at Mount Palomar. The radial velocity of this source indicates a distance of 700,000,000 light-years. Another source of radio energy Virgo A arises in the galaxy M87 which is a member of the Virgo cluster. It is an elliptical galaxy which displays a blue coloured jet. Yet another source Centaurus A is identified with the unusual elliptical galaxy NGC 5128 (Plate 43) whose centre is crossed by a remarkable dark band of absorption. The radio energy comes from two centres symmetrically placed with respect to the absorption band and outside the optically bright part of the galaxy. The radio source is remarkable for its great size as it extends more than $10°$ in the direction perpendicular to the dark band. By advances in techniques radio astronomers have improved the accuracy to which the positions of the sources can be given. A rapidly growing number of identifications is flowing from their collaboration with optical astronomers.

Observation of the identified *radio galaxies* yields some information about the source of the radiation. The radio waves from all three galaxies mentioned in the last paragraph is polarized and the optical radiation in the jet of M87 is polarized. The radio energy increases with wave-length. Thus the radiation is synchrotron radiation, of the kind requiring a magnetic field for its production, as in the case of the Crab Nebula in our own Galaxy. The polarization in Centaurus A measured by radio astronomers in Sydney extends over a large area and indicates a magnetic field of enormous size. Of the radio galaxies most are giant ellipticals and prove to consist of close pairs. Many of them show optical emission lines of the kind that arise in interstellar gas clouds near hot stars. A radio galaxy may give millions of times as much radio energy as an ordinary galaxy. Cygnus A emits more radio energy than optical.

Quasi-Stellar Objects

Radio astronomers have developed interferometer aerial systems which make use of the principle, used in optical astronomy to measure the diameter of stars, that some of the benefits of a very big receiver can be gained by an aerial which covers only part of the large area. These can be used to measure accurately the position and angular size of a source. Also, if a source lies in the path of the Moon, it may be occulted by the Moon. When the source fades, it must lie at the edge of the Moon in the position it occupies at the time. If several such observations are made, the position of the source may be accurately derived. The way in which the fading occurs gives information on the size of the source. Some of the sources investigated proved to have very small area and, moreover, the optical objects with which they were identified look like stars on the photographs. These are the *quasi-stellar objects* (or quasi-stellar sources, or "quasars").

Their remarkable character was revealed when radial velocities were measured. The Doppler shifts proved greater than any previously measured for galaxies, and interpreted in the usual way consequently yield distances running into thousands of millions of light-years. From this the absolute magnitudes are found and show that the quasi-stellar objects give a hundred times as much light as previously known giant galaxies. They are the brightest things in the universe—completely unsuspected before the first one was revealed in 1963. By the middle of 1965 more than 40 were known. The number is growing, and it may well be that a quarter of the radio sources will turn out to be of this kind.

The properties of the quasi-stellar objects may be displayed by discussing observations of some of them. The brightest known is 3C 273. The 3C stands for the Third Cambridge Catalogue of Radio Sources and 273 is the number in the Catalogue. The stellar object has apparent magnitude 12·8 and could therefore be observed by a good amateur telescope. The radial velocity is 30,000 miles per second which corresponds to a distance of 1,500 million light-years. The absolute magnitude is —26, the brightest single object known. The examination of previously taken photographs covering the area shows that the light varies through a few tenths of a magnitude over a period of a few years, with occasional changes lasting only a week or so.

Since the velocity of light is the limit of speed for any physical disturbance, it is argued that the portion of the object which varies in brightness must be very small judged by galactic standards. This part of the optical object may subtend an angle about a thousandth of a second of arc. The radio output of 3C 273 and several other quasi-stellar objects has also varied appreciably. 3C 47, one of the original quasi-stellar objects, has two radio components about a minute of arc apart and nearly symmetrical about the optical object. At the distance indicated by the high radial velocity the linear separation must be several hundred light-years; so the radio source is large. 3C 9 was found as a radio source of small diameter. Its optical counterpart, which is of magnitude 18, has a radial velocity measured as 149,000 miles per second—which implies a distance of several thousand million light-years. The red shift is so large that the line of hydrogen, related to its lowest energy state normally in the inaccessible ultraviolet, is observed for the first time from the Earth's surface. Once again emission lines are present in the spectrum. At the end of 1965 an even more distant object was reported from the work of the Parkes radio telescope and the 120-inch telescope at the Lick Observatory, California.

All of the optical objects have intense ultraviolet radiation. They are the most distant identified objects. In this account they are being treated as sharing the motions of the galaxies and as having distances corresponding to their radial motions. This is a natural interpretation, but it is as well to admit the possibility at this stage that this is an error, which might change the whole picture in the future.

The early quasi-stellar objects were revealed because they were radio sources of small angular size. Then the properties of the identified optical counterparts were found to be stellar appearance, large ultraviolet radiation, and high radial velocity, with implied immense distance and intrinsic luminosity. Broad emission lines and optical variability seem also to be properties of the objects. The next important step, to use other properties than radio energy of the quasi-stellar objects as indicators, was taken in 1965 by A. R. Sandage. If the magnitudes of any celestial body are measured in three colours—ultraviolet, blue and visual—two colour indices, ultraviolet minus blue and blue minus visual, are obtained. These may be plotted on a diagram with horizontal coordinate for one colour index and vertical coordinate for the other. Each body has a representative point on such a diagram, and the points for bodies of the same kind may lie on a characteristic curve. The points for the quasi-stellar objects indicated by their radio energy lie near a distinctive curve which corresponds to their high output in the ultraviolet.

For some time it has been known that in the areas of sky away from the Milky Way there are thousands of faint abnormally blue stars. These have been regarded as members of the halo of stars which surrounds the Milky Way. When the results of photometry are plotted on a two-colour diagram of the kind described, many of them, in fact most of those fainter than magnitude 15, lie near the line characteristic of the quasi-stellar objects. The next step is to try the indicated objects for some of the other properties of quasi-stellar objects. The spectra of some of them have been recorded to show emission and high radial velocities with consequent great distance and enormous intrinsic luminosity. They appear to have the properties of quasi-stellar objects, except the high emission of radio energy. They are several hundred times more frequent than the quasi-stellar sources. It seems natural to think that they represent a longer enduring state of the same kind of object that has a radio emitting phase in its life-time. While still thousands of times less common than normal galaxies they represent for research an important constituent of the universe. Sandage calls them quasi-stellar galaxies.

The Origin of the Energy

The source of the energy of the radio galaxies and quasi-stellar objects remains unknown. The difficulty is to suggest a mechanism which would provide the necessary huge amount of energy over a reasonable time. Any explanation must fit with several properties. The radio galaxies are massive but massive galaxies do not necessarily emit radio energy. They are sufficiently numerous to suggest that the circumstances in which they arise cannot be a rare one among galaxies. For the quasi-stellar objects the output varies, and both the radio source and its optical counterpart tend to be double. M82 is a double source in which the components are moving apart at high speed. The jets of M87 and the quasi-stellar sources 3C 48 and 3C 273 and other radio galaxies imply origin in large explosive events. Of course different explanations may be required in different cases and, in particular, the radio galaxies may well differ in origin from the quasi-stellar objects.

In preparing this section six suggestions were listed. Some of these have been virtually discarded and the others may be found unacceptable before this book can be published. However, to show the character of the thinking that is going on, some alternative suggested energy sources are outlined. The occurrence of a super-nova in a part of a galaxy crowded with stars might set off a chain reaction. The great energy radiated from the super-nova on reaching the surfaces of its near neighbours might heat them sufficiently to start atomic reactions causing these in turn to explode. Thus the wave of explosions would advance. For another suggestion, the existence of antimatter has been invoked. There appears to be no theoretical reason why matter should not exist with protons replaced by similar negative particles and electrons by positive electrons. If such matter were to meet the ordinary matter that occurs in our part of the universe the two kinds would mutually annihilate one another with the emission of a large amount of energy. However, there is no observational evidence of such matter.

The amount of energy arising from gravitational collapse of a large mass has been proposed. In ordinary stellar bodies the motion of the atoms and ions due to heating provides sufficient pressure to support the mass. According to this idea, a non-rotating cloud of gas with mass about a million times that of the Sun could collapse under its own gravitational attraction. From such an event there would be a release of potential energy at a very large rate. The theory has it that the collapse might continue to a stage in which the mass is so concentrated and the gravitational field so high that neither optical nor radio energy could escape. Such invisible collapsed bodies which would still exert a gravitational influence might explain the high mass of some galaxies revealed by dynamics of clusters.

Another idea, due to T. Gold, is that even in a dense assemblage of stars such as a globular cluster or an elliptical galaxy some will acquire sufficient velocity to escape. When this happens the escaping star carries away a small excess share of the energy. In the long run the assemblage shrinks in size to a point where the stars are so crowded together that collisions are frequent. This would provide very large amounts of energy and, with the collisions occurring in an irregular manner, would explain the observed variability.

Radio Astronomy and Cosmology

The objects directly detected by radio astronomy and the quasi-stellar objects whose presence has been revealed by radio astronomy are so energetic that they can be observed to enormous distances that cannot be explored in any other way. They may well make an important contribution to the understanding of the structure of the universe as a whole. Once again counts of the objects are compared with a formula derived by assuming that the distribution is uniform and that the numbers are proportional to the volume in which they are counted. The formula was given in the section of counts of galaxies, in the form appropriate when the energy received is expressed in magnitudes. The change in appearance of the formula when the energy is expressed in some other way makes no essential difference.

Catalogues of radio sources have been used to graph the number of sources to various energy limits. The counts appear to indicate an excess of faint sources over the number that would be expected from an assumption of uniform distribution. Directly interpreted this suggests a denser distribution of sources in distant parts of the universe.

Counts of the quasi-stellar objects also have interest in the same way. When the number of blue objects brighter than each magnitude limit is plotted against the magnitude, the slope of the curve is at first low, indicating that the population being counted is falling off in density. At about magnitude 15 the slope increases sharply. This verifies that the population being counted is changed, now consisting largely of the quasi-stellar objects. Even then the slope corresponds to a falling density, contrary to the indications of the last paragraph. The interpretation of these results being obtained is complicated by the allowance that must be made for the red shift and possibly unknown phenomena which affect the energy received. There is the possibility however that the observations might lead to better understanding of the structure of the distant universe, the evolution of galaxies and the character of events in the remote past when the radiation now reaching us set out on its long journey.

THE DARKNESS OF THE SKY

There has been some discussion of observations which use the greatest resources of astronomy, and appear to have importance in studying the structure of the universe as a whole. Yet a commonplace observation with the naked eye has significance. This is that the sky is dark at night.

To begin examining how much light should be expected four assumptions may be made. First, the universe is infinite and provided a sample is taken by including a large enough representative volume the average density and luminosity of the stars do not vary throughout space. Second, the average density and luminosity of the stars do not vary with time. Third, on a large enough scale the movements of the stars average out, so no large scale motions form an essential property of the universe. Fourth, the laws of physics apply everywhere and always. Now a line from the observer in any direction has, in a finite distance, some probability, even if small, of intersecting the surface of a star, and in an infinite universe to which the four assumptions apply this probability would in the long run amount to a certainty. In this circumstance there would be light coming to us from the surface of a star in every direction over the whole sky—which should therefore shine as a surface several thousand degrees in temperature. That it does not do so is a paradox, named after Olbers, who drew attention to it in 1826.

The paradox is not resolved by supposing that some intervening material prevents most of the radiation from reaching us. To obstruct the radiation such material would need to absorb energy until finally it was giving off as much as it received. So there must be something wrong with the commencing assumptions. The fourth assumption does not appear to be questioned, although if it were breached the consequences might be far reaching. We are thus led to see that the universe has one or more of the properties of being finite in extent, of having a finite age or of including motion as a property.

The observed law of the red shifts accords with the existence of large scale motions and could provide a way out. The more quickly an object is moving away from us the more the wave-lengths of its spectrum as received on Earth are lengthened. The longer wave-lengths have less energy and consequently the increasing velocities ensure that less and less energy is received from more remote parts of the universe. If the universe has existed for only a finite time, the radiation from sufficient distance would not yet have reached us. The equilibrium stage with sky shining as the surface of star would, supposing the stars to shine long enough, be in the far future. If the space in which stars are distributed is finite or if the distribution is not uniform, then the line outward from the observer need never intersect a stellar surface.

The interest in Olbers' paradox lies in the revelation that such a simple observation as the darkness of the sky must be taken into account in theories of the universe. When one or more of the original assumptions is dropped, it becomes a matter of complicated calculation to verify whether a suggested model of the universe conforms to the density of radiation which is actually observed. The absorption of energy by intervening matter does have an effect and the finite amount of energy available from each star must be taken into account. With the assumption about infinite age dropped it has been calculated that it would take 10^{23} years for the background radiation density to reach the value at the surface of the stars. But the radiating life of a star is much less than this especially taking into account that most of the radiation comes from giant stars whose life is comparatively short.

THE STRUCTURE OF THE UNIVERSE

Mankind has always pondered on what the universe as a whole must be like, but it is only since the recognition of the nature of the galaxies that observation appears to make real contribution to the problem. The galaxies can now be observed to distances where their recessional velocities are an appreciable proportion of the velocity of light. If it is accepted that the velocity of light is the greatest velocity at which an influence can be propagated, this appears to indicate that we must be observing a significant portion of the universe or at any rate of the part of it which is observable from the Earth. We must try to infer the properties of the whole from the part we see. There have been developed several theories of the universe which can be judged only by comparing their results with those obtainable from observation. Although what seems to be good progress has been made, cosmologists are still a long way from agreeing about the structure of the universe.

The Cosmological Principle

Cosmology differs from other branches of science in that the object of study is unique. There is only one universe only a part of which has been observed. In other branches of science a theory is usually arrived at by the study of many examples and tested in its final form by examination of consequences in still further cases or in specially devised experiments. The laws of gravitation and of motion which apply to every individual piece of matter are examples of this. In cosmology, instead of finding by abstraction from many cases laws which describe physical events, we are compelled to rely on deduction, depending with varied emphasis on credible assumptions about properties of the universe and extensions of the physics found from experience in our neighbourhood.

The most necessary assumption, common to all of the theories, is that the part near to us is a fair sample of the universe, which would have the same general aspect from whichever point it might be examined. This is called the *cosmological principle*. The laws of physics observed here are taken to be obeyed everywhere, or if any wider laws are found to belong to the cosmological theories, they must reach a close approximation to the usual laws when applied within the volumes, small compared with the whole universe, in which the terrestrial laws have been derived and in which they are known to apply with more or less accuracy. Some such axiom is necessary as a basis for progress in the problem of the structure of the universe, but in this case we are fairly familiar with the principle in a somewhat restricted form. The repetition of an experiment to test a fundamental rule of physics is expected to yield the same result whenever and wherever it is repeated. In fact, we would never have had any laws of nature if they depended on time and place because, owing to our motion in space, a repeated experiment always occurs at a point different in space as well as time. So, although it must be kept in mind that it is an assumption, the cosmological principle is of the most natural and minimal kind.

Observed Properties of the Universe

From observation is learned something of the composition, density and organization of the matter in the universe. To judge by our neighbourhood the constituents are mainly hydrogen and helium in the ratio about 2:1 by mass with only one or two per cent contributed by all of the remaining elements (mainly carbon, nitrogen, oxygen and metals).

The observable material is mainly in stars. However, about six or eight per cent is in the gas and dust of interstellar space and a much smaller proportion by mass is in the cosmic rays, which may nevertheless carry an appreciable proportion of the energy. This material is further organized into systems some tens of thousands of light-years across. The galaxies average perhaps three or four million light-years apart and, while showing a tendency to cluster, are scattered throughout the whole of the space that can be observed.

The average density of matter in the universe is low. An estimate from the observable material corresponds to a mass of the order of one pound in a cube of side 100,000 miles. This is a lower limit, for most of it is in the stars, and nothing can make distant matter so evident as collection into shining stars. There could be several times as much spread thinly in the space between the galaxies, perhaps in the form of hydrogen atoms, without it being observable by means so far available. The density of radiation, converted by the usual factor relating energy to matter, is only a very small fraction, about 1/100,000 of the density of the matter.

The remaining property is the relation between red shift and magnitude in the galaxies. According to this, the universe is in a state of expansion. With the red shift interpreted in the usual way the relative velocity between any two galaxies is such that they were close together about 10^{10} years ago.

Evolutionary Theories of the Universe

There is a group of theories in which, assuming our locality to be representative of the universe as a whole, there are sought the possible forms of the locally determined laws which can be solved to derive characteristics of the universe. The physics of either Newton or Einstein can be extended to yield cosmologies. Einstein was convinced that the theory of mechanics should reveal connections between local physics, on which it is based, and the constitution of the universe. The field equations of Einstein's theory of relativity have several solutions, each of which gives a corresponding model of the universe. It is a triumph of theory that the expansion of the universe was a feature of these solutions before it was discovered observationally. The phenomenon of expansion can also be fitted in with the Newtonian theories of mechanics and gravitation.

The formulation of the bases of the theories in a shape suitable for solution and the steps in the solution are mathematically technical, but the yielded models of the universe are easy to summarize. They are of two kinds. First, there are those in which an oscillation takes place between very small and very large radius. If the actual universe is of this kind our epoch is in an expanding phase. Second, there are those in which the universe began in a state of high density and small size from which the expansion will go on for infinite time. In a model of this kind—colloquially known as the *"big bang"* theory—the expansion began in an explosion which occurred presumably about 10^{10} years ago according to the present value of the Hubble constant. In this case the formation of the galaxies may have begun and the present abundance of the elements been set in the first stage of explosion rather than in later processes.

These two types of theory may be difficult to distinguish by observational tests. They are *evolutionary theories* and attribute to the universe a past and future different from the present. This appears to agree with the observed expansion and with the evolutionary processes occurring in the components of the universe. A feature of these models of the universe is the high density phase about 10^{10} years ago when the expansion began. The theories do not explain how this phase came about, what its previous history was nor how the expansion began.

The Steady-State Theory

Some cosmologists, instead of extending local physics to obtain a description of the universe, begin with assumptions about its general character and find its properties by deduction from these. To the cosmological principle is added the postulate that the universe also presents the same aspect through all time. This is called the *perfect cosmological principle*. This principle is not as artificial as may at first appear. In connection with the cosmological principle it was pointed out that an experiment is expected to give the same result not only wherever but also whenever it is repeated. Moreover, it is generally thought that there are connections between local physical laws and the universe at large. How else is it possible to explain that the rate of rotation of the Earth, found from mechanical experiments as described in Chapter 4, is the same as the rate found in relation to distant stars and to galaxies? Therefore, as soon as we postulate the constancy of the laws of physics, it is natural to think of a corresponding constancy in the universe. The surprisingly few and simple assumptions are sufficient basis for development of a cosmology which, since on a large scale the universe is unchanging, is called the *steady-state theory*.

Since this theory accepts three of the four postulates which lead to Olbers' paradox, it presents the conclusion that the universe is expanding as the observations have indicated. In the presence of such expansion the average density of the matter in the universe would be decreasing unless some compensating factor were present. Hence it is deduced that, to maintain the universe in a steady state, matter is being created at a rate to provide for the compensation. The rate at which matter would have to appear is so small as to be far below the possibility of direct observation. The new matter would most probably arrive in the form of atoms of hydrogen, which provides the raw material of which the universe is built. At a later stage the heavier atoms would be formed in stellar processes. While old galaxies of the same age are, owing to the expansion of the universe, drifting apart, new ones are forming from the incoming matter. So, young galaxies intermingle with the old, and, although any particular galaxy may be very ancient, the average age in a given volume of space is only about 4×10^9 years.

Observational Trial of Models of the Universe

The decision between the theories of the universe must rest upon the evidence of astronomical observation. It may be difficult to distinguish observationally between the different evolutionary models, but it may be possible in the not too distant future to decide whether the steady-state theory is possible or whether consideration must be confined to models in which evolution is taking place. It is a clear indication of the imperfect state of present knowledge that such very different points of view can be held by informed and expert cosmologists. The discrimination can be attempted when the theories give different results for a phenomenon accessible to observation. The attempts involve exploration to great distances and observations requiring the best resources of astronomy. The chance of choosing a unique model for the universe must still be remote.

An important contact between theory and observation occurs in the relation between red shift and magnitude for distant galaxies. It has been shown that all models which conform to the cosmological principle have at a given time a relation of the same mathematical form between distance and red shift. However, different models predict different variations with time of the velocities of recession, and so an observational test is provided. Because of the finite speed of light, the remote galaxies are observed with the velocities they had when the light left them. For example, if in the universe the velocity of expansion is decreasing, the distant galaxies will be receding faster than would be indicated from the relation determined from observation of nearby galaxies. Because different models predict different variations with time in the rate of expansion, there is a possibility that the relation between red shift and magnitude can be refined to provide a test between cosmological models, even different evolutionary models.

The relation between a count of galaxies and the limiting magnitude to which the count is made has been shown to give an indication of the distribution with distance. Such counts may be made either by optical or radio methods. Once again the fact that distant parts of space are observed at a remote epoch suggests a test of the theories. The steady-state theory indicates that the distribution of galaxies has not changed with time. However, evolutionary models, in which expansion occurs without compensation by the creation of new matter, predict that the space density of galaxies was greater in the past and hence that they should at faint magnitudes be more frequent than would correspond to a uniform distribution in space.

The different cosmological theories predict different forms for the population of galaxies. In the steady-state theory the population characteristics should everywhere be the same with the same proportion of young and old galaxies. In evolutionary theories the distant galaxies from which the light has taken so long to come to us should be seen at a younger age than the nearer ones, and so there should be, with distance, a variation in the fre-

P

quency of galaxies according to their stage of development. This is a difficult test to apply because the theories of evolution of galaxies are probably still inadequate, but even more because the lack of resolution in the small images of very distant galaxies makes them hard to classify in detail. A similar line of thought may apply to clusters of galaxies. If these are evolving they too might present different aspects when viewed at different distances and, consequently, at different times.

A theory of the universe should not be in conflict with fairly well-established knowledge of its component parts. In the evolutionary theories an apparent incompatibility exists because the age of the oldest stars is estimated to be somewhat more than the time allowed since the discontinuity in the history of the universe when the expansion began about 10^{10} years ago (as judged by the present value of the Hubble constant). In this respect the steady-state theory has an advantage. Then, too, the chemical composition of the universe must correspond to the theory. This will be different depending on whether it was set in a high density explosive epoch in which expansion began or has been determined by stellar processes throughout the ages.

In this century there has been an enormous expansion of our knowledge of the universe. Many of the techniques in which lie the hopes of finding the structure of the universe are in their infancy. The rate of advance is swift, although it sometimes appears more rapid than it really is in fundamentals. However, there is no manifest impassible barrier to further progress, and no one can foresee the direction it will be taking in 15 or 20 years time.

12

A CYCLE OF OBJECTS

THIS is a strictly practical chapter. Many readers will want to see and recognise objects mentioned in the text, and so tables of the most interesting ones are given. It is necessary only to give the right ascension and declination of such an object to enable its position to be located among the stars on the star maps and sought in the corresponding place in the sky. Many can be seen with the unaided eye—if not, a short search around the locality with a small telescope should be sufficient to find it. In most cases the magnitude will indicate the measures necessary, optical aid being needed when the object is fainter than sixth magnitude. To seventh or eighth magnitude field glasses or a small hand telescope suffice, and beyond that an appropriate telescope.

The lists should enable those who have telescopes soon to become familiar with a representative selection of objects and, if they so wish, should help them to prepare programmes for the entertainment of friends. This can be an endless source of pleasure to the interested amateur. Although the Moon is not listed—for it needs no directions for finding—it is as well to remember that, because so many details are easy to see, it provides the most fascination for the newcomer to the telescope. So it is well to arrange for demonstrations when the Moon is about first quarter and when, if possible, a planet is in the sky.

First are listed directions for finding the naked-eye planets from Mercury to Saturn. Their wanderings among the stars may be traced and, with a small telescope, their changes may be watched. Such changes include the phases of Venus, the phenomena of Jupiter's satellites or Saturn's rings, and the waxing and waning of the polar caps of Mars. Next are given representative lists of various objects more distant in space. In compiling these lists an effort has been made to select the objects from over as wide an area of sky as possible so that the observer may find examples whatever the season or wherever his situation in the world. Of course, we have to accept the heavens as they are and this effort has in some cases been only partly successful. The column headings of the tables show that in each case the object is given a name—for which, in the later tables, the NGC number is used—and the right ascension and declination for 1950. These should enable the object to be found by the use of the methods of Chapter 2. The visual magnitude is usually included, the distance in light-years and, for stellar objects, the spectral class. Then there may be columns to show type or alternative names which for objects in the later tables are often numbers in the Messier Catalogue of 1781. Since Messier observed with a small telescope, a Messier number is a guarantee that the object is fairly easy to observe. Numbers preceeded by a Greek Δ refer to the Catalogue, published in 1828, of James Dunlop, who observed at Parramatta near Sydney.

ON FINDING THE PLANETS

Mercury and Venus move so quickly that it would require an unduly long table to describe their motion in the sky with any detail. As they are both best seen near the times when the elongation—that is, angular distance from the Sun—is greatest, it seemed best to give a list of these times. For eastern elongations the planet is an evening star and for western elongations a morning star. The greatest elongations of Mercury are given in Table 9,

TABLE 9

Greatest Eastern Elongations of Mercury

1966	March 5, June 30, October 26.
1967	February 16, June 12, October 9.
1968	January 31, May 23, September 21.
1969	January 13, May 5, September 3, December 28.
1970	April 17, August 16, December 11.
1971	March 31, July 29, November 23.
1972	March 14, July 10, November 5.
1973	February 25, June 22, October 19.
1974	February 9, June 4, October 1.
1975	January 23, May 16, September 14.

Greatest Western Elongations of Mercury

1966	April 18, August 16, December 4.
1967	March 31, July 30, November 17.
1968	March 13, July 11, October 31.
1969	February 23, June 22, October 15.
1970	February 5, June 4, September 28.
1971	January 18, May 17, September 12.
1972	January 1, April 28, August 25, December 14.
1973	April 10, August 8, November 27.
1974	March 24, July 23, November 10.
1975	March 6, July 4, October 25.

and of Venus in Table 10. The approximate calculation may place the time in a date neighbouring the true one, which in any case would change for different standard times. Venus is so much brighter than any star that its identification is unmistakable if it is in the sky. Mercury, too, is bright enough to leave no ambiguity if the observer knows the first magnitude stars. Both planets remain fairly close to the ecliptic and so are highest above the horizon, when greatest elongation occurs, with the ecliptic tilted most steeply to the horizon. Thus, wherever the observer may be, elongations occurring in spring are best for evening apparitions of either planet, and in autumn for morning apparitions. Because of the large eccentricity of the orbit, the greatest elongations of Mercury range from 18° to 28°. Eastern elongations occurring in August and neighbouring months are best in

TABLE 10

Venus, Greatest Elongations

Eastern Elongation		Western Elongation	
1965	November 15	1966	April 7
1967	June 20	1967	November 9
1969	January 26	1969	June 18
1970	August 31	1971	January 21
1972	April 8	1972	August 27
1973	November 13	1974	April 4
1975	June 18	1975	November 7

this respect and western elongations about March and April. So, for southern observers, who have their spring in September, both the slope of the ecliptic and the angle from the Sun are favourable for eastern elongations around this time of the year. The two circumstances do not at any time work together for the northern observer. Since the angular distance of Mercury from the Sun is never large, the planet is best looked for fairly near the times of greatest elongation. The conditions are not so exacting for Venus, which may be well seen as an evening star for periods longer than from 100 days before to 50 days after greatest eastern elongation or as a morning star from 50 days before to 100 days after greatest western elongation. Venus if present in the sky is so bright as to be always obvious, indeed spectacular.

Tables 11, 12 and 13 give the right ascensions of Mars, Jupiter and Saturn to the decimal of an hour until the end of 1975. Since the planets are always not far from the ecliptic, provision of only the right ascensions enables them to be found. For example, in the middle of January 1968 Jupiter will have right ascension 10·4 hours which, including its proximity to the ecliptic, will place it on Map IV in the constellation Leo. Since Mars moves more quickly, it is necessary to tabulate its place at more frequent intervals than for Jupiter and Saturn. If the portion of the sky corresponding to the planet's place is above the horizon, it should be easy to find.

THE BRIGHT STARS

Table 14 includes particulars of all of the stars brighter than magnitude 1·5. An acquaintance with these stars is worthwhile as an aid to finding a way around the heavens. A column is added for the absolute magnitude, M—for which there may be more than one entry if the star is multiple, when there are also multiple entries in the column for the spectral class.

TABLE 11

Right Ascension of Mars

		1966	1967	1968	1969	1970	1971	1972	1973	1974	1975
		h	h	h	h	h	h	h	h	h	h
Jan.	1	20·6	12·9	21·7	14·0	22·9	14·9	0·2	15·9	2·0	16·9
	11	21·2	13·2	22·2	14·3	23·4	15·3	0·6	16·4	2·2	17·4
	21	21·7	13·4	22·7	14·7	23·8	15·8	1·0	16·9	2·5	17·9
	31	22·2	13·7	23·2	15·0	0·3	16·2	1·4	17·4	2·8	18·5
Feb.	10	22·7	13·9	23·7	15·4	0·7	16·6	1·8	17·9	3·2	19·0
	20	23·2	14·0	0·1	15·7	1·2	17·1	2·2	18·4	3·5	19·5
Mar.	2	23·6	14·1	0·7	16·0	1·6	17·5	2·7	18·9	3·9	20·0
	12	0·1	14·1	1·1	16·3	2·1	18·0	3·1	19·4	4·3	20·6
	22	0·6	14·0	1·6	16·5	2·5	18·4	3·6	19·9	4·7	21·1
Apr.	1	1·1	13·9	2·0	16·7	3·0	18·8	4·0	20·4	5·1	21·6
	11	1·5	13·7	2·5	16·9	3·5	19·2	4·5	20·9	5·6	22·1
	21	2·0	13·4	3·0	17·0	3·9	19·6	5·0	21·4	6·0	22·6
May	1	2·5	13·2	3·5	17·0	4·4	20·0	5·4	21·8	6·4	23·1
	11	3·0	13·0	4·0	16·9	4·9	20·4	5·9	22·3	6·9	23·5
	21	3·4	12·9	4·4	16·8	5·4	20·7	6·4	22·7	7·3	0·0
	31	3·9	12·9	4·9	16·5	5·9	21·0	6·9	23·2	7·8	0·5
Jun.	10	4·4	13·0	5·4	16·3	6·4	21·3	7·3	23·6	8·2	0·9
	20	4·9	13·1	5·9	16·1	6·8	21·5	7·8	0·0	8·6	1·4
	30	5·4	13·3	6·4	16·0	7·3	21·6	8·2	0·4	9·0	1·8

Jul. 10	5·9	13·5	6·9	15·9	7·8	21·7	8·6	0·8	9·4	2·3
20	6·4	13·8	7·4	16·0	8·2	21·7	9·1	1·2	9·8	2·7
30	6·9	14·1	7·8	16·1	8·7	21·6	9·5	1·5	10·2	3·2
Aug. 9	7·4	14·5	8·3	16·4	9·1	21·4	9·9	1·8	10·6	3·6
19	7·8	14·9	8·7	16·7	9·5	21·3	10·3	2·1	11·0	4·0
29	8·3	15·3	9·2	17·0	9·9	21·1	10·7	2·3	11·4	4·4
Sep. 8	8·7	15·7	9·6	17·4	10·4	21·1	11·1	2·4	11·8	4·8
18	9·1	16·2	10·0	17·8	10·7	21·1	11·5	2·5	12·2	5·2
28	9·6	16·7	10·4	18·3	11·1	21·2	11·9	2·5	12·6	5·5
Oct. 8	10·0	17·2	10·8	18·8	11·5	21·4	12·3	2·3	13·0	5·8
18	10·4	17·7	11·2	19·3	11·9	21·6	12·7	2·1	13·4	6·0
28	10·7	18·2	11·6	19·8	12·3	21·9	13·1	1·9	13·8	6·1
Nov. 7	11·1	18·8	11·9	20·3	12·7	22·2	13·5	1·7	14·3	6·2
17	11·4	19·3	12·3	20·8	13·1	22·5	13·9	1·6	14·7	6·1
27	11·8	19·9	12·7	21·3	13·5	22·9	14·3	1·6	15·2	5·9
Dec. 7	12·1	20·4	13·0	21·7	13·9	23·2	14·8	1·6	15·6	5·7
17	12·4	21·0	13·4	22·2	14·3	23·6	15·2	1·7	16·1	5·4
27	12·8	21·5	13·8	22·7	14·7	0·0	15·7	1·9	16·6	5·2

TABLE 12

Right Ascension of Jupiter

		1966 h	1967 h	1968 h	1969 h	1970 h	1971 h	1972 h	1973 h	1974 h	1975 h
Jan.	1	5·6	8·3	10·5	12·3	14·0	15·7	17·4	19·3	21·1	23·0
	21	5·4	8·1	10·4	12·4	14·2	15·9	17·7	19·6	21·4	23·2
Feb.	10	5·4	7·9	10·3	12·4	14·2	16·1	18·0	19·9	21·7	23·5
Mar.	2	5·4	7·8	10·1	12·2	14·2	16·2	18·3	20·2	22·0	23·8
	22	5·5	7·8	10·0	12·1	14·2	16·3	18·5	20·5	22·3	0·0
Apr.	11	5·7	7·8	9·9	11·9	14·0	16·3	18·6	20·7	22·6	0·3
May	1	5·9	7·9	9·9	11·8	13·9	16·1	18·6	20·9	22·8	0·6
	21	6·2	8·1	10·0	11·8	13·7	16·0	18·5	21·0	23·0	0·9
Jun.	10	6·5	8·4	10·1	11·8	13·6	15·8	18·4	20·9	23·2	1·1
	30	6·8	8·6	10·3	11·9	13·6	15·7	18·2	20·9	23·3	1·3
Jul.	20	7·2	8·9	10·5	12·0	13·7	15·6	18·0	20·7	23·3	1·5
Aug.	9	7·5	9·2	10·7	12·3	13·8	15·6	17·9	20·5	23·2	1·5
	29	7·8	9·5	11·0	12·5	14·0	15·7	17·9	20·4	23·0	1·5
Sep.	18	8·0	9·8	11·3	12·7	14·2	15·9	17·9	20·3	22·9	1·4
Oct.	8	8·2	10·0	11·6	13·0	14·5	16·1	18·1	20·3	22·8	1·3
	28	8·4	10·2	11·8	13·3	14·7	16·4	18·3	20·4	22·7	1·1
Nov.	17	8·4	10·4	12·0	13·5	15·0	16·7	18·6	20·6	22·7	1·0
Dec.	7	8·4	10·5	12·2	13·8	15·3	17·0	18·9	20·8	22·8	0·9
	27	8·3	10·5	12·3	14·0	15·6	17·3	19·2	21·1	22·9	0·9

TABLE 13

Right Ascension of Saturn

	1966	1967	1968	1969	1970	1971	1972	1973	1974	1975
	h	h	h	h	h	h	h	h	h	h
Jan. 1	23·0	23·7	0·4	1·2	2·0	2·9	3·9	4·9	6·0	7·1
31	23·1	23·8	0·5	1·3	2·1	2·9	3·8	4·8	5·8	7·0
Mar. 2	23·3	0·0	0·7	1·5	2·2	3·0	3·9	4·8	5·8	6·8
Apr. 1	23·6	0·3	1·0	1·7	2·4	3·2	4·1	4·9	5·9	6·9
May 1	23·8	0·5	1·2	1·9	2·7	3·4	4·3	5·2	6·1	7·0
31	23·9	0·7	1·4	2·1	2·9	3·7	4·6	5·4	6·3	7·2
Jun. 30	0·0	0·8	1·5	2·3	3·1	3·9	4·8	5·7	6·6	7·5
Jul. 30	0·0	0·8	1·6	2·4	3·3	4·2	5·1	6·0	6·8	7·7
Aug. 29	23·9	0·8	1·6	2·5	3·4	4·3	5·2	6·2	7·1	8·0
Sep. 28	23·8	0·6	1·5	2·4	3·3	4·3	5·3	6·3	7·3	8·2
Oct. 28	23·7	0·5	1·4	2·3	3·2	4·2	5·3	6·3	7·3	8·3
Nov. 27	23·6	0·4	1·2	2·1	3·1	4·1	5·1	6·2	7·3	8·3
Dec. 27	23·7	0·4	1·2	2·0	2·9	3·9	5·0	6·0	7·1	8·2

The list may be compared with Table 7, Chapter 9, with which there are only two stars in common. The tendency for stars to be multiple is exhibited in this list as it was among the nearby stars. The absolute magnitudes provide the great contrast with Table 7. Most of these stars are much brighter than the Sun, several are super-giant stars and two, Rigel and Deneb, appear to give out about 50,000 times as much light as the Sun.

TABLE 14

The Bright Stars

Name	R.A.		Dec.	Mag.	Distance	M	Spectrum
	h	m	o		l-y		
Achernar	1	36	−57·5	0·47	140	−2·6	B5
Aldebaran	4	33	+16·4	0·86	68	−0·6, +12	K5, M2
Rigel	5	12	− 8·2	0·08	1100	−7·5 0	B8
Capella	5	13	+46·0	0·09	45	−0·4, −0·3	G8, F
Betelgeuse	5	52	+ 7·4	0·8	650	−5	M2
Canopus	6	23	−52·7	−0·73	180	−4·6	F0
Sirius	6	43	−16·6	−1·47	8·7	+1·3, +10·0	A0, A5
Castor	7	31	+32·0	1·56	45	+1·2, +2·2	A1, A5
Procyon	7	37	+ 5·4	0·34	11·3	+2·8, +13	F5
Pollux	7	42	+28·1	1·15	35	+1·1	K0
Regulus	10	06	+12·2	1·36	83	−1·0, +5·3, +12	B7, K1
α Crucis	12	24	−62·8	0·83	260	−3·0, −2·5	B1, B3
β Crucis	12	45	−59·4	1·24	440	−4·5	B0
Spica	13	23	−10·9	0·96	155	−3·1	B1
β Centauri	14	0	−60·1	0·59	200	−5·0, −2	B1
Arcturus	14	13	+19·4	0·06	36	0·0	K2
α Centauri	14	36	−60·6	−0·27	4·3	+4·7, +6·1	G2, K1
Antares	16	26	−26·3	1·1	170	−2·4, +3	M1, B4
Vega	18	35	+38·7	0·04	26	+0·5	A0
Altair	19	48	+ 8·7	0·77	16·5	+2·3	A7
Deneb	20	40	+45·1	1·26		−7	A2
Fomalhaut	22	55	−29·9	1·16	22·6	+2·1	A3

Notes to Table 14:

     Aldebaran is a visual double. The companion has magnitude 13, distance 31″.

     Rigel is a visual double. The companion is distance 9″ and magnitude 7·4. The main star is a spectroscopic binary of period 9·9 days and the companion is a close visual binary.

     Capella is a spectroscopic binary of period 104 days. It has also been measured by an optical method.

     Betelgeuse is a semi-regular variable with period about 7 years varying from 0·4 to 1·3 magnitude.

     Sirius is in Tables 7 and 15, where there is a longer note in the text.

     Castor is in Table 15, where it is the subject of a note.

     Procyon is a double of period 40 years. The companion is a white dwarf.

     Regulus is triple. The B7 star has a seventh-magnitude companion at distance 176″. The companion has a thirteenth-magnitude component at distance 3″.

     α Crucis is in Table 15.

     Spica is a spectroscopic binary of period 4 days.

     β Centauri has a companion of magnitude 4·1 and distance 1·3″.

     α Centauri is in Tables 7 and 15, where there is a longer note.

     Antares is in Table 15, where there is a longer note. Antares is a semi-regular variable, 0·9 to 1·8.

DOUBLE AND MULTIPLE STARS

Pairs of physically associated stars may be separated by widely different distances. Some, like μ Scorpii, ϵ Scorpii and ϵ Lyrae, can be seen as double by the naked eye while others are so close as to defy the powers of the greatest telescopes in the world. It is only some of those divided by the telescope that are so close as to have an orbital period short enough for appreciable motion to be observed.

Particulars are given in Table 15 of some of the more interesting and observable doubles. Some of the stars in this Table are famous ones with interesting information in addition to that contained in the Table. All are visible to the naked eye. The magnitudes and spectra of the components are given in the fourth column. If the spectrum is composite or complicated in some way, it has sometimes not been given. In the fifth column the separation between the components is given. If the star is triple, the distances from the brightest component are in this column.

TABLE 15

Double and Multiple Stars

Name	R.A.		Dec.	Mag. Sp.	Sep.	Distance
	h	m	o		"	l-y
β Tucanae	0	29	−63·2	4·5, A2: 4·5, B9	27	110
γ Andromedae	2	01	+42·0	2·3, K0: 5·0, A0	10	
θ Eridani	2	56	−40·5	3·4, A2: 4·4, A2	9	120
32 Eridani	3	52	− 3·1	5·0, G8: 6·3, A1	7	
λ Orionis	5	32	+ 9·9	3·7, O5: 5·6	4·4	
σ Orionis	5	36	− 2·6	multiple		
β Monocerotis	6	26	− 7·0	4·7: 5·2: 5·6	7, 10	150
12 Lyncis	6	42	+59·5	5·3: 6·2: 8·5	2, 8	190
Sirius	6	43	−16·6	−1·6, A0: 7·1, A5		8·7
Castor	7	31	+32·0	2·0: 2·8		45
κ Puppis	7	37	−26·7	4·5, B8: 4·6, B3	10	
ι Cancri	8	44	+29·0	4·2, G8: 6·6, A3	30	160
γ Leonis	10	17	+20·1	2·6, K0: 3·8, G7	4·4	170
α Crucis	12	24	−62·8	1·6, B1: 2·1, B3	5	260
γ Virginis	12	39	− 1·2	3·7, F0: 3·7, F0		32
ζ Ursae Majoris	13	22	+55·2	2·4, A2: 4·0, A2	14·5	90
α Centauri	14	36	−60·6	0·3, G2: 1·7, K1		4·3
ϵ Boötis	14	43	+27·3	2·7, K0: 5·1, A2	2·7	
Antares	16	26	−26·3	1·2, M1: 6·5, B4	2·9	170
α Herculis	17	12	+14·5	3, M: 6·1, G	4·8	
ϵ Lyrae	18	43	+39·6	quadruple	207	
γ Coronae Austrinae	19	03	−37·1	5·0, F8: 5·0, F8	2	65
β Cygni	19	29	+27·9	3·2, K5: 5·4, B8	35	
γ Delphini	20	44	+16·0	4·5, K1: 5·5, F7	12	150
ζ Aquarii	22	26	− 0·3	4·4, F2: 4·6, F2		

From the point of view of spectacle the finest doubles are α Centauri, α Crucis and Castor. Interesting contrasts of colour occur when the components are widely different in spectral class. A beautiful example is ϵ Boötis. Others are γ Andromedae, 32 Eridani, ι Cancri and γ Delphini.

In β Tucanae the component whose spectrum is A2 is binary, of orbital period 43 years, too close for resolution except in a large telescope. The other star has a faint companion.

The fifth-magnitude star of γ Andromedae is double with components of magnitudes $5 \cdot 4$ and $6 \cdot 6$. The period is 310 years and the separation during the next few years about $0''.5$. The third magnitude component of θ Eridani is a spectroscopic binary. σ Orionis is a fine multiple star. The brightest star is a blue B0 star of magnitude $3 \cdot 8$, a spectroscopic binary, and there are several others visible in a small telescope.

Sirius, besides being the brightest star in the sky, has an interesting history. About 1844 Bessel noticed that its proper motion varied in a regular fashion. He was able to account for this by attributing to the star an invisible companion revolving about it and pulling it by gravitational attraction away from a straight path. This companion star was first seen in 1862 when a new telescope was being tested. The orbit was worked out and the mass of each component found. The mass of the main component is $2 \cdot 4$ times and of the faint one $0 \cdot 9$ times that of the Sun. But this was not the end of the story. The companion is so faint that it was naturally thought that it would prove to be a cool star not radiating much from each unit of area. However, when its spectrum was examined—a considerable feat in view of its closeness to so bright a star as Sirius—it was found to be much hotter than the Sun and correspondingly radiating a great deal more for each unit of its area. There was no escape therefore from the conclusion that its area, and radius, must be small and that it must have enormously high density. A ton of material of the average density of Sirius B would fit into a match box. Thus was discovered the first white dwarf. The period of revolution of the binary is 50 years. It is at greatest separation of $11''.2$ in about 1974 so that at present and for some time the companion is visible in comparatively small telescopes. The great brightness of the primary makes good atmospheric conditions necessary for it to be seen as double.

The orbital period of Castor is 380 years and the semi-major axis $5''.9$. It is expected to reach its smallest separation of $1''.7$ about 1969 after which it will open out again. Both components are spectroscopic binaries. The brighter component has a period of nine days and the fainter one three days. There is a star $73''$ away which varies from $8 \cdot 6$ to $9 \cdot 1$ mag. and has common proper motion with Castor. It, too, is a spectroscopic binary of period $0 \cdot 8$ day.

γ Leonis has a calculated orbital period of 620 years. Both components of α Crucis are spectroscopic binaries, each of period about a day. γ Virginis has a period of 171 years and semi-major axis $3''.7$. In 1965 its separation was $4''.8$ and in 1970 it will be $4''.6$.

The brighter component of ζ Ursae Majoris was the first spectroscopic binary to be discovered. It has a period of twenty days and has been observed by special techniques at the telescope although its semi-major axis is only $0''.01$, quite impossible to see visually with any telescope.

α Centauri is a famous double star with a period of 80 years and semi-major axis $17''.6$. It was closest in 1958 and at present is opening out. The separation was 12″·9 in 1965 and will be 18″·2 in 1970. The mean distance between the components is two-thousand-million miles. In 1839 the distance of Alpha Centauri, one of the first determined, was revealed from meridian observation at the Cape Observatory to be 4·3 light-years. In 1915, almost three degrees from it there was found a faint star, now named Proxima Centauri, which has a very similar proper motion and a distance measured at 4·2 light-years. These are the nearest stars to us. They occur also in Table 7.

Because of the difference in brightness good atmospheric conditions are needed to see Antares as double. The contrast of colour makes it interesting. The primary is a giant star of radius over 400,000,000 miles.

The bright component of α Herculis is an irregular variable of small range and period about 51 days. ϵ Lyrae is a naked-eye double each component of which proves to be double in the telescope. One star has components with magnitudes 5·0 and 6·0 and separation 3″ and the other 5·1, 5·4 and 2″. They are all physically connected with a common proper motion.

γ Coronae Austrinae has a period of 119 years and semi-major axis 2″·0. The bright component of β Cygni is a spectroscopic binary. ζ Aquarii has a period of 400 years and semi-major axis 3″·4. At present it is closing in. The distance in 1965 was 1″·5 and in 1970 will be 1″·2.

TABLE 16

Variable Stars

Name	R.A. h	m	Dec. o	Max.	Min.	Period days	Sp	Type
R Sculptoris	1	25	−32·8	5·8	7·7	376	N	long period
Mira	2	17	− 3·2	2·0	10·1	331	M6	long period
Algol	3	05	+40·8	2·2	3·5	2·9	B8	eclipsing
R Leporis	4	57	−14·9	5·5	10·7	436	N	long period
UU Aurigae	6	33	+38·5	5·1	6·8	3,400	N	semi-regular
L₂ Puppis	7	12	−44·6	3·4	6·2	140	M5	long period
1 Carinae	9	44	−62·3	5·0	6·0	36	F8–K0	cepheid
U Antliae	10	33	−39·3	5·7	6·8		N	irregular
U Hydrae	10	35	−13·1	4·8	5·8		N	irregular
Y Canum Ven.	12	43	+45·7	5·2	6·6	158	N	semi-regular
R Hydrae	13	27	−23·0	3·5	10·9	389	M7	long period
g Herculis	16	27	+42·0	4·6	6·0	80	M6	semi-regular
R Scuti	18	45	− 5·8	5·0	8·4	144	G0–M5	semi-regular
β Lyrae	18	48	+33·3	3·4	4·3	12·9	B8	eclipsing
κ Pavonis	18	52	−67·3	4·8	5·7	9·1	F5–G5	cepheid
χ Cygni	19	49	+32·8	2·3	14·3	407	M6	long period
μ Cephei	21	42	+58·6	3·6	5·1		M2	semi-regular
δ Cephei	22	27	+58·2	3·8	4·6	5·4	F5–G2	cepheid
19 Piscium	23	44	+ 3·2	6·7	7·7		N	irregular

VARIABLE STARS

It is interesting to watch the changing brightness of the variable stars some examples of which are given in Table 16. Columns 4, 5 and 6 give respectively the magnitude at maximum brightness, minimum brightness

Q

and the period. By comparing the brightness with that of nearby stars of similar magnitude the changes may be observed. The easiest ones to see are the long period variables Mira, L₂ Puppis, R Hydrae and χ Cygni. These are so very different at different times that casual observation will show the changes. The intrinsic variables of the Table are red stars. Those of spectral type N have been included partly because their red colour is so marked as to make them a striking spectacle worth looking at or showing to visitors to your telescope. It is desirable to remember that a star of great range of variation may be too faint to be obvious and that care is necessary if you want to avoid having to make explanations when you try to show an object which cannot be found.

Careful observation of variable stars is a field in which amateur astronomers do useful work. Most amateur astronomical societies have groups devoted to observation of variable stars. Charts are issued for finding the variable and suitable comparison stars, together with directions for making and recording the observations.

STAR CLUSTERS

The star clusters are among the most beautiful objects in the sky. Most of the galactic clusters on the list are visible to the naked eye, but the only globular clusters to be seen without optical aid are 47 Tucanae and ω Centauri. The Hyades are scattered in Taurus so that the members of the cluster are chiefly distinguished by their common proper motion. The Pleiades are best seen with binoculars or a telescope of low power although six of them are naked-eye stars for most people—and a few more for people

TABLE 17

Galactic Clusters

NGC	R.A.		Dec.	Total	Distance	
	h	m	o	Mag.	l-y	
752	1	55	+37·4	6	3,200	
869	2	16	+56·9	4	7,000	h Persei
884	2	19	+56·9	4	7,500	χ Persei
Pleiades	3	44	+24·0	2	400	M45
Hyades	4	18	+15·5	1	130	
1912	5	25	+35·8	7	3,200	M38
2168	6	06	+24·3	5	2,800	M35
2287	6	45	−20·7	5	2,500	M41
2516	8	00	−60·7	4	1,200	
2632	8	38	+19·9	4	520	M44 Praesepe
3114	10	01	−59·9	4	1,000	
3532	11	03	−58·4	3	1,400	
3766	11	34	−61·3	4	1,700	Δ289
4755	12	51	−60·1	5	5,200	κ Crucis
6231	16	51	−41·7	4	1,100	
6475	17	51	−34·8	4	700	M7
6494	17	54	−19·0	7	4,500	M23
6633	18	25	+ 6·5	6	1,100	
7092	21	30	+48·2	5	860	M39

with exceptionally keen eyes. Praesepe is resolved in binoculars. As a general rule a galactic cluster is best seen by the power with which it just fails to fill the field. The finest cluster is NGC 3532. All of the clusters with Messier numbers are worthy of acquaintance. The finest galactic star clusters, unlike some other objects, fully live up to the promise they offer in photographs with large instruments.

With binoculars the globular clusters show only as hazy patches of light but with sufficient optical power the clusters resolve into thousands of stars. It is interesting to view them in both ways. A telescope of about 6-inch aperture shows those on the list very nicely. The best ones are 47 Tucanae, ω Centauri and M13.

TABLE 18

Globular Clusters

NGC	R.A. h m	Dec. o	Mag.	Distance l-y	
104	0 22	−72·4	3·0	15,000	47 Tucanae
5139	13 24	−47·0	3·0	16,000	ω Centauri
5272	13 40	+28·6	6·4	43,000	M3
5904	15 16	+ 2·3	6·2	30,000	M5
6205	16 40	+36·6	5·7	27,000	M13
6656	18 33	−24·0	5·9	10,000	M22
7078	21 28	+12·0	6·0	43,000	M15

TABLE 19

Diffuse Nebulae

NGC	R.A. h m	Dec. o	Distance l-y	
1976	5 33	− 5·4	1,500	M42 Great Neb. in Orion
2070	5 40	−69·1	160,000	30 Doradus
3372	10 43	−59·4	5,200	Nebula about η Carinae
6514	17 59	−23·0	5,200	M20, Trifid
6523	18 02	−24·3	4,900	M8, Lagoon
6618	18 18	−16·2	5,900	M17, Horseshoe

GASEOUS NEBULAE

Three of the diffuse nebulae in Table 19, the Great Nebula in Orion, the nebulae about 30 Doradus and η Carinae are visible to the unaided eye. All six are beautiful objects in the telescope when viewed in a black sky on a moonless night. It is worthwhile to try various powers on them to find which one is best. The finest one is the Great Nebula in Orion when viewed with a high power which shows much detail, particularly in the central part. The beautiful multiple star θ Orionis is embedded within this nebulosity. It is often called the Trapezium because of its appearance in smaller telescopes, although with larger telescopes six components are seen. The star η Carinae has varied in brightness and has been classsified as a nova with maximum in 1843 although it does not appear by any means a normal nova. At maximum brightness, when the absolute magnitude was —13·5, it was giving 15,000,000 times as much light as the Sun. The nebula, too, has varied in brightness—as it required a telescope to see it in the 1830s, when Sir John Herchel was at the Cape of Good Hope. The Nebula about 30 Doradus is on a truly majestic scale to render it visible to the unaided eye from the distance of the Large Magellanic Cloud.

TABLE 20

Planetary Nebula

NGC	R.A. h m	Dec. o	Mag.	Distance l-y	
1952	5 32	+22·0	8·4	3,300	M1 Crab
2392	7 26	+21·0	8·3	2,300	
3132	10 05	−40·2	8·2	2,000	
3242	10 22	−18·4	9·0	2,000	
3918	11 48	−56·9	8·4	3,200	
6543	17 59	+66·6	8·8	2,100	
6720	18 52	+33·0	9·3	1,800	M57, Ring
6853	19 57	+22·6	7·6	700	M27, Dumbell
7009	21 01	−11·6	8·4	2,000	
7662	23 24	+42·2	8·9	2,600	

All of the planetary nebulae need a telescope to see them. They are intrinsically bright objects which can be seen at great distances. For good viewing they usually require more power than the diffuse nebulae. As their system extends outside the absorbing layer of the Milky Way and as much of their light is concentrated in accessible spectral lines, the observation of them has been useful in studies of the structure of the Galaxy.

Some of the diffuse nebulae, not represented in the tables, are reflection nebulae with a continuous spectrum. The best examples are M78 (R.A. 5 hours 42 minutes Dec. 0·°0) and the nebulosity around the Pleiades.

GALAXIES

Considering the fascinating story of the galaxies, their majestic size, and their dramatic appearance on photographs taken with the great telescopes of the world, their appearance visually is at first disappointing. Although the Andromeda Galaxy is visible to the naked eye, its spiral structure is not visible. Traces of structure can be observed for some of them—Lord Rosse's drawings, particularly of M51, showed the structure before they were photographed.

The galaxies listed in Table 21 provide a sample for the observer to look at. They are so far away that the distances are listed in millions of light-years. The Magellanic Couds are interesting with the naked eye, with binoculars, or with any telescopic power or photographic facility that may be available. The telescope shows M32 as a companion galaxy to the

Andromeda Galaxy. NGC 5128, the radio source, is divided by a rift into two portions. If a telescope of aperture four inches or more is available, it is worth searching with low power around an area centred about right ascension 12 hours 30 minutes declination $+13°$. The Virgo cluster of galaxies is here. Although none of these galaxies has striking appearance, there are more than a dozen Messier objects in the area, several of which may well be seen in the same field.

TABLE 21

Galaxies

NGC	R.A.	Dec.	Mag.	Type	Distance millions	
	h m	o			l-y	
55	0 12	−39·5	7·1	Sc	6	
224	0 40	+41·0	3·5	Sb	1·9	M31 Andromeda
253	0 45	−25·6	7·0	Sc	7	
SMC	0 50	−73·0	2·4	I	0·16	S.Magellanic C.
598	1 31	+30·4	5·8	Sc	2	M33
LMC	5 26	−69·0	0·1	I	0·16	L.Magellanic C.
3031	9 52	+69·3	6·9	Sb	10	M81
4594	12 37	−11·4	8·1	Sa	14	
4945	13 02	−49·0	7·0	S	16	
5128	13 22	−42·8	6·0	E	12	
5194	13 28	+47·4	8·3	Sc	6	M51
5236	13 34	−29·6	7·6	Sc	13	M83
5457	14 01	+54·6	8·1	Sc	10	M101

EPILOGUE

IT is the heavens that endure, not our ideas of them. Although observation of the sky is older than history, most of our astronomical knowledge has been recently acquired. Much of the narrative in the first three chapters about the sky visible to the naked eye would have seemed strange to our ancestors of only a few centuries ago. What was said in the later chapters would have been entirely foreign to them; much of our fundamental knowledge has been acquired in the present century.

The great leap forward began in the sixteenth and seventeenth centuries when the ideas of Copernicus were confirmed by the telescopic observations of Galileo and refined by Kepler who used as a foundation the great series of observations of Tycho.

Before this time, thought on the nature of the universe was crucially influenced by the fourth century B.C. writings of Aristotle. His main ideas were that the Earth is at rest in the centre of the universe, that the heavenly bodies are arranged on spherical shells simple movements of which explain the motions of the planets, that the outermost sphere held the fixed stars, and that the celestial luminaries were made of an element more "perfect" than those of which the Earth is constructed. In his thought the phenomena are deduced by argument from presupposed properties of the world, its inner nature and general principles. The universe, for example, has the quality of being "perfect" and so must be spherical—because the sphere is the sole perfect figure, in rotation always occupying the same space.

Thus the few years near the beginning of the seventeenth century saw the overthrow of ideas of the universe which were many centuries old, but gave no picture to replace them. However, in this adventure in thought, the gain was beyond measure—nothing less than the inductive character of modern science.

In the new method, so effective in the hands of Galileo and Newton, the principles are not pre-established but suggested by observation and experiment. Nothing is excluded as inadmissible provided that it and everything which may be deduced from it conforms to what is observed. Even Copernicus, following the habits of thought of his predecessors, regarded orbits as necessarily circular and velocities are necessarily uniform. For him the observations had to be fitted to such conditions. Newton, however, sought to derive from the observations themselves principles in terms of which the phenomena could be interpreted.

With a new structure for the solar system began the process—whose end remains obscure—of unfolding ideas of a universe immeasurably larger and more mysterious than previously conceived. The stars were now removed to depths of space where investigation of them seemed forever impossible. This was changed, however, by the development of telescopes of ever-increasing size and precision, and of spectroscopes and other accessories to analyse the light. Distance, physical constitution and chemical composition have all been made accessible to observation.

In our time a second "great leap" has originated with the disclosure of the nature of the galaxies. The advance of physics is providing new techniques for gathering observations and new ideas for interpreting them. Now radio astronomy and space science join with the traditional optical astronomy in further extending the horizon of our knowledge. The universe of man's understanding enlarges even more rapidly than the vast expansion of the physical universe he observes.

In all of this study it is impossible not to be struck by the interdependence of the fields of thought. Contribution to knowledge of the Earth is made by study of the planets and of the planets by study of the Earth. Work on populations of stars gives information on the characteristics and history of individual stars, while observation of one of their number, the Sun, makes a contribution to the knowledge of the many. Study of the galaxies brings understanding of the Milky Way, whose status was not appreciated until the character of the galaxies as star systems was realized.

The interdependence goes further than this, for it extends to different sciences. The methods of physics are primary tools for investigating the universe, but astronomy repays the debt by providing observations of matter in forms not accessible in Earth-bound laboratories. Space provides a better vacuum and the interior of stars a hotter environment than we can begin to command. Study of energy relations of quasi-stellar objects and of cosmic rays may lead to new and fundamental developments. Chemistry and meteorology contribute information for the study of planetary atmospheres, and biology aids space science and the search for life in other parts of the universe. Close investigation of other planets, should it become possible, may yield clues to the origin of life itself.

Man has come a long way from thinking of the Earth as the centre of the universe. The very material of which the Earth is made reveals it as a mere speck of impurity in the ubiquitous hydrogen-helium mixture. The Sun proves to be more representative than the Earth, both of the general chemical composition of the universe and also of the tendency for the material to gather into stars which in turn are organized into great systems like the Milky Way.

These systems are distributed to distances of several thousand million light-years, the furthest to which observation has been possible. Are we coming to a time when, rightly or wrongly, we shall again feel—as many pre-Copernican thinkers did—that we have an understanding of the universe as a whole? If this is happening one cannot help thinking that the advance is being made by a method which, with its cosmological principle—and even "perfect" cosmological principle—is much in the spirit of Aristotle.

BOOKS FOR FURTHER READING

For those who have the appetite for further study the following is a list of worthwhile books. The first seven are good general books on astronomy. Most of the others deal with only one aspect of astronomy and go further with it than has been possible in this book. None should be too technical for a reader who is willing to make a reasonable effort.

Abell, George O., *Exploration of the Universe*. Holt, Rinehart and Winston, New York.
Baker, R. H., *Astronomy*. Van Nostrand, Princeton.
De Vaucouleurs, G. and Rudaux, L., *Larousse Encyclopedia of Astronomy*. Paul Hamlyn, London (translated M. Guest and J. B. Sidgewick).
The Flammarion Book on Astronomy. George Allen and Unwin, London (translated A. and B. Pagel).
Jones, H. Spencer, *General Astronomy*. Edward Arnold, London.
McLaughlin, D. B., *Introduction to Astronomy*. Houghton Mifflin, Boston.
Wyatt, S. P., *Principles of Astronomy*. Allyn and Bacon, Boston.

Abetti, G., *Solar Research*. Eyre and Spottiswoode, London.
Abetti, G., *The Sun*. Faber and Faber, London (translated J. B. Sidgewick).
Alexander, A. F., *The Planet Saturn*. Faber and Faber, London.

Bates, D. R., *The Planet Earth*. Pergamon Press, London.
Beet, E. A., *Teaching Astronomy in Schools*. Cambridge University Press.
Berry, A., *A Short History of Astronomy*. Dover Publications, New York.
Bok, B. J., *The Astronomer's Universe*. Melbourne University Press.
Bok, B. J. and Bok, P. F., *The Milky Way*. Oxford University Press.
Bondi, H., *Cosmology*. Cambridge University Press.
Bondi, H., *Relativity and Common Sense*. Doubleday and Co., New York.
Bonner, W., *The Mystery of the Expanding Universe*. Eyre and Spottiswoode, London.
Bray, R. J. and Loughhead, R. E., *Sunspots*. Chapman and Hall, London.
Burgess, E., *Satellites and Spaceflight*. Chapman and Hall, London.

Campbell, L. and Jacchia, L., *The Story of Variable Stars*. Harvard University Press, Cambridge, Mass.

De Vaucouleurs, G., *Discovery of the Universe*. Faber and Faber, London.
De Vaucouleurs, G., *Physics of the Planet Mars*. Faber and Faber, London.
Dreyer, J. L. E., *A History of Astronomy from Thales to Kepler*. Dover Publications, New York.

Ellison, M. A., *The Sun and Its Influence*. Routledge and Kegan Paul, London.

Fielder, G., *The Structure of the Moon's Surface*. Pergamon Press, London.
Firsoff, V. A., *Exploring the Planets*. Sidgewick and Jackson, London.
Firsoff, V. A., *The Surface of the Moon*. Hutchinson, London.

Gamow, G., *A Planet Called Earth*. The Macmillan Co., New York.
Gamow, G., *A Star Called the Sun*. The Macmillan Co., New York.

Goldberg, L. and Aller, L. H., *Atoms, Stars and Nebulae*. Harvard University Press, Cambridge, Mass.

Howard, H. E., *Handbook of Telescope Making*. Faber and Faber, London.
Hubble, E. P., *The Realm of the Nebulae*. Dover Publications, New York.
Ingalls, A. G., *Amateur Telescope Making*. Scientific American, New York.
Inglis, R. M. G., *A New Popular Star Atlas*. Gall and Inglis, Edinburgh.

Kopal, Z., *The Moon, Our Nearest Celestial Neighbour*. Chapman and Hall, London.

Menzel, D. H., *Our Sun*. Harvard University Press, Cambridge, Mass.
Miczaika, G. R. and Sinton, W. M., *Tools of the Astronomer*. Harvard University Press, Cambridge, Mass.
Moore, P., *The Planet Venus*. The Macmillan Co., New York.
Moore, P., *A Survey of the Moon*. Eyre and Spottiswoode, London.
Muirden, J., *Astronomy with Binoculars*. Faber and Faber, London.

Nangle, J., *Stars of the Southern Heavens*. Angus and Robertson, Sydney.
Newton, H. W., *The Face of the Sun*. Penguin Books, London (Pelican series).
Norton, A. P., *A Star Atlas and Reference Handbook*. Gall and Inglis, Edinburgh.

Pannekoek, A., *A History of Astronomy*. George Allen and Unwin, London.
Piddington, J. H., *Radio Astronomy*. Hutchinson, London.

Richter, N. B., *The Nature of Comets*. Methuen and Co., London.

Shapley, H., *Galaxies*. Harvard University Press, Cambridge, Mass.
Shapley, H., *The Inner Metagalaxy*. Oxford University Press.
Smith, F. G., *Radio Astronomy*. Penguin Books, London.
Smith, S. W., *Teachers' Handbook of Astronautics*. British Interplanetary Society, London.

Thompson, A. J., *Making Your Own Telescope*. The Sky Publishing Corporation, Boston.

Watson, F. G., *Between the Planets*. Harvard University Press, Cambridge, Mass.
Whipple, F. L., *Earth, Moon and Planets*. Oxford University Press.
Whitrow, G. J., *The Structure and Evolution of the Universe*. Hutchinson, London.
Wood, Harley, *The Southern Sky*. Angus and Robertson, Sydney.

INDEX